A COMPLETE CATALOGUE

OF THE PAINTINGS OF

G·B·TIEPOLO

PHAIDON

ANTONIO MORASSI

A COMPLETE CATALOGUE
OF THE PAINTINGS OF
G·B·TIEPOLO

INCLUDING PICTURES BY HIS PUPILS AND FOLLOWERS

WRONGLY ATTRIBUTED TO HIM

WITH 429 ILLUSTRATIONS

PHAIDON PUBLISHERS INC
DISTRIBUTED BY
NEW YORK GRAPHIC SOCIETY PUBLISHERS, LTD
GREENWICH·CONNECTICUT

MADE IN GREAT BRITAIN

PRINTED BY HUNT BARNARD & CO · LTD · AYLESBURY · BUCKS

CONTENTS

PREFACE

THIS Catalogue forms the indispensable complement to my book on Tiepolo, published by the Phaidon Press in 1955, and was always planned as such: that it has taken so long to produce is due in part to technical considerations and in part to the complexity – which may easily be imagined – of the material itself. The catalogue includes every picture by Giambattista Tiepolo known to me, as well as all those destroyed in the War or through other causes, and those which are recorded in the literature, but which are now lost. Some of these may well turn up again, as has in fact happened in a few cases recently.

The whole of the literature on Tiepolo, whether old or modern, teems with wrong attributions, and even the greatest Museums continue to exhibit works labelled 'Tiepolo' which have no real connection with him; it has seemed worthwhile to include these as well, giving, when possible, the name of the actual painter. It is probable that the larger part of the works wrongly attributed to Giambattista are by his son Domenico, and I have noted those cases where, in the literature, there has been a confusion between father and son. Domenico was an infant prodigy in painting, brought up at the very centre of his father's art, later his indispensable assistant and finally his *alter ego*, so that in spite of his own artistic individuality he found himself often bound to speak with his father's voice, since he was working on pictures destined to pass as Giambattista's. The proof of this is the celebrated *Concilium in Arena*, at Udine, which was undoubtedly executed by Domenico although the contract was drawn up with Giambattista. The same can be said of some of the pictures once in the Algarotti Collection, catalogued by the famous connoisseur who owned them as by Giambattista, but in reality by Domenico. In short, 'Tiepolo' was the collective name for the workshop in which, from the Würzburg period (1750–53) onwards, Domenico was the most important collaborator; thus Goethe, in writing about the frescoes in the Villa Valmarana, speaks of 'Tiepolo' without distinguishing between father and son. For the critics and collectors it was unthinkable that Tiepolesque paintings of high quality should be by anyone other than Giambattista and so Domenico was pushed into the shade – sometimes in good faith, sometimes not. There have been cases where Domenico's signature has been obliterated, or the initials altered, it being simple enough to transform an original G.D. into a G.B. which was almost true. In other cases the distinction, on purely stylistic grounds, could be extremely difficult: for example, the two scenes in the Louvre, the *Minuet* and the *Charlatan*, which have been restored to Domenico only within recent years. The line of demarcation is by no means easy to draw, and, however much study is given to the problem, it is my opinion that there will always be a rather hazy zone between the two.

Nevertheless, it would not be an exaggeration to say that the imitators and followers of Giambattista, among his direct and indirect pupils, were legion, beginning with Giustino Menescardi, who painted in the Scuola dei Carmini, where his master had himself painted. There he executed several richly coloured and thickly painted canvases very close to Tiepolo even if inferior to his works. There are a good many pictures by Menescardi still attributed to Tiepolo, such as the *Erection of a Statue*, in the Uffizi, or the two *Historical Scenes*, in the Museum at Cleveland, all of which bear labels with Tiepolo's name. Another close follower was Francesco Zugno, especially in his early period and when, about 1754, he was painting frescoes side by side with Tiepolo in the Villa Soderini at Nervesa, near

Treviso. Giovanni Raggi, from Bergamo, became a pupil of Tiepolo while still very young, and, after assisting him with the frescoes of the Cappella Colleoni, followed his master to Venice and borrowed freely from him, especially at the beginning. Among others, Raggi made so faithful a copy of the *S. Joseph* that Tiepolo had painted for S. Salvatore in Bergamo that it was taken, in his own time and a few decades ago when it re-appeared, for an original or an autograph replica by Tiepolo himself.

There were many other followers and imitators in Venice and the Veneto – Francesco Fontebasso, Fabio and Giambattista Canal, Jacopo Guarana, Giambattista Mengardi, Costantino Cedini, and Francesco Lorenzi. There were still others in Friuli, like Francesco Chiaruttini, or in Lombardy, like Cesare Ligari, or Mattia Bortoloni, who, together with Giambattista Crosato, spread certain aspects of Tiepolo's art in Piedmont.

Wherever Tiepolo moved – to Udine or to Milan or to Vicenza or elsewhere – he was certain to create around himself a circle of younger artists. This happened even in Germany, where what can only be described as 'Tiepolism' occurred after his stay in Würzburg and became one of the most important characteristics in the development of Baroque painting in South Germany. Practically every painter working in the third quarter of the 18th century in Germany felt his influence to some degree: from Georg Anton Urlaub who was his collaborator and friend, to Johannes and Januarius Zick, from Christoph Fesel to Johann Holzer, from Franz Maulbertsch to Franz Sigrist, and many others. It was only in Spain that there was no real succession to Tiepolo and this may have been because when he arrived there he was already elderly, or it may have been that the Spanish school in those years was not endowed with much talent, or indeed it may have been that at that time Neoclassic ideals were beginning to gain their ascendancy in painting. Nevertheless, the influence of Tiepolo's art, transmitted through Domenico, was one of the factors in the artistic formation of Goya. After Giambattista's death his younger son Lorenzo, who was a good portrait painter, remained in Spain, and in that branch of the art continued his father's style, though in a rather more anecdotic and bourgeois manner more in keeping with the taste of the period.

After looking attentively for a long time at the works of Tiepolo there comes a certain moment when one finds oneself confronted with a mysterious element which is perhaps basic to his art. It is possible to take into account all the outside factors which determine the course of his development, but the essence of it is something spiritual which remains just out of reach. It is this element of mystery which one finds in the creation of all masterpieces and perhaps even in what appear to be the most obvious manifestations such as, to take a musical example, the works of a Mozart or a Verdi. In fact, the arts, when they reach their highest summits, cannot be defined by words for the good reason that at that point they are completely expressive in and for themselves alone and are, maybe for that reason, anti-literary.

One of the most singular aspects of Tiepolo's art, and of the whole world which he evokes, is that it is at one and the same time realistic and idealistic. His figures are drawn from nature and have a vital force and energy; but on account of the transparency of the colour and the treatment of the space which they inhabit, they lose their bodily weight in the atmosphere and become light and immaterial. If we think of Tiepolo's 'Heavens' our recollection is of something irradiated with light suggestive almost of a visionary sensation, supernatural and almost like a religious ecstasy. If, after the studies which have been undertaken in the last few decades, we know all, or almost all concerning the origins and development of Giambattista's art, and if it is now clear to us how he derived instruction and inspiration from contemporary painting and from the art of the past, yet the mysterious part begins when he leaves behind not only his immediate surroundings but his whole age. This is the moment in which he is no longer a follower of Piazzetta, or of Ricci, or of anyone else, but has become himself, so much so that he is unique and exceptional and can hardly be mistaken under any of his aspects.

Notwithstanding his mythological world, the exaltation of the gods and the heroes of antiquity, Tiepolo is nevertheless the fruit, and perhaps the finest as he is certainly the last, of the world of ideas of the Counter-Reformation; that is, he is the last exponent of those pictorial inventions which go back to Gaulli, to Padre Pozzo, and to Luca Giordano, and which were grafted on to the stock of Venetian art and the illusionism of the Bolognese school. To Bologna Tiepolo owed many ideas which came to him particularly through his faithful collaborator Gerolamo Mengozzi-Colonna, the specialist in perspective illusionism who worked for him from the time of the frescoes at Udine, or even earlier. Without his help, Giambattista would have had difficulty in giving form to his imagination and to his visionary illusions.

It is a comforting fact that in recent years art historians have entirely abandoned Neoclassic aversions from Venetian 18th century art, and that this field, in which Tiepolo occupies a pre-eminent position, has been the subject of a great growth of interest and has been explored with serious scholarship. It is with considerable satisfaction that I record here the most important recent studies on the painter published since my own monograph of 1955. These include the general treatments of Venetian 18th century painting which we owe to Decio Gioseffi (1956), Carlo Donzelli (1957), Michael Levey (1959), Eduard Hüttinger (1959) and the monumental work by Rodolfo Pallucchini (1960). There have been monographs by Freeden and Lamb on Tiepolo's frescoes at Würzburg (1956), the monograph by Paolo d'Ancona on the Palazzo Clerici (1956) and, finally, a book on the drawings of Tiepolo in the Victoria and Albert Museum by George Knox (1960). There have also been studies of particular problems connected with Tiepolo by O. Benesch, H. Voss, A. Riccoboni, W. R. Valentiner, J. Rubow, G. P. Mras, G. Biasutti, G. Vigni, J. J. Byam-Shaw, C. Boselli, M. Muraro, O. I. Lavrova, F. Haskell, M. Precerutti-Garberi to mention only the most notable. From all these studies the figure of Tiepolo as a painter emerges as somebody worthy of the deep respect in which he was held by the writers of his own time from Da Canal to Algarotti, from Moschini to Zanetti and Lanzi, and from Tessin to Cochin, Fragonard and Mariette and, indeed, by all the connoisseurs and patrons throughout Europe.

The criterion which has been adopted in drawing up this catalogue has been that of inclusiveness since, as I have already mentioned, it contains works wrongly attributed to Tiepolo as well as those really by him, and this was resolved upon in order to avoid perpetuating old and new confusions. At the same time, I wished to adopt a restrictive standard in the compilation of the individual entries which have been limited to a schematic presentation of the chronological facts, a brief note on the style and the importance of the individual work and on its relationship to other pictures by Tiepolo, whether small sketches or large frescoes, replicas or variants. The bibliographical references have been confined to the essentials and for the most part they give only the earliest recorded mention of the work together with a reference to the most important monograph which mentions it, that is to say, the monographs by Molmenti (1909) and Sack (1910) and a few others. For the same reasons, the collections through which individual works have passed have been given only when they were important.

Every picture by Giambattista which was not illustrated in my earlier monograph is reproduced here, with the exception of a very small number of pictures of which it was not possible to obtain good reproductions. This corpus of illustrations gives a complete idea of all Giambattista's work. It is, of course, risky to assert that it is complete. In any field of knowledge 'complete' is bound to be a relative term. This was well known to Goethe when he paraphrased a popular saying: 'It is easy enough to make a beginning but it is difficult to arrive at the supreme goal'.

My thanks are due to all those who have helped in so many ways in the preparation of this work, whether with photographs or information. I am grateful to the Directors of Museums and Galleries, to the collectors, scholars and friends who cannot be mentioned by name here since they would form too long a list. In particular, however, I should like to express my gratitude to Signora Mercedes Precerutti-Garberi, who has given invaluable help in the preparation of this catalogue; and to Dr. and Mrs. Peter Murray who have made the translation.

A.M.

CATALOGUE

NOTES TO THE CATALOGUE

1. The indication of the title of a painting followed by an indication of its date means that these works are, in my view, autograph paintings by Giambattista.

2. When the title of a picture is not followed by a date, it is to be understood that it is by some other artist.

3. Measurements are given with the height first, followed by the width.

4. Bibliographical references are simply to the name of the author followed by the year of publication. The full title of the book or article will be found in the bibliography on pages 71-77.

   When no date is given the following works are to be understood:

   > H. De CHENNEVIÈRES, *Les Tiepolo*, Paris, 1898
   >
   > A. DE VESME, *Le peintre-graveur italien*, Milan, 1906
   >
   > P. MOLMENTI, *G. B. Tiepolo*, Milan 1909 (when Molmenti's name is followed by the date 1911, the French edition is referred to since it contains some material not to be found in the Italian edition)
   >
   > E. SACK, *G. B. und D. Tiepolo*, Hamburg 1910
   >
   > M. GOERING, *Tiepolo*, in 'Thieme und Becker Künstlerlexikon', vol. XXXIII, Leipzig, 1939
   >
   > A. MORASSI, *G. B. Tiepolo*, Bergamo 1943, 1st edition
   >
   > G. LORENZETTI, '*Mostra del Tiepolo*' Catalogue, Venice, 1951.

5. When an attribution to Tiepolo is rejected but no bibliographical reference is given, it is to be understood that the actual attribution was made privately in a letter or a written certificate.

6. Most of Tiepolo's major works have been reproduced in my book *G. B. Tiepolo : His Life and Work*, London, Phaidon Press, 1955. In the present Catalogue, references to that volume are given in the form [1955].

CATALOGUE

AACHEN, Suermondt Coll.

THE LAST SUPPER
Canvas, 562 × 687 cm.

A picture mentioned by Waagen (*Katalog der Sammlung Suermondt*, 1859) with the attribution to Tiepolo (Sack, p. 233).
It is not known if Tiepolo ever executed any 'Supper' on such a large scale; the only link with this picture could perhaps be the notice in Da Canal, 1732, p. XXXIV, according to whom he painted in ten hours twelve life-size Apostles, with Christ administering the Eucharist. No other record existing.

AMIENS, Musée de Picardie

THE IMMACULATE CONCEPTION   Fig. 65
Canvas, 49 × 42 cm.; *c.* 1734-36.

Related to the Vicenza altarpiece, perhaps a first idea for it.
Ex coll. Lavalard, given to the Museum in 1890.
Sack, p. 211, fig. 206, records a similar sketch, formerly in the Weber Coll., Hamburg, now in Detroit, Art Institute (q.v.). Another canvas, identical with that at Amiens, but rectangular, was in the Exhibition 'Settecento Veneziano', Milan 1955, and is to be considered as a replica. An old copy of the Amiens sketch was in the Dr. Meller Coll., Paris, in 1948.

THE BAPTISM OF CHRIST
Canvas, 38 × 42 cm.

By a contemporary imitator of Tiepolo.
Copy after the fresco in Bergamo.
Ex coll. Lavalard.
Sack, p. 211, fig. 207; Molmenti, 1911, p. 192, both wrongly as by Giambattista Tiepolo.

THE BANQUET OF ANTONY AND CLEOPATRA
Canvas, 43 × 36 cm.

By a contemporary imitator of Tiepolo.
Related to the fresco in Venice, Pal. Labia. The original sketch is in the Stockholm University Museum. The sketch of the *Banquet* in the Alexander Coll., London, is closer to one of the canvases in Archangel.
Ex coll. Lavalard.
Molmenti, p. 284, as by Giambattista; Sack, p. 211, also as by Giambattista himself, whereas it is clearly a poor work of his school.
A similar *Banquet*, also by a follower of Tiepolo, is in the Cagnola Collection, Gazzada near Varese.

AMSTERDAM, Rijksmuseum

TELEMACHUS AND MENTOR   Fig. 236
Canvas, with added strips, 113 × 72 cm.; *c.* 1740-50.

Ex coll. Henry Rochefort, Paris; Cassirer, Berlin (when it was slightly restored); Duret, Paris; Amsterdam, 1922.
Molmenti, p. 259, fig. p. 255; Sack, p. 216, fig. 212; Venturi, 'Studi dal Vero', 1927, p. 399, fig. 275; Lorenzetti, p. 60, fig. 44.
A fragment, not of high quality.

THE CHILD MARY PRESENTED TO GOD THE FATHER   Fig. 68
Canvas, 47 × 27 cm.; 1759.

Sketch for the altarpiece in Dresden.
Ex coll. Benigno Crespi, Milan; Cassirer, Berlin; Tiedje, Amsterdam

till 1948; then to Museum. On the back a note in old writing: *Modello originale di Tiepolo fatto per la tavola dell'altare nel convento di S. Chiara in Cividale. Comprato dalla Galeria Bodese. Tiepolo per lire sessanta tre, li 23 maggio 1808.*
A. Venturi, 'La Galleria Crespi', Milan, 1900, pp. 179 ff., with repr. p. 181; Molmenti, p. 147; Sack, p. 172; Catalogue of the Crespi Sale, Petit, Paris, June 4, 1914, No. 85; Goering *ad vocem*; Catalogue of the Museum (Schilderijen), Amsterdam, 1951, p. 176.
A splendid work, in a very nervous style.

ALLEGORICAL FEMALE FIGURES   Figs. 379-380
Two canvases, oval, 81 × 65 cm. each; *c.* 1740-50.

Grisailles on golden background.
Belong to the series mentioned by Waagen in *Art Treasures etc.*, 1857, IV, p. 173 as in the Cheney Coll.
Companion pieces in the de Becker-Rothschild Coll., New York and in a Private Coll., Zurich.
Wrongly attributed to Domenico Tiepolo in the *Catalogue* of the Rijksmuseum, Amsterdam, 1951, p. 176.

THE FLIGHT INTO EGYPT
Canvas, 68 × 101 cm.

By Domenico.
Ex vom Rath Coll., Amsterdam.
Formerly attributed to Giambattista Tiepolo, exhibited in Venice, 1951, rightly as Domenico.
Catalogue of the Rijksmuseum, Amsterdam, 1951, p. 176, as Domenico.

AMSTERDAM, formerly E. vom Rath Coll.

ARMIDA CROWNING THE SLEEPING RINALDO WITH FLOWERS
ABRAHAM AND THE ANGELS
Two canvases, 50·5 × 120 cm.

Attributed erroneously to Tiepolo.
By a follower, very close to the Master, certainly F. Zugno.

AMSTERDAM, Sale of the 'Collection Royale de Tableaux venus de Saxe,' 1765

JULIUS CAESAR IN A SQUARE OF ALEXANDRIA CONTEMPLATING THE SEVERED HEAD OF POMPEY
Canvas, *c.* 135 × 185 cm.; 1743-46.

Commissioned from Tiepolo by Algarotti for King Augustus III in the spring of 1743; the painter was paid 130 'zecchini'.
Sent to Dresden in 1746. From the Royal Gallery of Dresden to Amsterdam, sold 22.5.1765 at Arnoldus Dankmeyer, Cat. No. 65. In the same sale there was sold the *Banquet of Cleopatra* now in Melbourne, which was acquired by Catherine II of Russia.
No further trace of the painting, whose present whereabouts is unknown.
The *modello* for the canvas once in the Giusti Coll., Modena (q.v.).
For the documents regarding the picture see the Chronological Table.
Algarotti, *Opere*, 1772, VI, p. 36; Posse, 1931, Beiheft; M. Precerutti-Garberi, in *Commentari*, April-June, 1958, p. 111 ff. with the complete story of the painting.

ANGERS, Musée des Beaux-Arts

APOTHEOSIS OF THE PISANI FAMILY   Fig. 339
Canvas, 134 × 80 cm.; 1761.

Sketch for the ceiling of the Villa Pisani, Strà. Bequeathed to the Museum in 1863 by Jean Robin de Chalonnes.
Molmenti, p. 247; Sack, p. 212; Morassi, p. 36; Lorenzetti, p. 131, fig. 93; Cat. Exhib. R.A., London, 1954–55, No. 492.
An important late masterpiece in excellent condition.

ARCHANGEL, Russia, Museum (National Trust), formerly Jusupov Gallery

THE MEETING OF ANTONY AND CLEOPATRA; CLEOPATRA'S BANQUET   Figs. 313, 311
Two canvases, each 338 × 600 cm.; the first is dated 1747.

Bought by Prince Jusupov, the Russian Ambassador at Turin, probably between 1783 and 1789, and since then in Russia.
Molmenti, p. 284; Sack, p. 208; Grabar, *The Art Review* ('Hckycctbo'), Leningrad, 1947, II, pp. 63–81, with several reproductions.
Very important works of his maturity. The sketch for the *Banquet* is in the Alexander Coll., London (q.v.); the one for the *Meeting* in the Rothschild Coll., Paris (q.v.). A copy of the *Meeting* (98 × 147 cm.) ascribed to Domenico, but by another pupil of Giambattista, perhaps Zugno, was on the market in Berlin before the war and is now in a Private Coll., Düsseldorf.
A *Banquet*, of the same size (99 × 146 cm.) was before the war in London, H. H. Buttery, later York Sale, Christie, London, 6.5.1927, No. 52. According to the Catalogue entry it was dated 1740 (perhaps an error for 1747?). This *Banquet*, exhibited as by Domenico in Amsterdam, 1934, No. 357 is also a work by a pupil.

ASCOTT, Wing, Leighton Buzzard, Bedfordshire (National Trust) Antony de Rothschild Coll.

THE ASSUMPTION OF THE VIRGIN   Fig. 106
Circular canvas, 51.5 cm. diameter; *c.* 1730–35.

Sketch for a ceiling.
Ex Coll. Battersea, London; Cheney Sale, Christie's 29.4.1885.
Sack, p. 226; Cat. Exhib. R.A., London, 1954–55, No. 516.
Stylistically related to the sketches in S. Daniele.
A copy in Le Havre (q.v.)

ATHENS, Museum of Fine Arts

REBECCA AT THE WELL   Fig. 7
Canvas, 146 × 197 cm.; *c.* 1730.

Molmenti, *Emporium*, 1914, pp. 314–315; E. Waldmann, La Pinacothèque d'Athènes, in *Callitechnis*, Athens, vol. A., p. 359; Goering, *ad vocem*, says that the *bozzetto* for this painting was in the Koetser Coll., London.
Certainly a good early work, but much and badly restored.
A similar subject in a Private Coll., New York (q.v.).

THE AGONY IN THE GARDEN
Canvas, 78 × 86 cm.

Certainly an old copy, perhaps by a pupil, after the picture in Hamburg, Kunsthalle.
Molmenti, *Emporium*, 1914, pp. 314, 315; E. Waldmann, op. cit. in *Callitechnis*, Athens, vol. A., p. 359, (both attributing it to G.B.).

ATLANTA, Georgia, Art Association Galleries

GIFTS OFFERED TO CLEOPATRA
Canvas, oval, 144 × 117 cm.; *c.* 1745–50.

Gift of Mr. Samuel H. Kress in 1932 (K. 161).
Excellent replica of the painting formerly in Turin, Colonna Coll., and now in the Necchi Coll., Pavia.
Lorenzetti, p. 87, believes the painting in Atlanta to be the original, the one in Pavia a replica; Goering, *ad vocem*, as by Giambattista.

DISEMBARKATION OF CLEOPATRA
Canvas, 155 × 280 cm.

By F. Zugno.

Ex coll. Brummer, New York.
Sometimes attributed to Giambattista or to Domenico, exhibited in St. Louis (U.S.A.) 1936, as Domenico.
Catalogue of the Exhibition, No. 44, with repr.

AUGSBURG, Museum

TARQUIN AND LUCRETIA   Fig. 289
Canvas, oval, 138 × 103 cm.; *c.* 1745–50.

Ex Coll. Thedy, Weimar; Haberstock Coll., Munich. Recently entered the Museum (Haberstock bequest).
One of the four overdoors formerly in the Palazzo Barbaro, Venice (Cf. Copenhagen, Museum; Pavia, Necchi Coll.; Washington, Nat. Gallery).
Some old copies, wrongly attributed to Tiepolo himself, were on the New York market years ago, another (143 × 110 cm.) on the Paris market, *c.* 1958.
Molmenti, p. 271, fig. p. 267; Sack, p. 150; Morassi, p. 20, fig. 69; Lorenzetti, p. 85, fig. 63.

BALTIMORE (Maryland), Walters Art Gallery

JUGURTHA BEFORE THE ROMAN CONSUL   Fig. 302
Canvas, 280 × 488 cm.; *c.* 1720–25.

Acquired by Henry Walters in 1902 from the Don Marcello Massarenti Coll., Rome. Listed in the *Catalogue du musée de peinture, sculpture et archéologie au Palais Accoramboni* (by E. Van Esbroeck) Rome, 1897, No. 404.
Morassi, Le Arti, 1942, p. 89, Pl. XXV, fig. 7; idem, 1950, p. 14.
A large and rather confused composition of his early period after the sketch in the Marinotti Coll., Milan (q.v.). Badly preserved, with repaints.
A first idea for this composition is, perhaps, the one in the Clifford Smith Coll., London (q.v.).

BALTIMORE (Maryland), Museum of Art

HEAD OF AN ORIENTAL
Canvas, *c.* 55 × 45 cm.

By Domenico. Attributed to Giambattista by the Museum.
Formerly Epstein Coll.
Engraved by Domenico in the 'Raccolta di Teste' with the inscription: *Joannes Batta Tiepolo inv.* (Molmenti, 1896, repr. p. 159 right).
The original by Giambattista, from which this copy was made, was formerly in the Orloff Coll., Paris.
Other 'Heads' like this are known, one sold at the American Art Association, New York, 1929, Pepoli Sale (q.v.); a second in Trieste, formerly Opuich–Fontana Coll. (q.v.).

BANBURY, Oxfordshire, Upton House (National Trust), Bearsted Coll.

MADONNA AND CHILD WITH S. ANTONY OF PADUA AND AN ABBOT   Fig. 91
Arched canvas, 98 × 61 cm., *c.* 1750–60.

Ex coll. Battersea; Sotheby Sale, London, 23.2.1938.
Berenson, 1902, p. 133; Sack, p. 226.
Not, as Sack says, a sketch but a finished *paletta*, i.e. small altarpiece or private devotional painting.
Engraved by Domenico.
Sack (p. 166) mentions a sketch (40 × 24 cm.) formerly in the Galleria Lochis in Bergamo, sold in Paris in 1887, and present whereabouts unknown.

BARCELONA, Museo de Arte

EUTERPE   Fig. 415
Canvas, 97 × 79 cm.; *c.* 1750–60.

Sale, Hôtel Drouot, Paris, 23.3.1903, p. 46; ex coll. Haberstock, Berlin; Trotti-Nicolle, Paris; Cambò, Barcelona.
Molmenti, fig. on p. 313, erroneously believes it to be by an imitator; Morassi, p. 28, fig. 72; Sánchez-Cantón, 1953, p. 27, fig. 39.
Fine work, light in colour.

BALLET and CHARLATAN
Two canvases, each 78.5 × 110 cm.

By Domenico.
Ex coll. Papadopoli, Venice; Cambò, Barcelona.
Molmenti, p. 206; Sack, p. 162, figs. 107–108 (both as by Giambattista);
Morassi, p. 33, figs 100–101 (as Domenico).
Masterpieces once attributed to Giambattista.
The *Charlatan* is dated 1756 on the banner at the left.

BARNARD CASTLE, Co. Durham, Bowes Museum

PHAETHON AND APOLLO   Fig. 242
Canvas, 95 × 70 cm.; 1731.

Sketch for the Palazzo Archinto, Milan.
Morassi, *Le Arti*, 1941–42, p. 265, fig. 17; Watson, Catalogue, 1951,
p. 34; Cat. Exhib. R.A., London, 1954–55, No. 488.
Very fine work in a grey-blue tonality: another excellent version is in
the Vienna Academy Gallery (q.v.).

BASLE, R. von Hirsch Coll.

TIME DISCOVERING TRUTH   Fig. 323
Canvas, 68.5 × 54.5 cm.; *c.* 1740–45.

Sketch for a circular ceiling. Closely related to the ceiling in the
Palazzo Barbarigo, Venice, and similar in composition to the painting
in the H. de Rothschild Coll., Paris (q.v.).
Ex coll. Trotti-Nicolle, Paris, 1932.
Exhib. Frankfurt, Staedel Institut, 1925, No. 212.

BASSANO, Museo Civico

THE CIRCUMCISION   Fig. 35
Canvas, 64 × 84 cm.; *c.* 1730–35.

Sack, p. 163; Morassi, *L'Arte*, 1944, p. 7, fig. 7.
Certainly autograph, but in very bad condition.
An old copy is in Tucson, Arizona (q.v.).

MADONNA AND CHILD
Canvas, 61 × 76 cm.; *c.* 1718–20 (?).

A very early work, rather damaged and much repainted. Recently
attributed to G.B. by the Director of the Museum, Dr. L. Magagnato.

BAYONNE, Musée Bonnat

APOTHEOSIS OF A WARRIOR
Canvas, shaped, 105 × 58 cm.

By Domenico.
Sketch for a ceiling, wrongly attributed to Giambattista in the Catalogue
of the Museum.

BELLAGIO, Princess Torre e Tasso Coll.

THE FLIGHT INTO EGYPT   Fig. 36
Canvas, 60 × 45 cm.; *c.* 1762–70.

G. Brauer, Nice; Prince Bobrinsky, Rome; Harris, London, 1929.
Morassi, p. 40, fig. 130.
Exquisite painting in light silver-blue colours, characteristic of his
more nervous style.

BENNEBROEK, Holland, von Pannwitz Coll.

S. ROCH   Fig. 166
S. ROCH   Fig. 170
Two canvases, 43 × 32.5 cm. each; *c.* 1730–35.

Form part of the series of the devotional pictures of St. Roch so
numerous in Tiepolo's work.
Catalogue 'Italiaansche Kunst in Nederlandsch Bezit,' Amsterdam,
1934, p. 113, No. 370–371.

BERGAMO, Galleria dell' Accademia Carrara

THE MARTYRDOM OF S. JOHN, BISHOP OF BERGAMO Fig. 129
Canvas, 40 × 22 cm.; 1743.

Sketch for the altarpiece in the Cathedral.
Molmenti, p. 132, fig. on p. 133; Sack, p. 164, fig. 151; Lorenzetti,
p. 70, fig. 53.
A very rapid sketch, almost a first idea, not so developed as the
modelletti generally are.

S. PROCULUS, BISHOP OF VERONA, VISITING SS. FERMUS AND
RUSTICUS   Fig. 137
Canvas, 57 × 32 cm.; *c.* 1740–45.

Sketch for an unknown or never executed altarpiece. Generally consi-
dered in relation with the altarpiece in S. Massimo at Padua and called
SS. Maximus and Oswald.
Good in quality, similar to the sketch in the National Gallery, London.
Another version (57 × 36 cm.) formerly in the Cavendish-Bentinck
Coll., London, is now in New York, Private Coll. Another one (also
called *SS. Maximus and Oswald*) is mentioned by Molmenti, p. 262 in
the Thiem Coll., San Remo. Another version in Moscow (q.v.).
Certainly Tiepolo saw S. Ricci's work, representing the same subject,
which was in the Bergamo Cathedral since 1704. C. Caversazzi, in
Emporium, 1899, p. 209, considered the sketch related to the tradition
of SS. Fermus and Rusticus of the Crotta Family; Molmenti, p. 262;
Sack, p. 106, fig. 155 and others always as 'SS. Maximus and Oswald'.

S. JOHN THE BAPTIST PREACHING
Canvas, 31 × 44 cm.

THE BAPTISM OF CHRIST
Canvas, 31 × 42 cm.

ST. JOHN NEPOMUK AND THE HOLY TRINITY
Arched canvas, 68 × 39 cm.

Three sketches from the studio of Tiepolo, but not autograph. The
original sketch of the *St. John preaching* is in Milan, Treccani Coll.
An original sketch of the *St. John Nepomuk* was formerly in the
Nicholson Coll., London (q.v.).

BERGAMO, Cathedral

THE MARTYRDOM OF S. JOHN, BISHOP OF BERGAMO Fig. 130
Canvas, 600 × 250 cm.; 1743.

In a letter of 31st July, 1743, Tiepolo agreed to paint the altarpiece,
which was despatched in the same year.
Molmenti, p. 132, fig. on p. 132a; Sack, p. 164, fig. 152; Pinetti, 1931,
p. 67, fig. p. 65; Lorenzetti, p. 70, fig. 52.
Masterpiece of his more dramatic style. Sketch in the Galleria at
Bergamo, above.

BERGAMO, Colleoni Chapel

JUSTICE, WISDOM, FAITH, CHARITY   Figs. 210–213
Frescoes in the supporting members of the vaulting; 1732.

S. MARK and MARTYRDOM OF S. BARTHOLOMEW
Frescoes in the lunettes of the choir; 1732.

S. JOHN THE BAPTIST PREACHING, THE BAPTISM OF CHRIST,
THE DECOLLATION OF S. JOHN THE BAPTIST Figs. 42–44
Frescoes in the three medallions of the chapel; 1733.

Signed and dated among the stuccoes: *Giov. Batt. Tiepolo 1733*. The
Governors of the *Luogo Pio* in Bergamo invited Tiepolo to paint these
frescoes on 4th July, 1731, and drew up a contract in July, 1733.
Molmenti, p. 128, figs. on pp. 126–132; Sack, pp. 163–164, figs. 43–48;
Morassi, pp. 19, 20, fig. 42.
The sketch for the *S. John preaching* is in the Treccani Coll., Milan.
The sketch for the *Decollation* is in Stockholm, Nat. Museum.
Another presumed sketch, rather big, for the *Baptism of Christ*, is

mentioned by Molmenti, 1911, p. 107, as in the Pio Fabbri Coll., Rome.
All the frescoes well preserved, except the *St. Mark*, which was damaged
by damp and badly repainted in the XIX century.

BERGAMO, S. Salvatore

S. JOSEPH WITH THE CHRIST CHILD   Fig. 178
Canvas, 140 × 120 cm., 1733.

Tassi, 1797, II, p. 104; Molmenti, p. 132, fig. on p. 134; Sack, p. 165,
fig. 153; Pinetti, 1931, p. 106, with repr.
A copy of this painting, certainly by Raggi (the same mentioned by
Tassi?), was *c.* 1930 on the art market in Milan, erroneously attributed
to Tiepolo.
Another picture with the same subject was recorded together with its
sketch by Rodella (or Carboni), 1760, p. 182, in the Barbisoni Coll. in
Brescia, as by the hand of Tiepolo.

BERGAMO, formerly Piccinelli Coll.

MADONNA AND CHILD WITH THREE SAINTS   Fig. 83
Canvas, 48 × 29 cm.; *c.* 1730–35.

An excellent *modello* for the altarpiece now in Moscow (q.v.), and
similar to the picture in Zurich, Private Coll. (q.v.).
Coll. Piccinelli; Bocchi Sale, Gall. Lurati, Milan, 1931 (65), repr. XI;
passed to Milan, Bordoni Coll.; sold Dec. 1933, Galleria Geri;
then to Rome, Meyer Coll. Present whereabouts unknown.
Caversazzi, *Emporium*, 1899, p. 212; Morassi, *Le Arti* 1942, pp. 266–67
with repr.

BERGAMO, Private Coll.

MADONNA AND CHILD WITH AN ANGEL   Fig. 80
Canvas 45 × 25 cm.; *c.* 1735.

Ex coll. Jaffé, Berlin.
Goering, *ad vocem*.
A fine sketch, related iconographically to the altarpiece in London,
J. B. Robinson Coll. (q.v.).

MADONNA AND CHILD   Fig. 78
Canvas, 60 × 50 cm.; *c.* 1720–25.

Ex coll. M. Crespi, Milan.
Modigliani, *Illustrazione Italiana*, Milan, 1924–25 (colour-plate); idem,
in *Dedalo*, 1933, p. 122, fig. p. 136.
Very characteristic of his early period.

CAPRICCIO ON THE FINDING OF MOSES   Fig. 18
COMPOSITION WITH APOLLO AND MIDAS   Fig. 240
Two grisaille frescoes, transferred to canvas, 154 × 210 cm. each;
c. 1750.

Originally in the Palazzo Sagredo, Venice, they were taken to Paris
(Clery Coll.) shortly before 1910 and have been back in Italy since 1949.
The ceiling related to these grisailles is in the M. Crespi Coll., Milan.
According to Sack, there was another ceiling fresco in the same Palace,
representing *Homage to Venice*, later completely repainted. A third
ceiling, fresco on canvas, was mentioned by Sack as having been taken
from Venice to the Stettiner Coll., Paris: present whereabouts unknown.
Sack, pp. 64, 153; Molmenti (French ed.) 1911, p. 198.

DIANA AND ACTAEON   Fig. 241
Canvas, 48 × 36 cm.; *c.* 1720–22.

Morassi, *Arte Veneta*, 1952, p. 91, fig. 90.
This very impetuous sketch, strong in chiaroscuro, dates from about
the same time as the four mythologies in the Academy at Venice.

BERGAMO, formerly Venanzi Coll.

THE CROWNING WITH THORNS
Canvas, of medium size.

Published by Caversazzi, *Emporium*, 1899, p. 211, as by Giambattista,
but it is the work of a pupil, as Sack rightly believed (p. 165).

BERLIN, Gemäldegalerie

THE MARTYRDOM OF S. AGATHA   [1955, pl. 51, Col. Pl. V]
Canvas, 184 × 131 cm.; *c.* 1745–50.

Painted originally for the church of the Benedictine nuns of Lendinara.
Engraved by Domenico Tiepolo when the painting was still arched in
the upper part, where were represented angels holding a symbolical
heart with a crown with thorns.
Ex coll. Munro, London; acquired by the Museum in 1878 from Paris.
Brandolese, 1795, p. 23; Molmenti, p. 264; Sack, p. 183; Cat. of the
Museum, 1931, p. 477; Morassi, p. 32, colour plate; Lorenzetti, p. 114,
fig. 81 bis.
One of Tiepolo's most moving masterpieces.

THE PROCESSION TO CALVARY   Fig. 54
Canvas, 52 × 63 cm.; *c.* 1738.

Sketch for the large painting in S. Alvise in Venice.
Ex coll. Algarotti, Venice; entered the Museum 1906.
Engraved by Pietro Monaco.
Molmenti, p. 265, fig. p. 57; Sack, p. 183; Cat. of the Museum, 1921,
p. 466; Morassi, p. 23.
It is the only autograph sketch that I know of the composition,
although there are many other small paintings of it by his pupils or
imitators. There are many differences between this sketch and the
large executed canvas (of which there is a copy by a contemporary
imitator in a private collection in Lugano (q.v.)), but the Berlin *modello*
is a masterpiece of freshness and impetuosity. It is not recorded in the
Catalogue of Algarotti's collection, printed after his death, and must
have been sold before then. The possession of the painting to Algarotti
is stated by Monaco's engraving.
Another version (79.5 × 89 cm.), very weak, was sold at the sale
'Kunstwerke aus dem Besitze der Staatlichen Museen Berlin,' Munich,
Böhler, 19–31.5.1937, cat. No. 672 (with repr.).

RINALDO IN THE GARDEN OF ARMIDA   [1955, fig. 37]
Canvas 39 × 62 cm.; *c.* 1751–53.

Formerly in a Russian Priv. Coll.; entered the Museum 1908 from
England.
Related to the larger painting in Munich (q.v.).
Molmenti, p. 265; Cat. of the Museum, 1931, p. 477; Morassi, p. 32,
colour plate; Lorenzetti, p. 107, fig. 78 bis.
The pendant to this charming painting is in the Cailleux Coll., Paris.

S. DOMINIC INSTITUTING THE ROSARY   Fig. 90
Canvas, 98 × 49 cm.; *c.* 1737.

Entered the Museum 1873 from Rome.
Sketch for the ceiling of the church of the Gesuati, Venice.
Molmenti, p. 265, fig. p. 51; Cat. of the Museum, 1931, p. 476.
A very fine *modelletto*. Another sketch, slightly varied, is in the M. Crespi
Coll., Milan (q.v.). The Berlin sketch differs considerably from the
finished fresco. Lost during the last war.

S. ROCH (full length, in profile, with a dog on the right)   Fig. 168
Canvas, 53 × 41.5 cm.; *c.* 1730–35.

One of the many devotional paintings for the brothers of the Scuola di
San Rocco.
Ex van Diemen Coll.; entered the Museum, 1931.
Cat. of the Museum, 1931, p. 478; Goering, *ad vocem*, as Domenico.

TWENTY-TWO MONOCHROME FRESCOES OF MYTHOLOGICAL
SUBJECTS

Formerly in the 'Stanza dei Satiri' in the Pal. Panigai, Nervesa. One is
dated 1754. Certainly painted with the collaboration of Domenico.
Entered the Museum from Venice 1902.
Five of them are still extant (four in the Gemäldegalerie, Berlin-
Dahlem; the fifth in the Bode Museum, Berlin-Ost). The others
were destroyed during the last war (1945).

Molmenti, pp. 265–266, fig. pp. 261–263; Sack, p. 183; Cat. of the Museum, 1931, p. 478. Morassi, pp. 32–33.

Wall paintings in a highly decorative style.

DEATH OF DIDO
Canvas, 39 × 57 cm.

Entered the Museum 1929 from the art-market.
By a pupil of Tiepolo. After the original by Tiepolo in Moscow.
Rather weak.
Cat. of the Museum, 1931, p. 478, wrongly as by G.B.

RECEPTION OF THE EMPEROR HENRY III AT THE VILLA CONTARINI ALLA MIRA IN 1574   [1955, fig. 42 with
Canvas 72 × 108 cm.   erroneous caption]

By an imitator of Tiepolo.
This picture differs from the fresco (now in Paris, Musée Jacquemart-André), and according to Sack, is a copy of the sketch once in the Rothschild Coll., Frankfurt, and later in the Rothschild Coll., Paris. This latter sketch is probably identical with the one mentioned in the Algarotti Catalogue, present whereabouts unknown.
Molmenti, p. 254; Sack, pp. 118, 183, fig. 106, as a shop work; *Catalogue of the Museum*, 1931, p. 647, as 'workshop'. Now in Trier, Kurfürstliches Palais.

TOILET OF VENUS
Canvas, 109 × 142 cm.

Attributed to Giambattista by Berenson, 1897, p. 132 and by Meissner, 1897, p. 78, fig. 64; assigned to S. Ricci, by Molmenti, p. 292; mentioned by Sack, p. 183 as a copy after Paolo Veronese by a pupil of Tiepolo.
Wrongly as Giambattista in the old *Guides* to the Museum, but rightly as S. Ricci, in the *Catalogue*, 1931, p. 394.

BERLIN, formerly Cassirer

MADONNA AND CHILD WITH S. CATHERINE, S. CHARLES BORROMEO AND S. JOHN, BISHOP
See: Munich, formerly von Nemes Coll.

ALLEGORY OF A QUEEN CRUSHING VICE
See New York, Wildenstein.

BERLIN, formerly Van Diemen Coll.

See New York, Baroness de Becker-Rothschild Coll.

BERLIN, formerly Van Dirksen Coll.

DIANA AND ENDYMION
APOLLO, PAN, AND MIDAS
ACHILLES AND TIRESIAS
Three grisailles on golden background, shaped on the shorter sides.
100 × 197.5 cm.; *c.* 1750–60.

Painted with much assistance from Domenico, certainly under the direction of Giambattista.
Another grisaille from the same series, *The Education of Bacchus*, was in Seusslitz, Fritz Harck Coll.
Later appeared on the Art Market in London (Agnew) *c.* 1934. Present whereabouts unknown.
Not seen by me. Photos in the Berenson Library.
Sack, p. 183, *Apollo*, 1935, XXI, 123, March; p. 171 (both as Giambattista).

BERLIN, formerly Jaffé Coll.

See Bergamo, Private Coll.

BERLIN, formerly Lippmann Coll.

THE CONTINENCE OF SCIPIO
Canvas, 61 × 44 cm.

According to Sack (p. 185) almost identical with the sketch (now in Stockholm Museum) for the fresco in the Villa Cordellina, Montecchio. Present whereabouts unknown.   Probably identical with the one exhibited in Paris (Chefs-d'oeuvre des Coll. Parisiennes) 1950, Cat. p. 42, fig. XVII, which is a very bad copy after the *modello* in Stockholm.

THE MYSTIC MARRIAGE OF S. CATHERINE
See Zurich, Hausammann Coll.

BERLIN, formerly Private Coll.

THE FLIGHT INTO EGYPT (with an angel bowed to the ground on the left.)   Fig. 37
Canvas, 59.4 × 40.8 cm.; *c.* 1762–70.

In the State Museum of Poltava, Ukraine, till 1930; now in New York. An excellent late work of the Spanish period, pale blue in colour and stylistically similar to those in Lisbon. Hitherto unpublished.

BERLIN, formerly Schwabach Coll.

MADONNA AND SAINTS
See Zurich, Private Coll.

BERLIN, formerly Simon Coll.

TULLIA DRIVING HER CHARIOT OVER THE BODY OF HER FATHER
Canvas, 35 × 70 cm.; *c.* 1716–20.   Fig. 301

Morassi, *Burlington Magazine*, Feb.-Mar., 1934, p. 86, fig. A.
Present whereabouts unknown.
One of the most interesting early works by Giambattista, wrongly attributed by Goering (*Guardi*, Vienna, 1944, p. 14, fig. 15) to F. Guardi.

APOTHEOSIS OF ORAZIO PORTO
See Seattle, U.S.A., Art Museum.

SIX MONOCHROMES OF ANCESTORS OF THE DA PORTO FAMILY
See Stockholm, National Museum.

BERLIN, formerly Dr. Voss Coll.

GROUP OF FIGURES   Fig. 409
Canvas 19 × 35 cm.; *c.* 1716–20.

Morassi, *Burlington Magazine*, Oct. 1935, p. 144, fig. C.
In the Exhib. Cat. Wiesbaden (H. Voss), 1935, it is called *The Triumph of David*.
Very early work, certainly autograph.
Now in Private Coll., Strasbourg.

BERLIN, formerly Weisbach Coll.

THE MARTYRDOM OF SS. FAUSTINUS AND JOVITA
Canvas, 49.5 × 69 cm., by Domenico.

Sketch for the fresco in SS. Faustinus and Jovita, Brescia. Pendant to the battle scene in the Brera at Milan.
Sack, p. 304, fig. 317, as painted under Giambattista's direction; Morassi, *Burlington Magazine*, Jan. 1955, p. 8.
Perhaps a work resulting from the collaboration of Giambattista and Domenico, in the sense that Giambattista may have inspired the composition. The frescoes in Brescia were executed by Domenico T. and G. Mengozzi-Colonna in 1754–55 as stated in the Addenda to the two MS. guides by Maccarinelli (*Le Glorie di Brescia*); see Boselli in 'Actes du Congrès int. d'Hist. de l'Art,' Venice, 1955.).

BERLIN, formerly Wertheim Gallery

TRIUMPH OF HERCULES
See Manchester, Currier Gallery of Art.

BERLIN, Art Market

MADONNA AND CHILD WITH A GOLDFINCH
Canvas, oval.

By Domenico.
Attributed to Giambattista, but judging from the reproduction (photo in the Kunsthist. Institut, Florence, 112370) certainly by Domenico, similar to the *Madonna* painted in fresco for the church in Zianigo, now in Ca' Rezzonico, Venice, (repr. in Molmenti, p. 337).

BERLIN-WANNSEE, formerly H. Feist Coll.

MADONNA AND CHILD
Canvas, 50 × 30 cm.

By Domenico, wrongly attributed to Giambattista.
Sale, Fischer, Lucerne, 25-27.5.1944, as Giambattista.

BERLIN-WANNSEE, formerly Grote Coll.

ANTONY AND CLEOPATRA
Canvas, 72 × 58 cm.

Attributed by Sack, p. 196, fig. 118 to Tiepolo, but probably, judging from the reproduction, a school work after an original sketch, present whereabouts unknown.

BESANÇON, Musée

S. ROCH   Fig. 167
Canvas, 62 × 41 cm.; *c.* 1730-35.

Sack, p. 212.
One of the numerous devotional paintings for the Confratelli of the Scuola di San Rocco. Certainly autograph.

S. JOHN THE BAPTIST PREACHING
Canvas 36 × 44 cm.

Old copy by a pupil of Tiepolo after the sketch in the Treccani Coll., Milan (q.v.), for the fresco in the Colleoni Chapel, Bergamo.
Molmenti, p. 248; Sack, p. 212; both as by G.B.

THE CIRCUMCISION
Canvas, 58 × 50 cm.

A work by G. Carpioni, in the Museum attributed to Tiepolo.

BÉZIERS, Musée Fabregat

MADONNA OF THE ROSARY
Canvas, 89 × 69 cm.

Assigned in the *Catalogue* of the Museum (No. 265) and by Galetti-Camesasca, *Enciclopedia della Pittura*, Milan, 1950, *ad vocem*, to Tiepolo, but is a weak painting by a follower.

BIADENE, Chiesa dell' Assunta

THE ASSUMPTION
Ceiling fresco, mentioned by Da Canal (1732, p. XXXII) as one of the first frescoes by Tiepolo. The fresco no longer exists and probably was never executed by Tiepolo since in the archives of the church there is no record of it. In the church there is instead a ceiling fresco with the *Glory of SS. Victor and Lucy*, painted after 1760 by Giambattista Canal.

BIELLA, C. Ajmone Marsan Coll.

MADONNA AND CHILD
See Florence, formerly Private Coll.

BILTMORE (Asheville), North Carolina, Biltmore House, formerly Vanderbilt

AURORA WITH ANGELS AND PUTTI
Ceiling fresco, believed to be by Tiepolo, but by C. A. Pellegrini.

Bought in Italy before 1914 as by Tiepolo.
This composition (or the sketch for it, or some drawing) certainly inspired Guardi's canvas of the same subject in the Palazzo Labia, Venice.
Morassi, in *Emporium*, Nov. 1958, p. 195 ff., Figs. 1-5.

BIRAGO (Lentate on Seveso, near Milan),
Palazzo formerly Casnedi-Raimondi

Frescoes in the main saloon and other rooms, wrongly attributed by Molfese Centelli, 1897, to Tiepolo and rightly doubted by Molmenti, p. 149, fig. p. 148; not mentioned by Sack. They are by the same hand as the frescoes in the Palace formerly Visconti at Brignano d'Adda (q.v.); that is, M. Bortoloni.

BOLOGNA, Ettore Modiano Coll.

ALEXANDER AND DIOGENES   Fig. 282
Canvas 43 × 54 cm.; *c.* 1730-35.

Morassi, *Le Arti*, II, 1942, p. 266, fig. 24; Morassi, p. 20, fig. 44.
Very characteristic and well preserved painting in a greyish blue tonality, of the period between Bergamo and Biron.
A weak contemporary copy (43 × 56 cm.) was on the market in Florence in 1957; another in Leningrad.

A MIRACLE OF S. ANTHONY   Fig. 131
Canvas, 48 × 29 cm.; *c.* 1754-60.

Sketch for the altarpiece at Mirano.
Fiocco, *Rivista di Venezia*, 1929, pp. 55, 66; Modigliani, *Dedalo*, 1933, p. 136; Lorenzetti, p. 105, fig. 77 bis.
The finished altarpiece shows many variations from this sketch.

BORDEAUX, Musée

REBECCA AND ELIEZER
Canvas, 97 × 137 cm.

By Molmenti, p. 247, fig. p. 250 and in the *Catalogue* of the Museum, 1933, and in the Museum itself attributed to Giambattista, whereas it is by Giambattista Pittoni.
Sack, p. 212, mentions it as not by Tiepolo.

BOSTON, Mass., Museum of Fine Arts

APOTHEOSIS OF AENEAS   [1955, fig. 57]
Canvas, 66 × 50 cm.; *c.* 1764-66.

S. de Vito-Battaglia, 1931, p. 6; L. Venturi, 1933, III, pl. 594; Morassi, p. 39; Lorenzetti, p. 156, fig. 96. This sketch is probably a preparatory study for the ceiling fresco in Madrid. It differs in composition from the finished work, whereas the sketch in Cambridge, Mass. (q.v.), is exactly like the fresco.

AURORA DISPERSING THE CLOUDS OF NIGHT   Fig. 340
Canvas, shaped for a ceiling, 183 × 137 cm.; *c.* 1755-60.

Removed from the Pal. Mocenigo, Venice.
Sack, p. 91; Constable, *Bulletin of the Museum*, Boston, VI, 1940, with reproductions.
A rather decorative ceiling composition, for a little room (*salotto*), with painted rocaille ornaments on the whole border.

ALLEGORY OF MERIT   Fig. 350
Canvas, oval, 33 × 42 cm.; *c.* 1755-60.

Ex coll. Ross, given to the Museum in 1906.
Sack, p. 227, as identical with the one formerly in the Sellar Coll., sold 1889 in Paris.
Sketch for a ceiling, in rapid and free brushwork.

BOSTON, Mass., Isabella Stewart Gardner Museum

THE MARRIAGE OF BARBAROSSA   [1955, fig. 34]
Canvas, 71 × 54 cm.; 1751-52.

One of the sketches for the fresco in the Kaisersaal at Würzburg.
Molmenti, p. 284; Hendy, *Catalogue of the Paintings in the Gardner Museum*, Boston, 1931, pp. 358–359, fig. p. 358.
Another sketch in London, National Gallery (q.v.), has many changes. The one in Boston differs greatly from the finished fresco. Freeden and Lamb, 1956, p. 43 (fig. 30), consider this sketch the first, that in London the second version for the fresco.

BREMEN, Kunsthalle

GLORY OF SAINTS
Canvas, 84 × 77 cm.; *c.* 1754–55.

From the Coll. of Baron von Stumm, German Ambassador in Rome before the first World War; Private Coll., Wiesbaden.
Sketch for a ceiling fresco, probably the preparatory study for the fresco in the church of SS. Faustino e Giovita, Brescia, which was executed by Domenico, *c.* 1754–55. The differences between the sketch and the fresco are very remarkable (see Morassi, *Brescia*, Rome 1939, p. 214, fig. 215). The two Saints in the upper part of the sketch are Faustino and Giovita, the female Saint is Afra, and the Bishop in the lower part may be S. Augustine. It can be assumed that Domenico helped his father in this painting and that the upper part may have been executed by him.
Exhib. Würzburg, 1951; *Cat.* by Freeden, p. 15; Morassi, in *The Burlington Magazine*, 1955, I, pp. 10–11, fig. II.

BRESCIA, Pinacoteca

S. SEBASTIAN
Canvas, 67 × 41 cm.

Old copy, perhaps by Raggi, of the sketch for the altarpiece in Diessen. Wrongly attributed to Tiepolo in the Museum *Catalogues*.
Filippini Bequest, No. 220.

BRESCIA, Chiesa dei SS. Faustino e Giovita

The frescoes on the ceiling of the presbytery, representing the *Glory of the Saints Faustinus and Giovita*, executed as is stated by the old *Guides*, by Domenico Tiepolo, have been recently attributed to Giambattista (A. Riccoboni, in *Acropoli*, Milano 1960–61, I, pp. 55, 56). This attribution is based on the sketch in Bremen, Kunsthalle (q.v.) and on supposed stylistic reasons.
As I have already pointed out, the ceiling frescoes in Brescia were certainly painted by Domenico following the directions of Giambattista. Domenico was the 'alter ego' who executed, in this case, the ideas of his father. He had painted in Würzburg side by side with Giambattista. Now (1754–55) he was ripe to work alone also in this large ceiling. The two lateral scenes in the same church were painted also by Domenico alone.
For the Bibliography of this question see principally: A. Morassi, in *The Burlington Magazine*, January, 1955, and the above mentioned article by Riccoboni.

BRESCIA, Palazzo Avogadro

Rodella (or Carboni) mentions in his volume of 1760, p. 182, three overdoors by G. B. Tiepolo as then existing in the Palazzo of the Conti Avogadro in the third room. Nothing more is known of these works.

BRESCIA, Conte Fausto Lechi Coll.

THE ASSUMPTION, WITH S. THERESA AND A BISHOP SAINT
Canvas, 47 × 35 cm.; *c.* 1735–40.   Fig. 150

A rather superficial sketch for an unknown or never executed painting. Hitherto unpublished.

BRESSANONE (Brixen), Museum Diocesanum

THE GATHERING OF THE MANNA
Canvas, copy after the original sketch for Verolanuova which is in Buenos Aires (q.v.).

On the back an old inscription with the date (17)41.

BRIGNANO D'ADDA, Castello formerly Visconti
(now of the Count G. Citterio)

SCENES FROM THE CRUSADES and ALLEGORICAL SCENES
Frescoes in the saloon, framed with feigned architecture in a Gothic-Baroque style. In the *Guides* of the T.C.I. and in the local literature attributed to Tiepolo, but the frescoes are certainly by Bortoloni.

BRUSSELS, Musée Royal des Beaux-Arts

SACRIFICE OF POLYXENA
Canvas, 94 × 128 cm.

Bought 1904 from the Somzée Coll.
Attributed by Molmenti to Tiepolo (p. 261, fig. p. 257) and by Sack (p. 223) to S. Ricci, but certainly by F. Bencovich.

BUDAPEST, Museum of Fine Arts

MADONNA WITH FIVE SAINTS   Fig. 85
Canvas, 73 × 56 cm., *c.* 1750–60.

Ex coll. J. L. Pyrker, Budapest.
Molmenti, p. 282; Sack, p. 201, fig. 199; A. Pigler, *Catalogue of the Paintings of the Museum*, Budapest, 1937, p. 255; Cat. of the Museum, 1954, p. 560.

S. JAMES OF COMPOSTELA   [1955, fig. 64]
Canvas, 317 × 162 cm.; *c.* 1767–70.

Signed *G. Tiepolo F.*
Painted for the Convent of Aranjuez, Spain, and mentioned by Bermudez and others as *S. Charles.*
Engraved by Domenico (De Vesme, 63) as *S. James on Horseback*, Madrid.
Formerly in the Esterhazy Coll. in Vienna, and afterwards in Budapest.
Molmenti, p. 282, fig. p. 280a; Sack, p. 200, fig. 132; A. Pigler, *Catalogue*, p. 254, Morassi, p. 39, fig. 128. M. Precerutti, in *Commentari*, April–June, 1958, pp. 118–120, fig. 5.

THE FLIGHT INTO EGYPT
Canvas, 48 × 65 cm.

By Domenico.
Formerly L. K. Beer Coll.
Molmenti, p. 179, fig. p. 179, wrongly attributed to Giambattista. Sack, p. 308, fig. 325, and A. Pigler, *Catalogue*, p. 225, as Domenico.

GOD THE FATHER
Canvas, 96 × 81 cm.

By Domenico.
Berenson, 1897, III ed., p. 133 as by Giambattista; Molmenti, p. 309, fig. p. 310, as by an imitator; Sack, p. 201, A. Pigler, *Catalogue* pp. 255–256, as Domenico.

THE VISION OF S. JEROME
Ascribed by Sack (p. 201–202) to Tiepolo, but it is by F. Fontebasso.

BUDAPEST, formerly in the Szapary Palace

APOTHEOSIS OF FRANCESCO MOROSINI PELOPONNESIACO
See Paris, A. de Rothschild Coll.

BUENOS AIRES, Museo Nacional de Bellas Artes

THE GATHERING OF THE MANNA   Fig. 21
THE SACRIFICE OF MELCHISEDEK   Fig. 9
Two canvases, each 91 × 67 cm.; *c.* 1735–40.

They are identical with the sketches once in the Maccari Coll., Venice. (Compare the illustrations in Molmenti, pp. 150–151).
Entered the Museum in 1938 as gift of Señora Maria Salome de Guerrico de Lamarca and S. Mercedes de Guerrico. Not seen by me. Judging on the photographs, I am convinced they are the autograph sketches for the large canvases in Verolanuova, from which they differ in

many parts. Copies of the *Gathering* in Bressanone and Oxford (q.v.).
Molmenti, pp. 150–151, as by a follower; Sack, p. 43, fig. 16 confusing
the version once in the Schloss Plausdorf (now in Oxford) with the
Maccari one.

THE FLIGHT INTO EGYPT
Canvas, 93 × 70 cm.

Wrongly attributed to Tiepolo in the Museum. The canvas is identifiable as the sketch for Andrea Pozzo's altarpiece of 1701, now in the
Chapel of the *Pia Congregazione dei Banchieri e Mercanti* in Turin
(reproduced in 'Torino,' June 1942, fig. 20).

GOD THE FATHER WITH THE GLOBE
Oil on paper, 45.5 × 40 cm.

Wrongly attributed to Tiepolo; a poor work which has nothing to do
with him.

BURANO, S. Martino

THE CRUCIFIXION   Fig. 58
Canvas 250 × 400 cm.; *c.* 1720–22. In bad condition.

In the bottom left-hand corner is the portrait of the donor, a pharmacist
of Burano. A drawing for this picture is in the Ferdinandeum, Innsbruck.
Molmenti, p. 51; Sack, p. 159; Fogolari, 1923, pp. 61–62; Morassi,
1943, p. 15; Pallucchini, 1944, p. 3 ff. with repr.
Very interesting work of the early period. It shows connections with
Tintoretto and is rather Piazzettesque in colour. Recently restored.

CADIZ, Museo Provincial de Bellas Artes

GIRL WITH A TAMBOURINE
Canvas, 64 × 50 cm.

By Domenico.
Molmenti, p. 197, fig. p. 198; Sack, p. 208; Sanchez-Cantón, 1953,
p. 24, all wrongly attributing it to Giambattista.
There is a drawing for this picture, also certainly by Domenico but
wrongly attributed to Giambattista, in the Museum at Bayonne.

CAEN, Musée des Beaux-Arts

ECCE HOMO   Fig. 52
Canvas, 57 × 37 cm.; *c.* 1760–70.

An impressive work, very close to Domenico.
G. Lefrançois Bequest, 1839.
De Chennevières, *Observations sur le Musée*, Argentan 1851, p. 18;
Molmenti, p. 309, fig. p. 310, as by an imitator; Sack, p. 212, as doubt-
ful; Catalogue du Musée de Caen, 1928, No. 38; *Exhib. Catalogue*,
Bordeaux 1956, p. 30.

CAMBRIDGE, Mass., Fogg Art Museum

S. ROCH   Fig. 159
Canvas, 44.5 × 31.5 cm.; *c.* 1730–35.

One of the many small devotional paintings for the brothers of the
Scuola di S. Rocco in Venice. A good contemporary copy was on the
market in Milan.
Entered the Museum from the Heimann Coll., New York.
Morassi, in *Le Arti*, 1942, p. 267, fig. 25; Morassi, p. 20.

APOTHEOSIS OF AENEAS   [1955, fig. 60]
Canvas, 71 × 51 cm.; 1764–66.

Sketch for the Royal Palace in Madrid.
Ex coll. Herzog, Budapest; Von Nemes, Munich; acquired by the
Museum, 1950.
Morassi, 1943, p. 38; Lorenzetti, p. 136, fig. 97.
This sketch is very similar to the finished fresco. Another sketch,
different in composition, but certainly also for the ceiling fresco in
Madrid, is in Boston (q.v.).

CAMBRIDGE, Mass., formerly Fogg Art Museum

THE VIRGIN HEARING THE PRAYERS OF S. DOMINIC   Fig. 94
Canvas, 38 × 52 cm.; *c.* 1737.

A *modello* (or a contemporary copy of an unknown original sketch)
for one of the smaller compartments of the ceiling of the church of the
Gesuati, Venice. The pendant, *Glory of S. Dominic*, is in the Johnson
Coll., Philadelphia.
This picture was lent to the Museum for the summer of 1923 by an
anonymous owner. Present whereabouts unknown. Not seen by me.
Photographs in the Frick Art Reference Library (neg. 1323) and in the
Witt Library.
Sack, p. 155, records two sketches once in the Sellar Coll., London,
sold in Paris, 1889: they are perhaps identical with this and the one in
Philadelphia.

CASTELGOMBERTO, Schio, Vicenza, Conte da Schio Coll.

ULYSSES DISCOVERING ACHILLES AMONG THE DAUGHTERS OF
LYCOMEDES
Canvas, 270 × 520 cm.

HERCULES AND ANTAEUS   [1955, fig. 11]
Canvas, 270 × 125 cm.

APOLLO AND MARSYAS
Canvas, 270 × 135 cm.

Three canvases, *c.* 1725, formerly in the Pal. Sandi, Venice.
Da Canal, 1732; Sack, p. 163; Morassi, p. 16, fig. 16; Lorenzetti, p. 21,
figs. 13–15.
Very impetuous paintings, heavily impasted, showing various Seicento
influences. In excellent state. They formerly belonged to the same room
as the ceiling frescoes of the Palazzo Sandi in Venice.

CHICAGO, Art Institute

RINALDO AND ARMIDA SURPRISED BY UBALDO AND GUELFO
RINALDO ENCHANTED BY ARMIDA   [1955, Pl. 69]
RINALDO ABANDONS ARMIDA
RINALDO AND THE OLD HERMIT   Figs. 273–275
The first two canvases, each 187 × 264 cm.; the other two, each 187 × 216
cm.; *c.* 1750–55.

Originally in the Palace of the Counts Serbelloni of Milan, in Venice
(according to Molmenti, 1911).
Ex coll. Cartier, Genoa; Sedelmayer, Paris; J. Deering, Chicago.
F. Malaguzzi-Valeri in *Rassegna d'Arte*, Oct. 1908, p. 179 ff., with repr.;
Molmenti, pp. 145–146, fig. pp. 145–146; Molmenti, 1911, p. 188;
Sack, p. 236; L. Venturi, 1933, III, pl. 589–592; Catton Rich, 1938
pp. 19–20; Morassi, p. 35, fig. 103.
The *Rinaldo enchanted by Armida* engraved by Domenico (De Vesme,
94); the *Rinaldo and Armida surprised* engraved by Lorenzo (De Vesme,
4). These four paintings, which show themes often repeated by Tiepolo
at Würzburg and in the Villa Valmarana, are excellent specimens of
his most decorative style of the 'fifties.

MADONNA WITH SS. DOMINIC AND HYACINTH   Fig. 96
Canvas, 275 × 138 cm.; *c.* 1730–35.

Ex coll. Morselli, Florence; Bloch, Vienna; Müller, Amsterdam (1905);
Kleinberger, New York; M. Ryerson, Chicago.
Sack, p. 205, fig. 71a; Molmenti, p. 263, fig. p. 258, mentions the
painting then in a Priv. Coll. in Dublin.
An altarpiece, painted in a fluent and grandiose style, for an unknown
church or private chapel.

S. DOMINIC INSTITUTING THE ROSARY
Canvas, 97 × 49 cm.

Ex coll. M. A. Ryerson, Chicago (1913).
Catton Rich, 1938, p. 18; Middeldorf, Bulletin of the Art Institute of
Chicago, 1940, pp. 54–57.
Probably a contemporary copy of the sketch in the Crespi Coll.,
Milan (q.v.). Another autograph version is in the Kaiser Friedrich
Museum, Berlin (q.v.).

S. JEROME IN THE DESERT
Canvas, 33 × 22 cm.; *c.* 1722–25.

Ex coll. G. Palumbo, Rome; Charles and Mary Worcester, Chicago (1928).
Catton Rich, 1938, p. 17; Lorenzetti, p. 45, fig. 32.
A rather weak and not very well preserved early work.

CHICAGO, Everett D. Graff Coll.

THE ANGEL APPEARING TO ABRAHAM AND SARAH

By Domenico.
See Paris, formerly Schloss Coll.

CHIOGGIA, Cathedral

SS. FELIX AND FORTUNATUS TORTURED
Large altarpiece.

By a follower of Tiepolo.
Given to the Republic of Venice by the Podestà of Chioggia, Agostino Maffetti (1729–31).
Molmenti, p. 108; Sack, p. 49; Goering, *ad vocem*, (as Giambattista in each case); Pallucchini, *Arte Veneta*, 1948, pp. 135–136, rightly believes the picture to be by a mediocre follower.

CHIOGGIA, Canonico Giovanni Vianelli Coll.

S. PAULINUS HEALING A POSSESSED MAN
Canvas, 46 × 35 cm.

Sketch for the altarpiece, engraved by Domenico, now in the Museo Civico in Padua, and known also as 'Miracle of S. Patrick of Ireland.' This sketch was recorded in 1790 in the Vianelli Coll. (*Catalogo dei quadri ecc.*, Venice, 1790), and after this year disappeared.
In the same Coll. there were also four 'Studies for Heads', now missing:
BUST OF A TURK
Canvas, 41.5 × 32.5 cm.
HEAD OF AN OLD MAN
Cardboard, 37.5 × 28.5 cm.
HEAD OF AN OLD MAN
Cardboard, 27.5 × 21 cm.
HEAD OF A BOY
Cardboard, 37.5 × 28.5 cm.
The first 'Head' (*Bust of a Turk*), was engraved by Domenico and passed later to the Bullo Coll., Venice (Molmenti, 1911, p. 91).
Sack, pp. 232–233.

CINCINNATI, Ohio, Art Museum

S. CHARLES BORROMEO   Fig. 190
Canvas, 124 × 112 cm.; *c.* 1767–69.

Fragment from the Aranjuez altarpiece. Acquired by the Museum in 1924.
Morassi, p. 38; Morassi, *Emporium*, 1950, XI, p. 208, fig. 13; Richardson, 1952, pp. 56–57, fig. 72.
The sketch or *modello* is in the coll. of Count Seilern, London (q.v.).
This is the central part of the altarpiece: nothing is known of the remainder.

CLEVELAND, Ohio, Museum of Art

THE MARTYRDOM OF S. SEBASTIAN   Fig. 116
Canvas, 53 × 31 cm.; *c.* 1739.

Modelletto for the altarpiece at Diessen. Perhaps the original sent for approval to the Augustinians. Formerly in the Convent at Diessen; ex coll. Dr. Kadisch, Vienna; Seligmann, Paris.
Molmenti, p. 160; Sack, p. 187; Froelich-Bume, *Burlington Magazine*, February, 1938, p. 82, fig. A; H. S. Francis, 1947, *Cleveland Bulletin*, XXXIV, I, p. 3.
This is the only original sketch for the Diessen altarpiece I know. The others (see e.g. Brescia) are copies or derivations. Another old copy is the sketch formerly in Holzhausen, v. Stumm Coll. (photo in the Kunsthist Inst., Florence, No. 62711).

APOTHEOSIS OF A WARRIOR   Fig. 356
Canvas, 41 × 34 cm.; *c.* 1750–60.

Sketch, in poor condition, for an unknown ceiling, iconographically very closely related to the *Apotheosis of Francesco Morosini* in Paris, A. de Rothschild Coll., now in Milan.
Gift of L. E. Holden, 1916.
Catalogue of the Collection of Paintings presented to the Cleveland Museum of Art by Mrs. Liberty E. Holden, Cleveland, 1917, pp. 35–36; H. S. Francis, *Cleveland Bulletin*, July, 1932, pp. 115–117.

PORTRAIT OF A LADY
Canvas, 62 × 51 cm.

By Domenico.
Ex coll. R. Owen, Paris; Agnew, London; Dalton Coll., Cleveland.
Venturi, *International Studio*, 1928, IV, p. 55, pl. CCCCXXX; L. Venturi, 1933, III, pl. 595; H. Tietze, *Meisterwerke Europæischer Malerei in Amerika*, Vienna 1934, Pl. 113; Catton Rich, 1938, p. 38, fig. 64; Sánchez-Cantón, 1953, p. 25, fig. 38. Exh. Cat., Bordeaux, 1956, No. 58. In each case attributed to Giambattista.

HORATIUS COCLES SWIMMING THE TIBER
THE FIGHT OF HORATIUS COCLES
Two canvases, each 140 × 204 cm.
Attributed to Giambattista; but by a pupil of his, certainly Menescardi. Once in the Demotte Coll., Paris; then in Venice. From the William H. Marlatt Fund to the Museum, 1949.
The Cleveland Museum of Art *Handbook*, 1958, No. 428, still attributing them to Giambattista.

COLOGNE, Wallraf-Richartz Museum

THE ADORATION OF THE MAGI
Canvas, 43 × 57 cm.

By Domenico.
Ex coll. Sthamer, Hamburg; acquired by the Museum in 1885.
Sack, p. 190, fig. 180, wrongly attributed to Giambattista. The pendant, an *Adoration of the Shepherds*, was also in the Sthamer Coll. in Hamburg, and is also reproduced by Sack (fig. 179) as by Giambattista.

COLOGNE, Baron Guillaume Coll.

APOTHEOSIS OF A WARRIOR   Fig. 369
Fresco, *c.* 10 m. in diameter; *c.* 1755–60 (?).

Circular ceiling, removed in 1909 from the Pal. Correr near Sta Fosca, Venice. Destroyed during the 1939–45 war.
It represented the glorification of a warrior (perhaps a member of the Correr family). The grisaille friezes by Domenico of a *Sacrifice* and a *Roman Triumph* are in the Pal. Polignac, Venice (q.v.), while the remaining friezes, of *Fauns and Faunesses*, and two other *Roman Scenes* are now lost or present whereabouts unknown. Not seen by me. Not possible to judge from the reproduction whether or not it is by Giambattista or Domenico.
A. Melani, in *Arte dec. ed ind.*, Nov. 1903, pp. 88–9 with reps.; Molmenti p. 273, fig. p. 272; Sack, p. 235.

COLOGNE, Pechmann Coll.

MADONNA AND CHILD
Canvas, 71 × 55 cm.

By Domenico.
Sack, fig. 227 as by Giambattista.

COPENHAGEN, Statens Museum for Kunst

THE BETROTHAL   Fig. 286
Canvas, oval, 140.5 × 109 cm.; *c.* 1745–50.

Taken to Paris in 1873; Camondo Coll., Paris; Baron Adolphe de Rothschild Coll., Paris; Dr. Kranz Coll., Vienna; von Auspitz Coll., Vienna. Acquired by the Museum in 1938. With three other canvases

(Augsburg; Washington, N.G.; Pavia, Necchi Coll.) it formed part of the decoration of Pal. Barbaro, Venice.
Molmenti, pp. 271, 274; Sack, pp. 113, 150, fig. 138; *Catalogue* of the Museum, 1946, p. 300.

APOLLO AND MARSYAS   Fig. 249
Canvas, 45.5×53 cm.; *c.* 1755–60.

Ex coll. A. von Nell, Trier; Scholz-Forni Coll., Hamburg; to the Museum *c.* 1950.
Sack, p. 196, fig. 193; A. v. Schneider, *Aus der Sammlung Scholz-Forni*, Hamburg, 1937, p. 158, fig. 159; Morassi, p. 35, fig. 105.
An excellent work in a light tonality.

CARNIVAL SCENE
Canvas, 35×57.5 cm.

By Domenico.
Acquired from Mrs. C. Lund, Copenhagen, in 1928.
It belongs to the same type as the four *Carnival Scenes* in Kansas City (q.v.).
Catalogue of the Museum, 1946, p. 301, attributed to the School of Giambattista Tiepolo.

THE MEETING OF ANTONY AND CLEOPATRA
Canvas, 76×53 cm.

Wrongly attributed to Giambattista; old copy of the fresco in the Palazzo Labia, Venice.
Formerly at Würzburg; Oppenheim Sale, Cologne, 1878; then acquired by the Glyptothek.
Sack, p. 205, attributed to Giambattista.

CRACOW, University Museum

ANGELICA AND MEDORO
Canvas, 52×40.7 cm.

By Domenico.
Probably from the Trotti Coll., Paris, because a photograph of this painting, labelled as Giambattista, was given to the Kunsthistorisches Institut in Florence by Count Trotti. *Catalogue* of the Exhibition of Italian Paintings in Polish Collections, Warsaw, 1956, No. 96, p. 107, fig. 106 (doubtfully as Giambattista).

CRACOW, Wawel Castle

DEATH OF S. JOSEPH
Canvas, 42×55 cm.

By a follower of Tiepolo, probably Domenico (judging by the photograph).
Attributed by A. Venturi (in the Inventory of the Collection) to Giambattista.
Catalogue of the Exhibition of Italian Paintings in Polish Collections, Warsaw 1956, No. 95, p. 107, fig. 107 (doubtfully as Giambattista.)

CRAUGLIO, (Friuli) Palazzo Steffaneo, formerly of the Counts Monaco

Frescoes attributed by Molmenti, p. 87, fig. p. 248 to Giambattista; they are by F. Chiaruttini (see Morassi, 1915, pp. 62–82 with repr.; C. Mutinelli, in 'Atti dell' Accademia di Scienze, Lettere ed Arti', Udine 1953, 257 ff.)

DARMSTADT, Coll. von Merk
MINUET
Canvas, 75.5×120 cm.

By Domenico.
Attributed to Giambattista by Molmenti, p. 206, fig. p. 204 and by Sack, p. 186, fig. III, has to be considered as a masterpiece by Domenico.

DESENZANO, Parish Church

THE LAST SUPPER   Fig. 49
Canvas, 284×138 cm.; 1738, or shortly before.

Signed on the step at the base of the picture: G. B. TIEPOLO O.
Engraved by Domenico (De Vesme 33). Placed in the church *c.* 1738; this date, which relates to the finishing of the Chapel, commissioned by Piero Panizza, is inscribed on a stone in the floor (Documents in the Parish Archives).
Molmenti, p. 149, fig, p. 149; Sack, p. 167; E. Calabi, *Catalogue*, Brescia, 1935, p. 112, (with the local literature); Panazza and Boselli, *Catalogue*, 1946, p. 159.
Not in very good condition, much restored. It is difficult to explain how some parts of this picture are so close to Domenico's style, in spite of the date resulting from the documents. Perhaps the painting was restored by Domenico himself at a later period.

DESSAU, Castle

S. ROCH AS A PILGRIM
Two canvases, 43×33 cm.; *c.* 1730–35.

Destroyed in the 1939–45 war; not seen by me.
Sack, p. 187; mentioned in the Catalogue of the Gemäldegalerie in Berlin, 1931, p. 478, as then in a private collection in Berlin.

DETROIT, Art Institute

MADONNA AND CHILD
Canvas, oval, 48×42 cm.; *c.* 1725–30.

W. Heil, in *Bulletin* of the Detroit Institute, 1929, X, III, p. 73; Heil, *Catalogue* of the Detroit Institute of Arts, 1930, No. 223 with repr.; Catton Rich, 1938, p. 18.
Rather weak early work, of which an old copy was on the American market. (Seligman Sale, Parke-Bernet, New York, 23–24.1.1947, No. 224.)

GIRL PLAYING A MANDOLINE   Fig. 414
Canvas, 93×74 cm.; *c.* 1755–60.

From the Biron Coll. (?), Paris (?); Private Coll., New York; in the Detroit Institute 1958.
One of Tiepolo's most beautiful portraits, undoubtedly representing his ideal model, the so-called 'Cristina'. Very close in style to the frescoes of the Villa Valmarana, with its broken draperies and nervous handwriting.
Morassi, in *Art Quarterly*, Summer 1958, pp. 177 ff., with repr.
An old, weak copy is in the Louvre (stores).

S. JOSEPH WITH THE CHRIST CHILD   Fig. 196
Canvas, 154×110 cm.; 1767–69.

Large fragment from the Aranjuez altarpiece.
Formerly in the Prado, Madrid; ex coll. Marques de Remisa, Madrid; Moret, Madrid; Moray Sale (Coll. Mme. L. K., Geneva), Sotheby, London, 9.6.1932.
Sack, p. 209, fig. 131a; W. R. Valentiner in *Bulletin* of the Detroit Institute, 1944–45, XXIV, p. 26; Richardson, 1952, pp. 57–58, fig. 73.
Splendid late work, pale blue in colour. A small fragment from this altarpiece of a *Cherub with a Crown of Lilies* is in the Prado, Madrid (q.v.), and another one in New York, formerly French (q.v.).

ALEXANDER AND THE DAUGHTERS OF DARIUS
Canvas, 118×97 cm.

By Domenico; probably a pendant to the *Continence of Scipio*, Frankfurt, Staedel Institute (q.v.).
Ex coll. Schnackenberg, Munich; Julius Böhler, Munich. C(lyde) B(urroughs), *Bulletin* of the Detroit Institute of Arts, 1925, VII, Nov., p. 13 with fig.; Venturi, *Studi dal vero*, 1927, pp. 399–400, fig. 276; Heil, *Catalogue*, 1930, No. 222 with repr.; Catton Rich, 1938, Cat. No. 15; Lorenzetti, p. 76, fig 56 bis. In each case wrongly attributed to Giambattista.

THE IMMACULATE CONCEPTION
Canvas, 36×30 cm.

Contemporary copy after the sketch in Amiens.
Formerly Vienna (1903); Weber Coll., Hamburg; von Nemes, Munich.
Molmenti, p. 311, fig. p. 317, as by an imitator; Sack, p. 188; Heil, *Catalogue*, 1930, No. 224 with repr., both attributing to Giambattista.

DIESSEN, Convent Church

THE MARTYRDOM OF S. SEBASTIAN   Fig. 119
Altarpiece 410×200 cm.; dated 1739.

Commissioned by the Augustinians of Diessen (when the church was rebuilt in 1739-40). They commissioned Pittoni's *Martyrdom of S. Stephen*, still in the church, at the same time.
Molmenti, p. 160, fig. p. 160; Sack, p. 187, fig. 56; Froehlich-Bume, *The Burlington Magazine*, 1938, February, p. 82; Goering, 1944, pp. 100-101, with figs.
The *modello* is in the Museum of Cleveland (q.v.).

DIJON, Musée des Beaux-Arts

THE EDUCATION OF THE VIRGIN   Fig. 70
Canvas, 48×27 cm.; c. 1720-25.

Dard Bequest.
Argan, 1933, p. 52 with fig.; Lorenzetti, p. 14, fig. 8.
Very early sketch for an unknown or never executed altarpiece. The same subject in another, later, sketch in the Cini Coll., Venice (q.v.), and another one in the Basevi Coll., Genoa (q.v.).

DRESDEN, Gallery

THE TRIUMPH OF AMPHITRITE   [1955, pl. 28]
Canvas, 188×442 cm.; c. 1740.

Originally in the Villa Girola, Como, and later with Artaria, Vienna.
Modern, 1902, pp. 239-241 with figs.; Molmenti, p. 277, fig. p. 278; Sack, p. 203, fig. 203; Morassi, p. 22, figs, 50-51.
With the two paintings now in the Timken Coll., New York, it formed a cycle representing the elements of *Water*, *Air* and *Earth*. We do not know if there was, as has been suggested, a fourth painting with the *Fire*. A sketch related to the *Triumph* is in Lisbon (q.v.); another (certainly by a pupil), in Trieste (q.v.). Taken to Moscow by the Russians in 1945, returned to Dresden, 1956. One of the most fascinating masterpieces by Tiepolo. The cycle was recorded in an *Inventory* of the Villa Girola, c. 1829.

THE CHILD MARY PRESENTED TO GOD THE FATHER   Fig. 69
Canvas, 244×121 cm.; signed and dated, '*GIO. BATTA. TIEPOLO, O. 1759.*'

In the Cloister of the Benedettine at Cividale until 1810; then Pinacoteca del Liceo di Udine, Udine. Disappeared; purchased by the Milanese dealer Sabajo before 1845; Coll. Don Agostino Quarzoli, Milan; ex coll. Crespi Milan; Crespi Sale, Petit, Paris, June 4, 1914.
Melani, *Arte e Storia*, IV, 1896; A. Venturi, 1900, pp. 179-183 with figs.; Molmenti, p. 147, fig. p. 144; Sack, p. 172, fig. 127.
Engraved by Lorenzo (De Vesme, 1).
The sketch is in the Rijksmuseum, Amsterdam (q.v.). In the background is a view of Cividale.
This masterpiece, requested for the Exhibition in Venice, 1896, was not recognised as an original by Tiepolo, and refused (Melani, *loc. cit.* 1896).

THE PRESENTATION IN THE TEMPLE
Canvas, 40×38.5 cm.

By Domenico.
Molmenti, p. 271, correctly attributing it to Domenico; Sack, p. 187, fig. 30, assigns it to Giambattista. The same composition occurs in the picture by Domenico in Milan, Ambrosiana.

DUBLIN, National Gallery of Ireland

CHRIST AND THE MAGDALEN IN THE HOUSE OF THE PHARISEE
Canvas, 130×160 cm.; c. 1760-61.   Fig. 47

Copy of a painting by Paolo Veronese; executed for Count Algarotti.
Ex coll. Colchester, Walcot, Purford, Surrey; T. Barlow, London.
Molmenti, p. 236, fig. p. 257, Sack, p. 232, who lists it among the lost works; Morassi, p. 35, fig. 107; Catton Rich, 1938, p. 17, fig. p. 60.
Most interesting specimen of the style of Tiepolo in copying Veronese, his favourite master. The original painting by Veronese, in the Pal. Durazzo (later Reale) in Genoa until the mid-19th Cent., is now in the Pinacoteca, Turin.
It is probably to this canvas that Tiepolo's letter to Algarotti refers (16th March, 1761), in which he writes that the '*Cena*' was almost finished. Another probable reference to the picture is in a letter of 4th April, 1761, where it is mentioned as finished. From some letters it is interesting to learn that Tiepolo was commissioned by Count Algarotti to repaint for him an old copy of the '*Cena*' (the large painting originally executed by Veronese for the Chiesa dei Servi in Venice now in the Louvre). This old copy was never freshened up because of Tiepolo's departure for Spain (letter of 9th January, 1762, by Tiepolo). Another copy after Veronese by Tiepolo, of the *Rape of Europa*, was once in the A. L. Cliffe Coll., London (q.v.); another splendid interpretation after Veronese, in Melbourne (q.v.).

THE TRIUMPH OF FAITH (or, more correctly, ALLEGORY OF THE IMMACULATE VIRGIN)   Fig. 72
Canvas 58×44 cm.; c. 1760-70.

Wrongly said (by Sack) to be a sketch for the ceiling of the Church of the Pietà, Venice.
Molmenti, p. 263; Sack, p.223.

DÜSSELDORF, Exh. of Paintings from Private Collections, 1929

MADONNA AND SAINTS
See Wiesbaden, formerly Dr. Hohmann Coll.

EDINBURGH, National Gallery of Scotland

MOSES SAVED FROM THE WATERS   [1955, pls. 70-71]
Canvas, 200×339 cm.; c. 1755-60.

Originally in the Pal. Barbarigo, Venice; Thomas Hamlet Coll., Denham Court, Bucks, Sale 22nd May, 1841; presented to the Royal Institution, Edinburgh, in 1845. A *Halberdier*, cut from the right-hand side of this picture was formerly in the Fauchier-Magnan Coll., Paris, and later in the Tree Coll., London (q.v.).
Waagen, 1854, vol. III, p. 271; Berenson, *Venetian Painters*, 1894, p. 133; Molmenti, p. 263; Sack, p. 223; *Der Cicerone*, January-February, 1913; *Catalogue* of the Gallery, 1936, p. 299; Morassi, p. 35, fig. 106.
Exhibited together with the *Halberdier* at the Exhibition of Italian Art, Royal Academy, London, 1930 (*Catalogue*, No. 518, 519).
An old copy of this painting, including the *Halberdier*, is in the Gallery at Stuttgart (q.v.). Another copy (78×61 cm.) of the main part, similar to the Stuttgart one in style, was with Dowdeswell and Kay.

THE MEETING OF ANTONY AND CLEOPATRA   [1955, fig. 33]
Canvas, 66×38 cm.; c. 1745-50.

Purchased in Venice for the Royal Institution, Edinburgh, 1845.
Sack, p. 223; *Catalogue* of the Gallery, 1936, p. 229; Morassi, p. 29, fig. 78.
Excellent sketch for the fresco in the Pal. Labia, Venice.
An old copy (97×56 cm.) once in the Gnecco Coll., Genoa, is now in a Private Coll., Milan. Another (106×78 cm.) was exhibited in Würzburg, 1951 (*Catalogue*, V., 4), belonging to the Mainfränkisches Museum.

EL PASO, Texas, Museum of Art

LADY WITH A PARROT
LADY WITH A FUR
Two pastels, 66×52 cm.

Copies, probably by Lorenzo Tiepolo after originals by Giambattista
Tiepolo, formerly in London, executed about 1750–60. The original
painting of the *Lady with a Parrot* was in the Durlacher Coll., London,
and is now in Oxford. The present whereabouts of the other is unknown. Ex coll. Labia, Venice; S. H. Kress Collection 1931; National
Gallery of Art, Washington, 1941–61. Gift of the S. H. Kress Foundation 1961.
Fiocco, *Pantheon*, 1931, with repr. as by Giambattista; Cat. of the
Nat. Gall. of Art, Washington, 1941, p. 192, also as by Giambattista;
Morassi, p. 28, as copies; The S. H. Kress Collection, El Paso Museum
of Art, 1961, no. 40 with repr.

ESTE, Chiesa delle Grazie (abbaziale di S. Tecla)

S. Thecla Delivering the City from the Plague [1955, pl. 75]
Canvas, 675×390 cm.; 1759. Signed: *Giô. Batta Tiepolo f.*

Engraved by Lorenzo Tiepolo (De Vesme, 3).
Pietrograande, *Descrizione*, 1885; Molmenti, p. III, fig. p. III; Sack,
p. 167, fig. 126; Morassi, p. 36, fig. 113; Pallucchini, *Cinque secoli*,
(Exhibition Catalogue), 1945, p. 129.
Placed on the high altar on Christmas Eve, 1759. One of the most
impressive religious creations of Tiepolo's maturity.
Sketch in the Metropolitan Museum, New York (q.v.).

FLORENCE, Uffizi

Two Putti
Canvas 67×77 cm.; fragment; *c.* 1740–50.

From the Pal. Grimani ai Servi, Venice; formerly in the Giacomo
Favretto Coll.; later Luigi Nono Coll., Venice.
Molmenti, p. 53, fig. p. 47; Sack, p. 167.
Another fragment from this ceiling—the *Angel of Fame*—was once in
the Ventura Coll., Florence (q.v.).

Portrait of a Page (half length)
Canvas, 64×46 cm.

By Domenico.
Attributed by Sack, p. 168, to Giambattista.

Erection of a Statue
Canvas, 420×175 cm.

Ceiling removed from the Seminary at Udine.
By a follower, certainly Menescardi.
Molmenti, p. 245, fig. p. 247; Sack, p. 167, fig. 157; both wrongly
attribute it to Giambattista, as do all other writers although the style is
patently not Tiepolo's.

FLORENCE, Bardini Coll.
Triumph of Venus

Fresco removed from the ceiling of the Villa Steffaneo, Crauglio,
(Friuli), to Florence.
By F. Chiaruttini.
Molmenti, pp. 87, 246, fig. p. 248, as by Giambattista: returned to
Chiaruttini by Morassi, *Jahrbuch d. Zentralkommission f. Denkmalpflege*,
Vienna, 1916.

FLORENCE, Contini-Bonacossi Coll.

Marriage Allegory of the Casa Cornaro   [1955, fig. 26]
Canvas 342×169 cm.; *c.* 1745–50.

Ceiling, originally in the Pal. Corner-Mocenigo a S. Polo, Venice, and
later in the Edward Cheney Coll., from whence it passed to the
Capel-Cure Coll., Badger Hall.
Berenson, *Venetian Painters*, 1894, p. 132; Sack, p. 152; Morassi, p. 27,
fig. 66; *Catalogue* Exhib. Paris, 1935, p. 199. Generally incorrectly dated
at *c.* 1720.

Triumph of Virtue and Fortitude   Fig. 351
Canvas 299×379 cm.; *c.* 1740–50.

Ceiling, originally in the Pal. Manin, Venice, and later in the Edward

Cheney Coll.; Capel-Cure Coll. at Badger Hall, England.
Berenson, *Venetian Painters*, 1894, p. 132; Molmenti, 1911, p. 187 note I;
Sack, p. 153; Vigni, 1951, pl. VII.
Engraved by Domenico Tiepolo (De Vesme 102).
Sack lists the ceiling once more under 'Lost Works' (p. 228) and men-
tions a sketch for it (oval, 30×38 cm.) in the Rothan Coll., Paris,
sold at auction in 1890.

FLORENCE, formerly Costantini Coll.

Head of an Oriental Holding a Book
By a follower of Tiepolo.
Wrongly attributed to Tiepolo (Photo Brogi, 19042).

FLORENCE, formerly Private Coll.

Madonna and Child   Fig. 76
Canvas, 50×40 cm.; *c.* 1720–22.

Now in Biella, G. Ajmone Marsan Coll.
Morassi, *Burlington Magazine*, 1935, Oct., p. 148, pl. IIIC.

FLORENCE, formerly Ventura Coll.

The Angel of Fame
Fragment of a ceiling fresco, 110×109 cm.; *c.* 1740–50. Originally in
the Pal. Grimani ai Servi, Venice. Another fragment, of two *putti*, is in
the Uffizi, Florence (q.v.).
Molmenti, p. 53, fig. p. 47; *Catalogue* of the Ventura Sale, Scopinich
Gall. Milan, 6.4.1932, No. 48.

FOLZANO, Parish Church

The Baptism of Constantine   Fig. III
Canvas, shaped at the bottom, 325×173 cm.; *c.* 1757–1759.

Commissioned 1757 and dedicated in Sept. 1759.
Molmenti, p. 152, fig. 152; Sack, p. 230 fig. 223 after the engraving,
under 'Lost Works'; E. Calabi, *Catalogue* Brescia, 1935, p. 112, pl.
XXXI (with the local literature). Engraved by Domenico (De Vesme,
82).
A masterpiece, almost unknown, in very good preservation. Tiepolo
may have delivered his work in March, 1759, when a letter of the 14th
to Frugoni says that he is staying in Brescia (probably on his way from
Folzano to Venice).

FRANKFURT, Staedel Institute

Patron Saints of the Crotta Family   Fig. 109
Canvas, 71×108 cm.; *c.* 1750 (?).

Pal. Calbo-Crotta, Venice, till 1902; Bardini of Florence sold it to
Frankfurt.
Engraved by Domenico (De Vesme, 74) and Pietro Monaco.
Caversazzi, *Emporium*, March, 1899; Molmenti, pp. 72, 270, fig. p. 66;
Sack, p. 188, fig. 100; Morassi, p. 32.
The scene represents some patron saints of members of the Crotta
family; S. Lupus as Doge of Bergamo, with S. Adelaide near him.
Their daughter S. Grata stands in front of them with the head of
S. Alexander, whose blood is transformed into flowers. Beside her are
her brothers SS. Fermus and Rusticus with the palms of martyrdom.
One of Tiepolo's most important religious pictures for a private house.
The style is that of the 'fifties, after his return from Würzburg.

Head of an Old Man
Canvas, 65×51 cm.

By Domenico. Engraved by Domenico in his 'Raccolta di teste,' No. 13.
Molmenti, p. 270; Sack, p. 188, both as by Giambattista.

The Continence of Scipio
Canvas, 121×97 cm.

Ex coll. Martinengo, Würzburg; sold 1861 (Sale Cat. 77).
By Domenico.

Molmenti, p. 270 as by Giambattista; Sack, p. 188, fig. 176, rightly as by Domenico.
Probably pendant to the *Alexander and the Daughters of Darius* in Detroit (q.v.).

FRANKFURT, formerly Rothschild Coll.

THE RECEPTION OF HENRY III AT THE VILLA ALLA MIRA
Canvas, 71 × 108 cm.; *c.* 1750 (?).

Perhaps the original sketch once in the possession of Count Algarotti. Molmenti, p. 254; Sack, p. 188, says that it went to Paris.
Not seen by me. Present whereabouts unknown.
Another sketch of the *Reception* is in the Berlin Museum (q.v.), attributed to Giambattista by Molmenti, p. 254, whereas it is certainly a contemporary copy.

FÜRTH, Bavaria, Städtisches Museum

DAVID AND ABIGAIL
Fig. 23
Canvas, 82 × 105 cm.; *c.* 1751–53.

Goering (1944) writes that it is signed G.B.T. on the back at the right. Also called *The Queen of Sheba bringing Gifts to Solomon.* Certainly of the Würzburg period, probably painted there. Related (or, better, pendant) to the *Esther and Ahasuerus* formerly in the Gulbransson Coll., Munich (q.v.) and stylistically very near to the two paintings in the University Museum, Wurzburg.
Goering, *ad vocem*; Goering, 1944, p. 104, with fig.

GENEVA, André Pereire Coll.

ECCE HOMO
Fig. 53
Canvas, 66 × 42.5 cm.; *c.* 1750–60.

Ex coll. Beurnonville, Paris, Sale 1881, No. 702 (sold for 3,100 fr.); Signol Coll., Paris.
Sack, p. 218; Mireur, 1912, VII, *ad vocem; Catalogue*, Exhib. *Collections Romandes*, Geneva, 1954, No. 10; Pallucchini, in *Arte Veneta*, 1955, p 233, fig. 315.
Excellent autograph sketch of Tiepolo's maturity.

GENOA, Alessandro Basevi Coll.

THE EDUCATION OF THE VIRGIN
Fig. 74
Canvas, oval, 78.5 × 62 cm.; *c.* 1720.

Morassi, *Catalogue*, Genoa, 1947, p. 111, fig. 91.
A very good early work, slightly earlier than the one in Dijon (q.v.).

GENOA, formerly Private Coll.

HEAD OF AN ANGEL
Canvas, 40 × 30 cm.

By a pupil of Tiepolo and attributed by some critics to Tiepolo himself. Now in a Private Coll. in Milan.

GOTHA, Museum

ESTHER AND AHASUERUS

Ascribed in the Museum to Tiepolo, it is a work of the Bolognese school at the beginning of the XVIIIth Century.

GRAZ, Museum Johanneum

MARTYRDOM OF A FEMALE SAINT
Canvas 42 × 22.7 cm.

A school work, attributed by Sack, p. 202, to Giambattista.

HAMBURG, Kunsthalle

THE AGONY IN THE GARDEN   [1955, pls. 30, 33]
THE CROWNING WITH THORNS   [1955, pls. 31, 32]
Two canvases, each 79 × 90 cm.; *c.* 1745–50.

The first was painted for Giacomo Concolo of Venice according to the engraving by Pietro Monaco (1771).
Ex coll. Miethke, Vienna; Seeger, Berlin. Entered the Museum 1925.
Sack, p. 184, figs. 172–173; Cat. of the Museum, 1930, p. 163; Lorenzetti, p. 58, figs. 42–43.
These two belong to a cycle of many paintings of the Passion of Christ. The *Last Supper* in the Louvre certainly forms part of it, and very probably also the *Crucifixion* at St. Louis or the *Crucifixion* at Vierhouten, Holland (q.v.).
There are many copies of the Hamburg pair: one of the *Agony* in Athens (q.v.); another, of the *Crowning*, in the Museum at Vicenza, ascribed to Domenico and not catalogued here. Others are in Paris, Venice, New York, etc.

THE SACRIFICE OF IPHIGENIA
Canvas, 39 × 62 cm.; 1740–50.

Formerly G. von Falcke Coll., Cologne. From the Wedells Coll., Hamburg bequeathed to Hamburg in 1921 and lent to the Kunsthalle. Excellent autograph replica of the painting in Paris, Patino Coll. (q.v.). Sack, p. 190; G. Pauli, in *Pantheon*, XIX, 1937, p. 136; Goering, *ad vocem*.

HAMBURG, formerly Sack Coll.

S. JOSEPH WITH THE CHRIST CHILD
Canvas, 57 × 51 cm.

The Saint with the Child on his right arm; two heads of cherubs on clouds in the upper right part.
Mentioned by Sack, p. 190, as by G.B., *c.* 1720–30 and as showing S. Ricci's influence. Missing.

HAMBURG, formerly Scholz-Forni Coll.

APOLLO AND MARSYAS
See Copenhagen, Statens Museum.

HAMBURG, formerly Sthamer Coll.

THE ADORATION OF THE SHEPHERDS
Canvas, 43 × 57 cm.

By Domenico.
The pendant, of the *Nativity*, is in the Wallraf-Richartz Museum, Cologne.
Sack, p. 190, fig. 179, as by Giambattista.

HAMBURG, formerly Weber Coll.

HEAD OF AN ORIENTAL
Canvas, 61 × 51.5 cm.

On the art market at Kissingen, 1906; Weber Sale, 1912, Cat. No. 162 (for 13.000 marks).
Sack, p. 189, as one of the most brilliant examples of the Master's *Heads* (describing it as in half-bust, turned half to the right, bearded, looking at the spectator, with a turban and a large collar).

HEAD OF AN ORIENTAL
Canvas, 43.5 × 36.5 cm.

In the Schewitsch Coll., Paris, 1906 (repr. in the Cat. of the Collection); Weber Sale, Hamburg, 1912, Cat. No. 161 (for 2.500 marks).
Sack, p. 189.
Both not identifiable, perhaps missing.

HARTFORD, Conn., Wadsworth Atheneum

SUSANNA AND THE ELDERS
Fig. 31
Canvas, 56 × 43 cm.; *c.* 1718–20.

Morassi, 1949, pp. 75–76, fig. 66.
Very characteristic sketch in the style of his youth, related to Piazzetta, but in light colours.
Entered the Museum in 1954 (Erlanger Gift), from the Schaeffer Gall., New York.

A contemporary copy (65×55 cm.) was on the market in Venice, 1955, together with a pendant of *Bathsheba at the Bath*, certainly also a copy after Tiepolo of which the original is unknown.

THE LAST SUPPER
Canvas, 66×42 cm.

By Domenico.
Generally attributed to Giambattista, but given to Domenico by Morassi, in *Emporium*, 1941, p. 279, and by Lorenzetti, *Catalogue*, 1951, p. 175, fig. 126.

THE BUILDING OF THE TROJAN HORSE
Canvas, 190×340 cm.

By Domenico; attributed in the Museum to Giambattista.
Another small picture of the same subject, also by Domenico, is in the National Gallery, London.
Wadsworth Atheneum Report, 1950.

HELSINKI, Ateneum

THE RAPE OF THE SABINES   [1955, fig. 7]
Canvas, 45×74 cm.; *c.* 1720–22.

Sketch for the picture in Leningrad.
E. von Engestrom Coll.; J. Ahrenberg Coll.; entered the Museum 1892.
Morassi, 1942, p. 88; Lorenzetti, p. 13, fig. 6.
A very spirited composition, close to the finished picture.

INNSBRUCK, Ferdinandeum

ALLEGORY OF WEALTH AND STRENGTH
Canvas, 71.5×58 cm.

By an imitator of Tiepolo.
Sketch after the ceiling now in the house of Baroness Elly de Rothschild in Paris (q.v.).
Molmenti, p. 255 (cf. fig. 253) also as Giambattista; Sack, p. 202, rightly as by a follower.

INTRA, Lago Maggiore, Heirs of Count Alessandro Poss

THE LAST JUDGEMENT   Fig. 222
Canvas, 150×200 cm.; *c.* 1735–40.

Sketch for a ceiling.
Modigliani, *Dedalo*, 1933, XIII, p. 138, figs. pp. 143–146 dates it 1745–1750.
It is not known if this sketch was ever executed as a ceiling painting. The composition is rather strange in its dispersed elements, but there is no doubt of the authenticity of the picture, which reveals analogies of style with the sketches of his Lombard period and the *modelli* of the Scalzi. In the group of the devils there are some similarities with the ceiling of the Scalone in Udine.

JACKSONVILLE, Florida, DeEtte Holden Cummer Museum Foundation

S. PETER   Fig. 191
Canvas, oval, 45×37 cm.; *c.* 1718–20.

From a Private Coll., Zürich (where is preserved the 'pendant' with *S. John the Baptist*, q.v.), to the Museum.
Head in natural size. Hitherto unknown.
Very Piazzettesque in style, but with a more developed coloristic sense.
Formed perhaps part of a series of Apostles.

KAMMENDORF, Landhaus (Kamiona, district of Wroclaw-Breslau), Poland

NIGHT

Ceiling-painting mentioned by Goering in *Thieme-Becker* as doubtfully by Tiepolo.
Nothing more is known of it.
Through the courtesy of Prof. S. Lorentz, Director of the National Museum in Warsaw, I understand that the ceiling was possibly removed during the last war.

KANSAS CITY, William Rockhill Nelson Gallery of Art

HAGAR AND ISHMAEL
Canvas, 84×104 cm.

By Domenico.
Sack, p. 192; fig. 185, rightly as Domenico; A. Venturi, *Studi dal vero*, Milano, 1927, pp. 403–405, fig. 279, as Giambattista; Catton Rich, 1938, p. 25, as Giambattista; Cat. of the Gall., III ed. (1959?), p. 48 as by G.B.

KANSAS CITY, formerly Consul Maxwell Blake Coll. (formerly in Tangiers)

THE CHARLATAN
34×58 cm.

THE TOOTH-DRAWER
36×58 cm.

THE TRIUMPH OF PULCINELLA
33×58 cm.

THE STORYTELLER
36×58 cm.

Four canvases. Certainly by Domenico.
All were engraved by Wagner, and in these engravings, two were stated to be by Domenico.
Morassi, 1941, pp. 271–72 with repr., as by Domenico; Lorenzetti, pp. 145–46, 147, figs. 103–105, 118, wrongly attributing the first three to Giambattista.
Recently acquired by a Private Coll. in Rome.

KIEW, Museum of Fine Arts

THE SUMMONS TO CINCINNATUS
Canvas.

Believed to be an original sketch for the large painting in Leningrad (q.v.), whereas judging from the reproduction, it seems to be a copy after the autograph sketch in Munich, formerly Caspari Coll. (q.v.).
M. J. Scerbaciova, 1941, p. 26, with repr. as by Giambattista.

LAKE FOREST, Ill., Alfred E. Hamill Coll.

APOLLO AND DAPHNE
Canvas, 94×74 cm.

Old copy after the Louvre picture.
Said to come from the Mocenigo family, Venice.
Catton Rich, 1938, p. 24, as by Giambattista.

LAUSANNE, formerly Private Coll.

RINALDO AND ARMIDA IN THE GARDEN   Fig. 276
Canvas, 42×37 cm.; *c.* 1725.

Stylistically related to the earlier *Susanna and the Elders*, Hartford, Wadsworth Atheneum; to the *Venus with a Mirror*, Milan, Private Coll., and especially to the *Alexander and Campaspe* in Montreal; both the latter being of about the same period. This very charming painting is the first early version known of the subject of Rinaldo and Armida, dear to Tiepolo in his maturity (see the late versions in Berlin, Chicago, New York).
Hitherto unpublished.

LE HAVRE, Musée

THE ASSUMPTION
Canvas, 71×56 cm.

Given to the Museum by the curator Galbrun.
Old copy of the sketch in Ascott (q.v.).
Molmenti, p. 248; Sack, p. 212, fig. 208, believes it may be the sketch for the ceiling painted by Tiepolo for the church of Biadene near Treviso in his early youth (Da Canal, p. XXXII), but the actual ceiling in the church is by G. Canal, not Tiepolo.
Wrongly attributed to Giambattista (Exh. Cat., Bordeaux, 1956, p. 24).

ASSUMPTION OF A SAINT
Canvas, 55×38 cm.

Assigned to Tiepolo in the old *Catalogues* of the Museum, it is by a pupil, as Sack rightly believed (p. 212).

LENINGRAD, Hermitage

THE ANNUNCIATION Fig. 32
Canvas, 46×38 cm.; *c.* 1720.

Entered the Museum 1924 from the W. D. Dourdine Coll.
Catalogue Exhibition 'Starye-Gody', 1908, p. 41, No. 210 as by Domenico Tiepolo; Weiner-Liphart, *Les Anciennes écoles...*, Bruxelles, 1910, p. 112; by A. Benois believed to be by Domenico.
In the Museum with an attribution to the Tiepolo School. Recently restored.
Undoubtedly painted by Giambattista in his early period, about 1720, and stylistically related to the fresco with the *Glory of S. Theresa* in the Chiesa degli Scalzi, Venice.

THE RAPE OF THE SABINES Fig. 300
Canvas, 288×588 cm.; *c.* 1720–22.

The sketch for it is at Helsinki.
Ex coll. Prince S. M. Wolkonsky, St. Petersburg; entered the Museum, 1910, as by S. Ricci. First given to Tiepolo by Voss (1922).
Da Canal, 1732, p. XXXIV; Sack, p. 231; Weiner, in *L'Arte*, 1910, pp. 146, 147; Woinoff, in 'Starye Gody', Jan.-March, 1911, pp. 34–37; *Catalogue* of the Hermitage, 1916, No. 1942; Morassi, 1941–42, XII-I, p. 88, fig 3.
This picture, mentioned by Sack among the lost works, was executed, according to Da Canal, for N. H. Jacopo Zorzi delle Zattere. It passed into the coll. of Maffeo Pinelli and was sold in Venice in 1785. The Sale Catalogue gives the measurements.

THE TRIUMPH OF SCIPIO
546×322 cm. Fig. 295

VOLUMNIA AND HER CHILDREN BEFORE CORIOLANUS Fig. 298
387×224 cm.

MUCIUS SCAEVOLA BEFORE PORSENNA Fig. 299
387×227 cm.

FABIUS MAXIMUS BEFORE THE SENATE OF CARTHAGE Fig. 297
387×224 cm.
Engraved by the Abbé Saint-Non after a drawing by Fragonard (G. Wildenstein, *Fragonard Aquafortiste*, Paris 1956, p. 22).

THE DICTATORSHIP OFFERED TO CINCINNATUS Fig. 296
387×224 cm.

Five of the ten canvases originally executed for the extant large principal hall in the Ca' Dolfin, Venice, *c.* 1725–30. Miller von Aicholz Coll., Vienna, in 1870; A. A. Polovtzef Coll., St. Petersburg, from whence given to the Stieglitz Museum; entered the Hermitage 1934. Two others from this cycle are in the Museum, Vienna; three in the Castiglioni Coll., New York.
Da Canal, 1732, XXXIV; Bergeret et Fragonard, 1773–4, p. 386; Moschini, 1806, III, p. 75; Molmenti, p. 276; Sack, p. 151; P. Weiner, *Les anciennes écoles...*, 1910, I, p. 138; M. I. Scerbaciova, 1941, with reprs.; Morassi, 1942, IV-V, pp. 259–264; figs. 5, 8–11; Morassi, 1950, p. 16, figs. 32–33.; Cat. of the Museum, 1958, pp. 196–200 with reprs.
The sketch for *Cinnatus* was in the Caspari Coll., Munich (q.v.).
The original sketch for the *Mucius Scaevola* is in the Musée Magnin, Dijon (see Addenda); a small copy is in the Museo Civico, Padua (q.v.); another one, certainly by Antonio Guardi, in a Private Coll., Milan (q.v.). Scerbaciova (1941) records that the restoration of the five paintings revealed old inscriptions in Latin referring to the Roman history (*Epitome*) by Annaeus Florus. (The inscriptions are still extant on the two canvases in the Museum at Vienna.)

FOUR FLYING PUTTI CARRYING GRAPES
Canvas, 140×147 cm.; *c.* 1740–45. Fig. 401

Ex coll. Princess Maria Nicolaevna; later Princess Elena Grigorievna Cheremetieva; entered the Museum 1924.
Attributed in the Hermitage to Domenico. Judging from the photograph it seems an excellent original by Giambattista and close in style to the *Putti* in the Talleyrand Coll., Paris.
N. Wrangel, *The Inheritance of the Princess Maria Nicolaevna*, St. Petersburg, 1912, II, 68, repr. 28.

THE BANQUET OF ANTHONY AND CLEOPATRA
See Melbourne.

MAECENAS PRESENTING THE ARTS TO AUGUSTUS Fig. 312
Canvas, 69.5×89 cm.; 1743—beginning of 1744.

Commissioned by Algarotti, together with the *Triumph of Flora* (now in San Francisco), for Count Brühl in July, 1743 (see the Chronological Table).
Sent to Dresden, probably in March, 1744, together with other paintings acquired in Venice by Algarotti for Augustus III of Poland (among them was the *Banquet*, now in Melbourne).
Acquired in 1769 by Catherine II of Russia; temporarily in the Palace at Gatchina and from there to the Hermitage (1882).
A record of it, perhaps in watercolour, belonged to Count Algarotti and was engraved by Leonardis in 1766 (*Catalogue... du feu Comte Algarotti*, n.d. (*c.* 1766), p. 54): it was still in the Algarotti Coll. in 1854 (cf. *Galleria Particolare* of Lauro Bernardino Corniani de' Conti Algarotti, 1854, p. 8).
Molmenti, p. 282; Sack, p. 206, fig. 204; Liphart, in 'Starye Gody,' Jan.-March, 1910, p. 13; *Catalogue* of the Hermitage, 1911, No. 1671; Fogolari, 1913; H. Posse, in *Prussian Jahrbuch*, 1931, p. 49; Levey, in *Burlington Magazine*, March, 1957, p. 89; Cat. of the Museum, 1958, p. 200, fig. 23.

ALEXANDER AND DIOGENES
Canvas, 47×60 cm.

A studio copy after the original by Giambattista in the Modiano Coll., Bologna (q.v.).
Attributed by the Museum to Domenico and wrongly said to be the pendant to the *Prodigal Son* (by Domenico) in the Museum at Moscow. (Kindly communicated by Mrs. M. Scerbaciova).
Catalogue of the Jusopov Coll., 1920, p. 12, No. 199.

GOD THE FATHER IN THE CLOUDS
Canvas, 33×49 cm.

By Domenico.
Entered the Museum, 1920.
Judging from the photograph, kindly sent to me by Mrs. Maria Scerbaciova, certainly a work by Domenico, rather late.
Cat. of the Museum, 1958, p. 200 as by G.B.

LENINGRAD, formerly Delaroff Coll.

PARIS IN A LANDSCAPE
See Munich, formerly D. Heinemann Coll.

LILLE, Musée

S. AUGUSTINE AND OTHER SAINTS
Canvas, 60×34 cm.

By an imitator of Tiepolo.
Bought at the Camille Rogier Sale, 1896.
Molmenti, p. 236, says the Museum attributed it to Domenico; Sack, p. 220, wrongly as a replica. It is a copy, rather late, after the painting in the National Gallery, London.

LISBON, Museu Nacional de Arte Antiga

ALLEGORY OF THE ARTS   Fig. 338
Canvas, 55 × 72 cm.; c. 1731.

To the Museum, 1920, from the Palacio Nacional da Ajuda.
Sketch related to the ceiling of the Pal. Archinto, Milan (1731).
Fiocco, 1940, pp. 8–9 pl. 1, attributes it wrongly to the Spanish period;
Morassi, 1941, IV-V, p. 253 recognising the relation with Pal. Archinto;
Cat. of the Museum, 1951, p. 127.
This sketch, closely connected with the ceiling of Pal. Archinto, is not a
preparatory study, but rather a *ricordo* of the finished fresco.

THE FLIGHT INTO EGYPT   [1955; pl. 92]
Canvas, 57 × 44 cm.; c. 1762–70.

From D. Maria Helena Garcês Ferreira Pinto Basto Coll. to the
Museum, 1946.
Fiocco, 1940, p. 12, pl. IV; Morassi, p. 39, fig. 133; Cat. of the Museum,
1951, p. 127.
Forms part of the series in Lisbon, E. Pinto Basto Coll.; Bellagio and
Berlin (q.v.).

LISBON, formerly Espirito Santo Silva Coll.

YOUNG LADY HOLDING A MANDOLINE (with flowers and pearls
in her hair, half length.)
Canvas, 59 × 48 cm.

By Domenico.
Formerly attributed to Giambattista, and as Giambattista sold at
Charpentier, 9.12.1952, No. 22. The same model as in the Lazaro
Galdiano Museum, Madrid (q.v.).

LISBON, Edoardo Ferreira Pinto-Basto Coll.

CHRONOS ENTRUSTING CUPID TO VENUS   Fig. 353
Canvas, 46 × 57 cm.; c. 1762–70.

The drawing and the engraving are in the Cooper Union Museum,
New York.
Molmenti, p. 223, repr. of the drawing; Fiocco, 1940, p. 12, pl. III.
Excellent work of the late Spanish period.

THE FLIGHT INTO EGYPT (with boat)   [1955, pl. 93]
Canvas, 57 × 43.5 cm.; c. 1762–70.

Fiocco, 1940, p. 12, pl. V; Morassi, p. 39, fig. 132.
Belongs to a cycle of variations on the *Flight* like the painting in Lisbon
mentioned below, and the paintings in Bellagio and Berlin.

TRIUMPH OF AMPHITRITE
Canvas, 40.5 × 59 cm.

Sketch related to the Dresden picture (or, possibly, a workshop copy
like the one in Trieste).
Fiocco, 1940, p. 11, pl. II, as by Giambattista.
A rather weak painting, certainly not a preliminary study for the large
finished work in Dresden.

THE ENTOMBMENT   [1955, fig. 56]
Canvas, 57 × 43 cm.; c. 1762–70.

Fiocco, 1940, p. 12, pl. IV; Morassi, p. 39, fig. 133.
Very impressive and dramatic creation of Tiepolo's last years.

LISBON, formerly D. Maria Helena Garcês Ferreira Pinto Basto

THE FLIGHT INTO EGYPT
See Lisbon, Museu Nacional de Arte Antiga.

LONDON, National Gallery

S. PROCULUS, BISHOP OF VERONA, VISITING SS. FERMUS AND
RUSTICUS   Fig. 138
Canvas, 58 × 32 cm.; c. 1740–45.

Lord Ward Coll. by 1854; Earl of Dudley Sale, London, 3.5.1884 (lot

83); bought by C. Beckett Denison; Beckett Denison Sale, London,
6.6.1885, bought for the National Gallery.
Certainly autograph. Like the sketch in Bergamo and the other versions
(E. Drey Coll., New York; Thiem Coll., San Remo), it was wrongly
called *SS. Maximus and Oswald* and related to the altarpiece in Padua,
S. Massimo, whereas it can be shown to represent SS. Fermus and
Rusticus by comparison with the same saints in the later *Crotta Family
Saints* in Frankfurt.
A copy is in Rennes; another was in the Pasquinelli Coll., Milan.
See also Bergamo, Carrara Gallery.
Formerly also called *Henry IV of Germany at Canossa.*
Molmenti, p. 262, fig. p. 107; Sack, p. 224, fig. 216, Levey, *Catalogue,*
1956, pp. 92–96.

S. AUGUSTINE AND OTHER SAINTS (*Louis of France, John the
Evangelist and a Bishop Saint*)   Fig. 110
Canvas, 58 × 32.5 cm.; c. 1737 (?).

Lord Ward Coll. c. 1855; Earl of Dudley Sale 1884; purchased by the
N. G. at the Beckett Denison Sale, 6.6.1885 (lot 884).
Related to the altarpiece (now lost) in San Salvatore, Venice (1737–38);
probably a *prima idea* for it (cf. the drawing after the altarpiece in Sack,
p. 157). The sketch for, or, better, a record of, the lost canvas is in the
Lycett Green Coll., City of York Art Gallery (q.v.).
A copy of the National Gallery painting is in the Museum at Lille.
Another copy in Rennes.
Modern, 1902, p. 29; Molmenti, p. 262, fig. p. 46; Sack, p. 224, fig. 217
(both wrongly believing the present sketch to come from the Algarotti
Coll.); Levey, *Burlington Magazine*, IV, 1955, p. 119, fig. 22; Levey,
Catalogue, 1956, p. 96.
In the *Catalogue* of the Nat. Gallery, 1929, it is called *Henry IV of Ger-
many at Canossa* (?), No. 1193.

MADONNA AND CHILD WITH SAINTS   Fig. 86
Canvas, 52.7 × 31.8 cm.; c. 1730–35.

Salting Coll., by 1883; Salting Bequest 1910.
Probably a *modello* for an unknown or never executed altarpiece. Once
attributed to Domenico and only recently, by the present writer,
restored to Giambattista.
Catalogue of the Nat. Gall., 1929 (No. 2513), p. 361 as Domenico;
Levey, *Catalogue,* 1956, pp. 99–100 as G.B.
Cleaned in 1955. A good workshop replica (50 × 30 cm.) in a Private
Coll., Bergamo.

POPE S. CLEMENT ADORING THE HOLY TRINITY   Fig. 127
Canvas, 70.2 × 57 cm.; c. 1734–37.

Excellent *modello* for the Nymphenburg altarpiece (now in the Pina-
kothek in Munich).
A copy of this sketch is in the Metropolitan Museum, New York, and is
perhaps identifiable with the one mentioned by Sack, p. 192, in the
Hauser Coll., Munich.
Bought by the National Gallery in 1957 from the New York market
(Weitzner).
Levey, in *Burlington Magazine*, August 1957, pp. 256–261, with repr.;
Morassi, in 'Arte Veneta', 1957, p. 173, fig. 187.

THE MARRIAGE OF BARBAROSSA   Fig. 315
Canvas, 72.4 × 52.7 cm.; c. 1751.

Sketch for the fresco at Würzburg.
Boursault Sale, Paris, 7.5.1832 (lot 89); bought by Evans; by 1841 in the
Edmund Higginson Coll. at Saltmarshe; Ch. Scarisbrick Coll.; Gold-
smith Coll.; John Samuel Coll.; bequeathed by the Misses Cohen to
the Gallery, 1906.
Another *modello* for the same fresco, in Boston, Gardner Museum
(q.v.), is also autograph. Freeden and Lamb consider the present as the
second version for the fresco. Levey attributes the London example to
Domenico, but it seems rather doubtful that he prepared the *modello* to
be executed by his father. (In this connection, compare the two *modelli*
for the overdoors of Würzburg, sketched by Domenico, now in the

Mainfrankisches Museum at Würzburg, where the difference in style and quality is quite evident.)
Molmenti, p. 262 (calling it *Bozzetto embrionale* by Giambattista); Fiocco, 1929, p. 70 (attributing to Domenico); Vigni, 1951, fig. 96 (as Giambattista); Freeden and Lamb, 1956, p. 43, fig. 31; Levey, *Catalogue*, 1956, pp. 102–105, as by Domenico.

TWO BEARDED ORIENTALS   Fig. 277
RINALDO LOOKING AT HIS REFLECTION IN HIS SHIELD
TWO TURBANED TURKS
A SEATED MAN AND A YOUNG WOMAN WITH A VESSEL
Four canvases, 158 × 53 cm. each; *c.* 1750–55.

Ex Coll. Festetits, Vienna (until 1883); Rothschild, Frankfurt, Schloss Grueneburg; Talleyrand, Rome; Baroness de Becker-Rothschild, New York; entered the National Gallery 1961.
Two of the canvases were engraved by Domenico (De Vesme, 110, 111) and a third by Lorenzo (De Vesme, 5).
Sack, p. 188; Art Bulletin, XXVIII, 1935, p. 405 with repr.
Exhibited Amsterdam, 'Italiaansche Kunst in Nederlandsch Bezit', 1934, Cat. No. 359, with fig. These very decorative pictures are related to the compositions from the *Gerusalemme Liberata* at Chicago and to the frescoes of the Villa Valmarana. Two other scenes of *Rinaldo and Armida* in a similar style, also by Giambattista, are in the Wrightsman Coll., New York (q.v.).

THE DEPOSITION   Fig. 59
Canvas, 64 × 42 cm.; *c.* 1750–60.

Ex coll. Passaro, Venice; Cavendish-Bentinck Sale, 1891; Nat. Gall. No. 1333.
In spite of a certain weakness in the execution of some figures, the present writer is inclined to believe that this composition on the whole is a work by Giambattista resulting from a collaboration with Domenico.
Molmenti, p. 262; Sack, p. 224, fig. 215, as by Giambattista; Goering, *ad vocem*, as possibly Domenico; Watson, *Catalogue*, London, 1951, p. 36, No. 133 as Domenico; Levey, *Catalogue*, 1956, pp. 101–102 as Domenico.
Certainly influenced by Rembrandt's *Deposition* (London, N.G.), which was in the Consul Smith Coll., Venice, from before 1738 until it was acquired with the rest of the Smith Coll. by George III in 1762. Perhaps Tiepolo based his painting on the chiaroscuro woodcut made by J. B. Jackson while the Rembrandt was still in Smith's possession.

THE DEPOSITION   Fig. 63
Canvas, 80 × 89.2 cm.; *c.* 1750–60.

Ex coll. Secrétan, Paris; Kann, Paris; Sir Joseph Duveen, 1907; Miss Emilie Yznaga, 1936; Yznaga bequest, 1945. (N.G. No. 5589).
W. von Bode, *Die Sammlung Kann*, Vienna 1900; Sack, p. 222, fig. 214 both as by Giambattista; Goering, *ad vocem*, as Domenico; Levey, *Catalogue*, 1956, pp. 107–108 as Domenico.
Very similar to the preceding *Deposition* and almost identical in some parts. Collaboration with Domenico must also be assumed for this work.
Another version, very weak, to be attributed to the shop of Tiepolo, was in the Strauss Sale, Charpentier, 27.5.1949, Paris, *Catalogue* No. 38 with repr. (76 × 87 cm.), here not catalogued.

THE FINDING OF MOSES
Canvas, 53 × 80 cm.

By a follower of Tiepolo, probably Zugno.
Bought from Colnaghi and presented by A. A. de Pass, 1920.
Sack, p. 223, lists it in the Capel Cure Coll., Badger Hall, as Giambattista. *Catalogue* of the Nat. Gall., 1929, p. 361, No. 3542, as Domenico. Fiocco, 1929, p. 70, as by Zugno, followed by Levey, *Catalogue*, 1956, p. 111.

THE BUILDING OF THE TROJAN HORSE
Canvas, 38 × 66 cm.

By Domenico.
Catalogue of the Nat. Gall., 1929, p. 360, No. 3318, wrongly attributed to Giambattista; Goering, *ad vocem;* Morassi, 1941, VI, p. 279 (both as by Domenico); Levey, *Catalogue*, 1956, pp. 105–106, as Domenico. Another large picture of the same subject and almost identical, also by Domenico, is in the Wadsworth Atheneum, Hartford (q.v.).

THE PROCESSION OF THE TROJAN HORSE
Canvas, 38 × 66 cm.

By Domenico.
Catalogue of the Nat. Gall., 1929, p. 360, No. 3319, wrongly attributed to Giambattista; Goering, *ad vocem;* Morassi, 1941, VI, p. 279 (both as by Domenico); Levey, *Catalogue*, 1956, pp. 106–107 (as Domenico). Another scene of the *Trojan Horse*, also wrongly attributed to Giambattista, in Paris, d'Atri, published in *Pantheon*, 1930, V, 4th April.

LONDON, Victoria and Albert Museum

GLORIFICATION OF POPE LEO IX
Circular canvas, 71.5 cm. diam.

By Domenico.
Ex coll. Ionides, London; given to the Museum in 1901.
Sketch for the ceiling fresco by Domenico in San Lio, Venice, 1783–84.
Exhib. Venetian Painting, New Gallery, London, 1894–95.
Sack, p. 225, attributes it to Giambattista as *Apotheosis of a Pope*; Byam-Shaw, in *The Burlington Magazine*, Dec. 1959, pp. 447–51, rightly as Domenico.

LONDON, Dulwich College Gallery

JOSEPH RECEIVING PHARAOH'S RING   Fig. 13
Canvas, 101 × 178 cm.; *c.* 1735.

A very fine work, in good condition, related in style to the Venice *Brazen Serpent*. Wrongly believed to be by Domenico.
Catalogue of the Gallery, 1953, No. 158, as Domenico; Morassi in *Burlington Mag.* I, 1955, p. 11, fig. 12, restoring it to Giambattista.

ALLEGORY OF FORTITUDE AND WISDOM   Fig. 346
Canvas, 65 × 35 cm., shaped for a ceiling, 1743.

Bourgeois Bequest, 1811.
Sketch for the ceiling in the Villa Cordellina, Montecchio Maggiore, painted Oct.–Nov. 1743.
Molmenti, p. 264; Sack, p. 225, fig. 77; *Catalogue* of the Gallery, 1953, No. 278; Cat. Exhib. R.A., London, 1954–55, No. 485.

DIANA   Fig. 355
Canvas, shaped, 32 × 32 cm.; *c.* 1735–40.

Bourgeois Bequest, 1811.
Sketch for a ceiling.
Sack, p. 225; *Catalogue* of the Gallery, 1953, No. 186; Cat. Exhib. R.A., London, 1954–55, No. 490; Morassi, *Burlington Mag.* I, 1955, p. 11, n. 23.

APOLLO AND A GODDESS   Fig. 355
Canvas, shaped, 32 × 32 cm.; *c.* 1735–40.

Bourgeois Bequest, 1811.
Sketch for a ceiling, lower half of the previous sketch.
Bibl. as above. These two fragments originally formed the *modello* for the ceiling in the Villa Cornaro in Merlengo.

LONDON, formerly Agnew

TWO DECORATIVE PANELS   Fig. 402
Canvas 186 × 70 cm.; *c.* 1740–50.

Each representing one vase on a little console, with grapes and ears of corn, and in the upper part heads of putti.
Not seen by me, but, judging from the reproduction (Kunsthistorisches Institut, Florence, Photo No. 55764–5) certainly autograph. The two heads of putti have been added later to the decorative motives of the vases. The two putti representing *Summer* and *Autumn* in Paris, Talleyrand Coll., certainly formed part of this decorative cycle to which are probably related also the *Four putti* in Leningrad (q.v.).

DIANA AND ENDYMION
APOLLO, PAN AND MIDAS
ACHILLES AND TIRESIAS
See Berlin, formerly Van Dirksen Coll.

LONDON, Alexander Coll.

THE BANQUET OF CLEOPATRA   [1955, fig. 31]
Canvas, 46×67 cm.; c. 1747.

Sketch for the large canvas in Archangel (1747).
Ex coll. Cavendish-Bentinck, London; Sale 11.7.1891.
Molmenti, p. 263; Sack, p. 127; Morassi, p. 29; Lorenzetti, p. 89,
fig. 65. Cat. Exhib., R.A., London, 1954–55, No. 513.
One of the most freshly sketched and lightly coloured *modelli* by
Giambattista.
There is a related drawing in the Victoria and Albert Museum.

LONDON, formerly Barlow Coll.

CHRIST AND THE MAGDALEN IN THE HOUSE OF THE PHARISEE
See: Dublin; National Gallery of Ireland.

LONDON, formerly Battersea Coll.

See Banbury, Bearsted Coll.

LONDON, formerly Bischoffsheim Coll.

ALLEGORY OF VENUS ENTRUSTING CUPID TO TIME
Ceiling.
Mentioned by Molmenti, 1911, p. 201, as coming from a Venetian
Palace. Probably the same which was engraved by Domenico.
Present whereabouts unknown.

Four oval grisailles representing:
PEACE AND WAR
POLITICS
ART
THE PUBLIC WEAL
All with coupled figures.
Frescoes transferred to canvas on gold background.
Reproduced in De Chennevierès, figs. pp. 94–95; Sack, p. 226; Leroi,
'L'Art,' 1876, repr. after the engravings by Boetzel, pp. 294–297, as
forming part of a ceiling in one of the grandest houses in Mayfair,
London (p. 298). Present whereabouts unknown.

EDUCATION OF THE INFANTE OF SPAIN AT PARMA
Two canvases, each 40×80 cm.

By Domenico. One signed by Domenico on the label over the mantel-
piece.
In 1826 described in the Baron V. Denon Coll., Paris; ex Mayfair Coll.
Engraved by Ad. Lalauze in *L'Art*, 1876, p. 298 r. (as by Giambattista).
Bischoffsheim Sale, Christie's, London, 7.5.1926; André de Limur
Coll., Washington, D.C.
Now New York, Private Coll.
Molmenti, p. 210, fig. p. 216; Sack, p. 226; both as by Giambattista, as
also Sánchez-Cantón, 1953, p. 22, figs. 32–33.
One picture shows the Infante present at a performance of a scene
from Roman history, the second the same Infante witnessing the
burning of heretical books in a monastery: this is iconographically
dependent on Magnasco.
The two pictures are very impressive examples of Domenico's art,
clearly showing his influence upon Goya.

LONDON, formerly Bowyer Nichols Coll.

STANDING FIGURE OF S. ROCH, WITH A DOG   Fig. 169
Canvas, 39.5×34 cm.; c. 1730–35.

One of the many pictures of this subject painted for new members of
the Confraternity of the Scuola di San Rocco.
Arundel Club Exhibition, London, 1913, *Cat.* No. 286. Photograph in
the Witt Library.

LONDON, formerly Edward Brandus Gallery

ON THE TERRACE
Canvas, medium size (?).

Some people playing cards on a terrace with an architectural background; in the foreground some stairs with a boy and a dog.
Photograph in the Witt Library, as attributed to Tiepolo, whereas the
painting seems certainly to be by Zugno.

LONDON, formerly Cavendish-Bentinck Coll.

DEATH OF A CAPUCHIN MONK   Fig. 136
Canvas, 54.5×40.5 cm.; c. 1735–40.

In the Cavendish-Bentinck Coll., 1891; Martin Sale, Christie's,
28.3.1924, No. 117.
The only known example of Tiepolo working in the style of Magnasco,
whose influence is evident also in the choice of subject.
Sack, No. 581, as a Lost Work, once belonging to Count Algarotti.

LONDON, formerly A. L. Cliffe Coll.

THE RAPE OF EUROPA   Fig. 243
Canvas, 75×66 cm.; 1743.

Copy made for Count Algarotti, of the well known Veronese bought
by him from Teresa Negrenzi in Venice and sent to Dresden in 1743.
Identical with the painting listed in the Algarotti Coll. (*Catalogue*,
1779), as 'copia mirabile dell' originale di Paolo Veronese ch'è nella
Galleria Elettorale di Dresda, e che viene mentovata dal Ridolfi, parte I,
pag. 330 . . . Alto p. 2, onc. 4, largo p. 2.' (The measurements correspond
to the present work.)
Sack, p. 232, No. 588, under 'Lost Works,' but with erroneous measure-
ments resulting from a mistake in calculating; M. Levey, in *The
Burlington Magazine*, June 1960, pp. 250, 257, fig. 28.
A copy of another *Rape* after Paolo Veronese, mentioned in a letter of
Algarotti to his brother Bonomo (16.1.1761) is not to be identified with
the present one, of an earlier period.
From the Cliffe Coll. to the L. A. Nicholson Coll., London, 1927;
Agnew, London, 1929; now Sir Steven Runciman Coll., London.
Exhibited at Agnew, June–July, 1956, No. 15.

LONDON, Colnaghi

A STORM AT SEA
LANDSCAPE AFTER A STORM
Two canvases, 94×144 cm. each; c. 1725–29.

The two landscapes by Marco Ricci, the little figures ('macchiette') by
G. B. Tiepolo.
Formerly R. B. Cheney Coll., Badger Hall, England. J. J. Byam-Shaw,
Paintings by Old Masters, London, May, 1958, N. 3 and 5 noting that
'the figures are noticeably Tiepolesque'; A. Morassi, in *The Burlington
Magazine*, June, 1959, p. 231, figs 24–27.

LONDON, formerly Earl of Dudley Coll.

A BISHOP SAYING MASS
See Milan, formerly Chiesa Coll.

LONDON, Marquess of Dufferin Coll.

THE ASTRONOMER   Fig. 419
Canvas 62×85 cm.; c. 1740–50.

Catalogue of the Loan Exhib. of Venetian Painting, Agnew, London,
May–June, 1953, No. 24 with ill.
A very good picture, hitherto unrecorded.

LONDON, formerly Durlacher Coll.

PORTRAIT OF A LADY WITH A PARROT
See: Oxford, Ashmolean Museum.

LONDON, formerly Eckstein Coll.

BACCHUS AND ARIADNE ON CLOUDS   Fig. 261
Canvas, 46×38 cm.; *c.* 1730–35.

Sketch for a ceiling in the style of the Palazzo Archinto period (1731).
Another sketch, probably autograph, almost identical, was in the
Kleinberger Coll., Paris (reproduced by Sack, fig. 211). A fragment of
another replica is in the Broglio Coll., Paris.
Sotheby Sale, 8.12.1948; Sotheby Sale, 16.11.1955, No. 54, wrongly
described as probably identical with the picture in the Kleinberger Coll.,
Paris, mentioned above.
Now in the J. Hasson Coll., London.

LONDON, formerly Fischmann Coll.

THE PRESENTATION IN THE TEMPLE
Canvas, 38×48.5 cm.

By Domenico.
Attributed to Giambattista at the Ticpolo Exhibition in Chicago, 1938,
No. 2. The painting is almost identical with the same subject in Milan,
Ambrosiana, and with the one in Dresden, both by Domenico.
Later in the L. Charles Wallach Coll., The Grange, Alresford, Hants.
Catton Rich, *Catalogue*, 1938, p. 21.

LONDON, Hamalton Trust

A BOY WITH A DOG   Fig. 418
Canvas, 120×105 cm.; *c.* 1740.

Fragment of a large composition, probably a *Banquet of Anthony and
Cleopatra* which was left unfinished and cut (no traces of other fragments
known). The impetuous brushwork shows the structure of Tiepolo's
painting in a stage just before completion.
A. Morassi, in *The Connoisseur*, Nov., 1958, p. 178 with repr.

LONDON, formerly T. Harris Coll.

PORTRAIT OF A YOUNG LADY (with flowers in her hair, called
'Christine.').
Canvas, 60×48 cm.

By Domenico.
Always attributed to Giambattista, in *Pantheon*, 1932, p. 238 with ill.;
in the *Connoisseur*, 1934, p. 133; in *Art News*, 1936, June 6th; Catton
Rich, 1938, p. 31, No. 38.
The same type of female figure in the Lazaro-Galdiano Coll., Madrid.
Present whereabouts unknown.

LONDON, Lord Kinnaird Coll.

THE IMMACULATE CONCEPTION   Fig. 71
Canvas 53.5×35.5 cm.; *c.* 1767–69.

Coll. Bayeu (Inv. No. 38); L. Chopinot; in the Coll. of the 9th Lord
Kinnaird—by whom it was probably acquired—at Rossie Priory by
1826.
Sketch for the picture now in the Prado, Madrid, originally
painted for the church at Aranjuez. One of the series of sketches for
Aranjuez now in Count Seilern's Coll., London (q.v.).
The sketch differs from the executed altarpiece only in a few details.
Berenson, *Venetian Painters*, 1894, p. 98; Sack, p. 226; Cat. Exhibition,
R.A., London, 1954–55, No. 498; Morassi, *Burlington Mag.*, Jan., 1955,
p. 11, fig. 1.
Attributed not at all convincingly to Domenico by G. Knox in
Connoisseur, Feb., 1955, p. 39.

LONDON, D. Koetser

JUGURTHA BEFORE THE ROMAN CONSUL
See: London, formerly C. Smith Coll.

LONDON, formerly Koetser

MADONNA AND CHILD
Canvas, 52×45 cm.

By a contemporary imitator of Tiepolo.
Attributed by Borenius in *Burlington Mag.*, March, 1935, to Giambattista; by A. Venturi to him, in collaboration with Domenico. This
painting is identical with that once in the Sabin Coll., London, but
considerably cut down to rectangular shape.
Parke-Bernet, New York, 4.5.1955 (65).

LONDON, formerly Nicholson

THE HOLY TRINITY WITH THE MARTYRDOM OF S. JOHN
NEPOMUK   Fig. 128
Canvas 61×34 cm.; *c.* 1730–35 (?).

In the Bass Sale, Parke-Bernet, New York, 25th January, 1945. Sketch
similar to that in the Galleria Carrara, Bergamo, but of better quality.
Present whereabouts unknown.
Another version (55×33 cm.) was in the Cheremetjew Coll., Russia
(perhaps identical with the present?). Another, rather weak, version
was with Rothmann, London, 1939.

LONDON, formerly Northwick Coll. (sold 1859 to Mr. G. Daubeny)

S. CHARLES BORROMEO BEFORE THE GRATE OF A HOSPITAL
The picture appeared in 1888 at the George Redford Sale, London,
with the attribution to Giambattista.
Sack, p. 233.
No further trace exists of the picture.

LONDON, formerly Private Coll.

BUST OF DAVID
Canvas, 60×45 cm.

Attributed to Tiepolo, but by a follower, perhaps by Domenico
Tiepolo. (Photo Cooper 80467).

LONDON, formerly J. B. Robinson Coll.

THE MADONNA OF THE ROSARY   Fig. 81
Canvas, 236 × 152 cm.; signed and dated JOA. BATTA TIEPOLUS.
F./1735.

Formerly John Webb Coll.; Peacock sale, Foster's, 28th February, 1844;
H. A. J. Munro of Novar sale, 1st June, 1878; Sedelmeyer Coll., Paris,
sold before 1898; Robinson sale, Christie's, London 8th July, 1923,
bought back by J. B. Robinson himself. Now in the coll. of Princess
Labia (on loan, with the whole Robinson Coll., to the National Gallery
of Cape Town, South Africa).
Exhibited at the Royal Academy, London, 1958, *Catalogue* of the
Robinson Collection, No. 35, with repr.
An interesting and well preserved altarpiece of Tiepolo's first maturity,
comparable with the *Adoration of the Infant Jesus* in St. Mark's, Venice;
the *Madonna and Female Saints* of the Gesuati, Venice; the *Madonna
with SS. Dominic and Hyacinth*, of the Art Institute of Chicago, etc.
A sketch, related to the present altarpiece, in Bergamo, Private Coll.
Sack, p. 219, fig. 212a, noting the picture in the Sedelmeyer Coll.,
Paris.

LONDON, Earl of Rosebery Coll.

THE MIRACLE OF THE HOLY HOUSE OF LORETO   Fig. 88
Canvas, oval, 123×77 cm.; *c.* 1743.

Coll. Edward Cheney; Sale Christie's 29.3.1885; 5th Earl of Rosebery.
Modelletto for the ceiling of the church of the Scalzi, Venice (1743–44),
similar to that in the Accademia, Venice.
Watson, *Catalogue*, 1951, p. 34, fig. p. 22; Lorenzetti, pp. 67–69, fig.
51; Cat. Exhib. R.A., London, 1954–55, No. 504.
Excellent study for the fresco, differing somewhat from the other
sketch in Venice Academy; but both are of very high quality.

THE TRIUMPH OF FAITH   Fig. 226
Canvas, oval, 90×60 cm.; c. 1754.

Modelletto for the ceiling of the church of the Pietà, Venice (1754–55).
Watson, *Catalogue*, 1951, p. 34; Lorenzetti, p. 111, fig. 80 *bis*.
Preliminary study, of high quality, with many variations from the
executed ceiling.

HEAD OF CLEOPATRA
Canvas, 38×28.5 cm.

Contemporary copy by a pupil of Tiepolo after his *Banquet of Anthony
and Cleopatra*, now in Melbourne.
Bought presumably in Venice from Casa Correr by Edward Cheney,
Cheney Sale, 29.4.1885 (158).
Watson, *Catalogue*, 1951, p. 35, as by Giambattista.

LONDON, Sir S. Runciman Coll.

RAPE OF EUROPE
See: London, formerly Cliffe Coll.

LONDON, formerly Sabin

MADONNA AND CHILD IN SWADDLING CLOTHES
Canvas, oval 81×64 cm.

By a contemporary imitator.
T. Borenius, in *The Burlington Magazine*, March, 1935, as Giambattista.
(See London, formerly Koetser.)

LONDON, Count Seilern Coll.

APOTHEOSIS OF S. LOUIS GONZAGA   Fig. 113
Canvas, 58×44.7 cm.; c. 1726.

Formerly in the Casa Fantoni, Rovetta sopra Bergamo.
Morassi, 1938, X, p. 141, ff., p. 1; Cat. Exhib., R.A., London,
1954–55, No. 478.
The sketch was, so far as we know, never executed as a large painting.
It bears on the back an inscription: GIO: BATTA: TIEPOLO 1735,
which refers not to the origin but to the date of the gift (probably to the
sculptor Fantoni). Professor Wilde suggested that the canvas was painted
on the occasion of the Saint's canonization in 1726.

S. ROCH   Fig. 163
Canvas, 44×33 cm.; c. 1730–35.

One of the numerous paintings for the members of the Scuola di S.
Rocco.
Bought at Christie's, 1905, with a 'pendant' (also a *S. Roch* in profile)
and sold by Böhler, Munich, 1906, to Baron von Stumm, Holzhausen.
Morassi, *Emporium*, Nov., 1950, p. 209, note 4; *Italian Paintings at 56
Princes Gate, London*, London, 1959, p. 160, Pl. CXXXIV.

S. PASCAL BAYLON   [1955, fig. 63]
S. FRANCIS OF ASSISI   [1955, pl. 91]
S. CHARLES BORROMEO   [1955, fig. 61]
S. JOSEPH WITH THE CHRIST CHILD   [1955, fig. 62]
Four canvases, each 63×38 cm.; c. 1767–69.

Ex coll. Bayeu (Inv. Nos. 133, 138, 139, 137).
L. Chopinot Coll. (the *S. Pascal* and the *S. Francis* later Hulot Coll.,
Sale G. Petit, Paris, 10.5.1892; Priv. Coll., Brazil).
Modelletti for the altarpieces painted for the church of Aranjuez. The
first two are now in the Prado, Madrid, where there is also a fragment
of the *S. Joseph*; the *S. Charles* is in Cincinnati; the *S. Joseph* in Detroit.
A. L. Mayer, *Revista Española de Arte*, IV, Sept., 1935, p. 300, with fig.;
L. Coletti, 1936, p. 171, with repr.; Morassi, 1939, figs. 126–27;
Morassi, 1950, XI, pp. 206–208, figs., I, 12; Lorenzetti, p. 140, figs.
98–101; Cat. Exhib., R.A., London, 1954–55, Nos. 500, 507, 508, 501;
Italian Paintings and Drawings at 56 Princes Gate, London, London, 1959,
pp. 161–65, Pl. CXXXV-CXXXVIII.
Very important and excellently preserved sketches of Tiepolo's late
period.

They wandered from Spain to Paris, then to South America; from there
to Italy (about 1930) and finally to London.
Lord Kinnaird's *Immaculate Conception* (see above) belongs to the same
series.

LONDON, formerly Clifford Smith Coll.

JUGURTHA BEFORE THE ROMAN CONSUL   Fig. 303
Canvas, 28×58.5 cm.; c. 1718–20.

Possibly the first idea for the painting in Baltimore.
Morassi, 1950, XI, p. 196, fig. 2.
Formerly ascribed to Piazzetta (Burlington Fine Arts Club, London,
1917). It was exhibited (not in Catalogue) in the 'Eighteenth Century
Venice' Exhib., London, Whitechapel Gallery, 1951.
Very early and dark in colour.
Now with D. Koetser, London.

LONDON, Sotheby's sale, 28th Nov. 1956

A BEARDED MAN (half-length, in turban and a fur cloak, holding a
sword)
Canvas, 58×47.5 cm.

By Domenico.
Attributed to Giambattista in the Sale Catalogue, No. 25.

LONDON, formerly M. Tree Coll.

HALBERDIER   Fig. 20
Canvas, 205×132 cm.; c. 1755–60.

Ex coll. Lord Blantyre, Scotland; Fauchier-Magnan, Paris; Winterfield
Sale (Arion Coll.), Sotheby, London, 9.12.1936.
Forms part of the *Moses saved from the Waters*, now in the National
Gallery of Scotland, Edinburgh (q.v.).
Cf. under Edinburgh, National Gallery, for literature; Bodkin,
Dismembered Masterpieces, pls. 42, 43; Loan Exhibition of Venetian
Paintings, Agnew, 1953, p. 25.
Now in a Private Coll., Turin.

LOVERE (Lago d'Iseo), Tadini Museum

S. PHILIP AND S. FRANCIS OF SALES
Canvas, 48.5×27 cm.

By Domenico.
Attributed traditionally to Giambattista, and also by Sack (p. 168).
Very low in quality.
From the Coll. of Bishop Morosini in Verona.
R. Bassi-Rathgeb, 1953, p. 177, fig. 157 as by Domenico.

APOTHEOSIS OF A BISHOP SAINT
Canvas, 83×42 cm.

Wrongly attributed to Giambattista traditionally and by Sack (p. 168).
It is a weak work of Tiepolo's school. In the Gallery erroneously as by
Fontebasso.
Cat. of the Museum, 1929, p. 46 as by G.B.; R. Bassi-Rathgeb, 1953,
p. 177, fig. 158 as by C. Ligari.

LUGANO, Thyssen Coll.

THE DEATH OF HYACINTH   [1955, fig. 41]
Canvas, 287×235 cm.; c. 1752–53.

Ex coll. Fürst von Bückeburg; Schloss zu Stadthagen.
Sack, p. 186, fig. 97a; Heinemann, *Sammlung Schloss Rohoncz*, Lugano,
1937, p. 149, fig. 228 (both with bibliography); A. Morassi, p. 32,
fig. 89.
Bought by the Fürst von Bückeburg, perhaps direct from Tiepolo, for
200 zecchini.
One of the most glowing and superb paintings by the Master.

APOTHEOSIS OF HERCULES
Canvas, 102 × 85.5 cm.

By Domenico.
Sketch for a ceiling. Engraved by Domenico (De Vesme, 101).
Ex coll. Fritz August von Kaulbach, Munich.
Heinemann, *ibid.*, 1937, p. 149, fig. 227; Morassi, p. 39, fig. 123;
Cat. of the Gallery, 1958, p. 106 (in each case wrongly as by G.B.).
The engraving states that the invention and the execution are by
Domenico; *Joannes Dominicus Tiepolo invenit, pinxit, et delineavit, inc.*
This sketch was carried out on a large scale by Domenico for the
Imperial Court of St. Petersburg; the other canvases for the same Court
were by his father.
A similar sketch (88.5 × 62 cm.), clearly by Domenico, was in Vienna,
Strauss Sale, Wawra, No. 41, 22–23.3.1926, reproduced in Suida,
Kunstschätze der Sammlung Dr. Max Strauss, Vienna, 1921.

THE PROCESSION TO CALVARY
Canvas, 79 × 86 cm.

By a contemporary follower.
Brentano Coll., Frankfurt, until 1870; Weber, Hamburg; Knoedler,
New York; Ventura, Florence; Private Coll., Milan.
Molmenti, p. 273; Sack, p. 189, fig. 178; Catton-Rich, 1938, p. 22;
Catalogue, Sammlung Schloss Rohoncz, 1958, p. 105, as by G.B.
In the Brentano Coll. this was a pendant to the *Crucifixion* now in St.
Louis but it is not by the same hand. The *Crucifixion* is undoubtedly by
Tiepolo himself, but this is clearly a school piece, copied from the
large canvas in Sant'Alvise, Venice, of 1738–40. The only autograph
sketch for the Sant'Alvise picture is in the Museum at Berlin. Originally
both paintings were taller in size, with added strips 18 cm. high, as in
Sack's reproductions (figs. 177, 178).
Another rather weak version was sold at the Sale 'Kunstwerke aus dem
Besitz der Staatlichen Museen Berlin' in Munich, 19–31.5.1937,
Catalogue No. 627 with repr.

MADRID, Royal Palace

APOTHEOSIS OF SPAIN   [1955, pls. 80–90]
Fresco on the ceiling of the Throne Room. Signed and dated: *Tiepolo A*
1764.
In the same room two overdoors in grisaille fresco, one representing
Merit and Virtue, the other an old man with two warriors symbolizing,
probably, the *Power of Government.*

AENEAS CONDUCTED TO THE TEMPLE OF VENUS [1955, fig. 58]
Fresco in the ceiling of the Guard Room, 1764–66.

APOTHEOSIS OF THE SPANISH MONARCHY   [1955, fig. 59]
Fresco in the ceiling of the 'Saleta', 1764–66.

Ponz, *Viaje de España,* Madrid, 1776, VI; Bermudez, *Diccionario,*
Madrid, 1800, p. 45 ff; Fabre, *Descripcion de las alegorias pintadas en las
bovedas del Real Palacio de Madrid,* Madrid, 1829, pp. 99–132, 168–174;
Molmenti, pp. 183–191, figs. pp. 184–193; Sack, pp. 208–209; figs.
131c, 134, 136a; Morassi, p. 37, figs. 118–122; Sánchez-Cantón, 1953.
A large *modello* for the *Apotheosis of Spain* is in Washington; two
sketches related to the *Aeneas,* one in Boston, the other in Cambridge,
Mass.; two sketches for the *Apotheosis of the Spanish Monarchy,* one in
the Metropolitan Museum, the other in the Wrightsman Coll., New
York (q.v.).
According to Zannandreis, 1891, p. 429, Tiepolo during his stay in
Verona for the frescoes in the Palazzo Canossa, asked his pupil, the
Veronese Francesco Lorenzi, to suggest a subject for the Throne Room
in Madrid. Lorenzi agreed, describing carefully the theme on four pages
that were highly praised by Tiepolo, who is said to have promised to
follow his pupil's suggestions. It is an interesting anecdote, but to be
regarded as a news item of local interest, for Zannandreis's purpose was
to praise the artists of Verona.
The frescoes have been variously judged in the literature. Some critics
praised them as sublime creation, others, who inclined to the new neo-
classical current, contrasted them unfavourably with Mengs. There is no

doubt that, in comparison with the frescoes in Würzburg, the present
cycle does not show the same force and originality of imagination. We
cannot speak of decline but of a relaxed inventive power.

S. PETER OF ALCANTARA   Fig. 187
Canvas, oval, 217 × 167 cm.; 1767–69. Signed *D. Juan Batta Tiepolo inv.
et pinx.*

Originally at Aranjuez.
Molmenti, p. 197; Sack, p. 209, fig. 131b; Morassi, p. 38; Gerstenberg,
1952; Sánchez-Cantón, 1953, p. 21, fig. 29.
Found in the Royal Palace stores in 1875, rolled up and completely
neglected.

MADRID, Prado

THE IMMACULATE CONCEPTION   Fig. 67
Canvas, 279 × 152 cm.; *c.* 1767–69. Signed: *Dn. Juan Batta Tiepolo inv:
et pinx.*

Painted for the altar on the Gospel side of the church of S. Pascal at
Aranjuez.
Molmenti, p. 196, fig. p. 194; Sack, p. 209, fig. 133; Sánchez-Cantón,
Cat., 1942, p. 627; Morassi, p. 38; Sánchez-Cantón, 1953, p. 19, fig. 21.
Entered the Prado in 1828.
The sketch is in Lord Kinnaird's Coll., London (q.v.).

ANGEL BEARING THE EUCHARIST   Fig. 198
Canvas, 185 × 178 cm.; *c.* 1767–69 (1770?).

Fragment of the upper part of the altarpiece of *S. Pascal Baylon,* painted
for the church of Aranjuez.
Molmenti, p. 196, fig. p. 194; Sack, p. 209, fig. 135; Sánchez-Cantón,
Catalogue, 1942, p. 627; Morassi, p. 38; Sánchez-Cantón, 1953, p. 18 ff,
fig. 19.
This painting was soon replaced in the church by an altarpiece by
Mengs. The lower part is the next painting. Sánchez-Cantón states that
a drawing of this part of the painting was in the M. H. Oppenheimer
Coll., London (not known to me).

S. PASCAL BAYLON   Fig. 197
Canvas, 153 × 112 cm.; *c.* 1767–69 (1770?).

Fragment of the lower part of the altarpiece painted for the church at
Aranjuez (see above). The complete altarpiece was engraved by
Domenico with the inscription: *Joan Bapta Tiepolo Venet. Pict. apud
Hisp. Reg. inv. et pinx., an 1770 ante suum decessum. Joan Dominicus
Filius Inc. Hisp.*
Molmenti, p. 196, repr. of the engraving, p. 193; Sack, p. 209, repr. of
the engraving, fig. 136; Morassi, p. 38; Sánchez-Cantón, 1953, p. 18 ff,
figs. 18, 20.
The inscription on the engraving seems to contradict the statement in
a letter of 29 August, 1769, written by Tiepolo himself to the Secretary
Miguel de Muzquiz, in which he affirms that all paintings for Aranjuez
were at that time finished. We can, however, easily imagine that
Tiepolo could call 'finished' a painting which was about to be completed and therefore we are inclined to believe Domenico's statement
and to think that this canvas was really the last on which Giambattista
worked.
The sketch is in the Count Seilern Coll., London (q.v.).

TRIUMPH OF VENUS   Fig. 341
Canvas, 86 × 62 cm.; *c.* 1762–70.

Sketch for a ceiling.
Molmenti, p. 197, fig. p. 195 wrongly connects the sketch with the
ceiling in the Bardini Coll., Florence, which is by F. Chiaruttini; Sack,
p. 209, fig. 130; *Cat.* of the Museum, 1942, p. 628; Morassi, p. 39;
Sánchez-Cantón, 1953, p. 18, fig. 16.
Called *Olympus* in the Prado (in the centre: Venus with her chariot;
around: Jupiter, Juno, Diana, Mercury, Minerva and Saturn). It is the
sketch for the ceiling painted by Giambattista for the Imperial Court at
St. Petersburg (now lost) and engraved by Lorenzo (De Vesme 9). In
the Prado by 1834.

S. Francis of Assisi Receiving the Stigmata   Fig. 195
Canvas, 278 × 153 cm.; *c*. 1767–69. Signed: *Dn. Juan Tiepolo inv. et pinx.*
Painted for the church of Aranjuez.
Sánchez-Cantón, 1929, pp. 137–143; *idem*, Cat. 1942, p. 628; Sánchez-Cantón, 1953, p. 18 ff., fig. 25.
This painting, removed from Aranjuez, was rediscovered in 1914 in the Prado, rolled up and in a very bad state. The sketch is in the Seilern Coll. London (q.v.).

Abraham and the Angels   Fig. 4
Canvas, 197 × 151 cm.; *c*. 1762–70.
Given to the Museum in 1924 by the de Sainz family.
Sánchez-Cantón, Catalogue, 1942, p. 629; Morassi, p. 39; Sánchez-Cantón, 1953, p. 24, fig. 36.
It is not known for whom it was painted; probably for some church or private chapel in Madrid.

Cherub with a Crown of Lilies   Fig. 199
Canvas, 40 × 53 cm.; *c*. 1767–69.
Formerly in the Coll. Eugenio Lucas, sold at Charpentier, Paris (Coll. de M. de Frey), Cat. No. 36, June 1933. Fragment of the altarpiece of *S. Joseph* painted for Aranjuez, and now in Detroit. Acquired by the Prado in 1953.
This fragment belonged to a larger fragment of the above *S. Joseph*, including the two cherubs formerly in New York, French (q.v.). The larger fragment was in Munich, Caspari Coll. (q.v.) until about 1930, when it was cut in two parts—the present one and that in New York.
Sánchez-Cantón, Catalogue, 1942, pp. 628–629; Morassi, p. 38; Sánchez-Cantón, 1953, p. 18 ff., fig. 30.

S. Pascal Baylon
Canvas, *c*. 45 × 35 cm.
Acquired in 1946, and exhibited as by Giambattista.
Not by Tiepolo, but probably by a Spanish painter of the late 18th Century (Bayeu?).
Sánchez-Cantón, 1953, p. 19, as not by Tiepolo.

S. Peter Delivered from Prison
Sketch, 25 × 18 cm.
Mentioned in the *Catalogue* of the Prado, 1942, p. 629 as 'Tiepolo(?)' but clearly not by him.

MADRID, Museo Cerralbo

Sketch for an Allegorical Ceiling
Canvas, 94 × 73 cm.
Wrongly attributed to Tiepolo in the Guide of the Museum, 1956, p. 46.
By a rather late follower of Tiepolo.

MADRID, Museo Lazaro Galdiano

Three Heads of Bearded Old Orientals and Three Heads of Young Ladies
Six canvases, in different sizes from 42 × 36 to 60 × 45 cm. Four from the Lazaro Coll., two from the Marquess of Salamanca.
All by Domenico; except two heads of bearded men, which are by an imitator of Domenico.
Della Pergola, 1937, p. 252 with figs.; J. Camón Aznar, *Guia del Museo Lazaro Galdiano*, Madrid, 1951, p. 138; both wrongly attribute them to Giambattista.

MADRID, Academia de San Fernando

Head of a Bearded Man
Canvas, 60 × 50 cm.
By Domenico.
Represented *en face* with a barret, like the engraving of the 'Raccolta di Teste' (Molmenti, *Acqueforti*, 1896, p. 159, 1), but without a hand.

Originally in the Coll. de Godoy, Principe de la Paz, Minister of Charles IV of Spain.
Attributed in the Academy to Giambattista.

MADRID, Aznar Coll.

Blonde Girl with Flowers
Dark Girl with Flowers
Two canvases, each 60 × 50 cm.
Generally ascribed to Giambattista, but characteristic of Domenico's Spanish period.

MADRID, Marquesa de Balboa Coll.

Dancing Dogs
The Charlatan
Il Mondo Nuovo (Carnival Scene)
Three canvases, 40 × 64 cm. each.
Attributed always to Giambattista (Sanchez-Cantón, 1953, p. 27, figs. 42–43) and also exhibited in Bordeaux (*Catalogue* 1956), they are typical works by Domenico.

MADRID, formerly Valentino de Carderera Coll.

Portrait of Maria Amalia of Saxony, Wife of Charles III of Spain
Attributed by Leroi in 'L'Art', IV, 1876, p. 320, to Giambattista Tiepolo, but contested by Molmenti, p. 198, who remarks that Amalia died two years before Tiepolo's arrival in Madrid.
Nothing else is known of this portrait.

MADRID, Duke of Luna-Villahermosa Coll.

Abraham and the Angels   Fig. 3
The Annunciation   Fig. 34
Two canvases, each 57 × 42 cm.; *c*. 1762–70.
Ex coll. Don Valentino Carderera, Madrid; ex coll. Duchess of Villahermosa, Madrid.
Molmenti, p, 197, fig. p. 196; Sack, p. 210, figs. 134a, 134b; Morassi, p. 39; Sánchez-Cantón, 1953, p. 23, figs. 34–35.
Painted in very light colours and silver-blue tonality, in a flowing and nervous style.

MADRID, Count de Mora Coll.

The Continence of Scipio   Fig. 308
Canvas, *c*. 250 × 500 cm.; *c*. 1720–25.
Morassi, p. 14; Morassi, 1950, XI, p. 196, fig. 3F; Sánchez-Cantón, 1953, p. 26, fig. 41.
Provenance unknown. In style and composition very closely related to the *Jugurtha* in Baltimore.

MADRID, formerly Marques de Perinat Coll.

Heads of Orientals
Four canvases, each 57 × 48 cm.
Perhaps by Domenico.
Sack, p. 211, figs. 205a, 205b.
Three of them were engraved by Domenico in 'Raccolta di teste', nos. 6, 7, 24. (De Vesme, 122, 123, 140.)
Not known to me. The two reproductions in Sack seem rather to suggest Domenico. Sánchez-Cantón, 1953, p. 24, mentions four heads of women in the same coll., possibly by Giambattista.

MADRID, Private Coll.

Allegory of Merit between Nobility and Virtue
Canvas, 53 × 65 cm.; *c*. 1758.
Ex coll. Bayeu, the painter.
Sánchez-Cantón, 1953, pp. 25, 36, fig. 40.
To judge from the reproduction it is, as Sánchez-Cantón suggests, very probably Tiepolo's first idea for the fresco in Palazzo Rezzonico, Venice.

MADRID, formerly Private Coll.

TIME DISCOVERING TRUTH
Canvas, 38 × 25 cm.

Sketch believed to be by Tiepolo, but by a contemporary pupil.
Catalogue of the Sale in Cologne, Nov. 1955, as Giambattista.

MADRID, formerly Conte de Quintanilla Coll.

THE DEPARTURE WITH THE GONDOLA
See: New York, Wrightsman Coll.

MADRID, Rodriguez Bauza Coll.

S. ANTHONY OF PADUA WITH THE CHRIST CHILD   Fig. 179
Canvas, oval, 245 × 196 cm.; 1767–69.

Painted for the church at Aranjuez.
Fiocco, 1937, p. 322; Morassi, p. 38; Sánchez-Cantón, 1953, p. 18 ff.;
figs. 28, 31.
This fine and simple work closely resembles the *S. Peter of Alcantara* in
Madrid, Royal Palace, and was probably a pendant to it at Aranjuez.

MADRID, Marques de Casa Torres Coll.

S. JOHN THE BAPTIST PREACHING
Small canvas.

Judging from the photograph, it is a copy after the sketch in the
Treccani Coll., Milan, for the fresco in the Colleoni Chapel, Bergamo.
Sánchez-Cantón, Madrid, 1925, p. 4, fig. 3a; *id*; 1953, p. 25, as an
original by Giambattista.

MAINZ, Museum

ENCAMPMENT OF GYPSIES
Canvas, 77 × 122 cm.

By Domenico
Molmenti, p. 209, fig. p. 206; Sack, p. 309, fig. 327; both wrongly
attribute it to Giambattista.

MANCHESTER, New Hampshire, U.S.A., Currier Gallery of Art

TRIUMPH OF HERCULES   Fig. 254
Canvas, 90.5 × 67.8 cm.; *c.* 1761

Ex coll. Baron von Stumm, German Ambassador at Madrid; van
Diemen Gallery, Berlin; Jacob Goldschmidt, Berlin and New York;
Baroness de Becker-Rothschild, New York.
Modello for the Palazzo Canossa ceiling, in Verona, from which it
shows many differences.
Exhibited at the Wertheim Gallery, Berlin, 1927 (*Cat.* 'Italienische
Malerei im 17. und 18. Jahrhundert').
Morassi, p. 39.

MELBOURNE, National Gallery of Victoria

THE BANQUET OF CLEOPATRA   [1955, fig. 28]
Canvas, 249 × 346 cm.; last months of 1743–beginning of 1744.

Originally commissioned from Tiepolo by Smith (?) in Venice and
bought from the painter for the Royal Gallery at Dresden by Algarotti
in January, 1744, for 300 zecchini (see the Chronological Table, p. 82,
for the documents). Sent to Dresden in March, 1744, together with the
Old Masters bought by Algarotti for Augustus III and the *Triumph of
Flora* (now in San Francisco) and *Maecenas presenting the Arts to Augustus*
(now in Leningrad), the two latter having been painted for Count
Brühl. From the Royal Gallery in Dresden to Amsterdam, Sale of the
"Collection royale de tableaux, venus de Saxe', 22.5.1765, at Dankmeyer's, *Catalogue* No. 54; bought by Catherine II of Russia; during
the reign of Paul I temporarily in the Michel Castle in S. Petersburg, as
a ceiling; entered the Hermitage, whence it was sold to Melbourne in
1932.
The painting in Paris, Musée Cognacq-Jay, must be regarded as the
modello for this large *Banquet*.

A very important work of Tiepolo's maturity, well documented in the
correspondence of Algarotti to Brühl (published by Posse, 1931,
Beiheft).
A copy by another hand is mentioned by Sack as in Wörlitz.
Algarotti, *Opere*, Venice, 1791–94, VI, p. 35; Ferrari, in *L'Arte*, III,
1900, pp. 150–154; Molmenti, p. 282, fig. p. 68b; Sack, p. 207, fig. 81;
R. Fry, 1933, p. 133; Morassi, p. 29; Cat. of the Nat. Gall. of Victoria,
Melbourne, 1948, pp. 150–151; Cat. Exhib. R.A., London, 1954–55,
No. 51; Watson in *Connoisseur*, Nov. 1955, p. 214; Levey, in *Arte
Veneta*, 1955, pp. 199–203; Haskell, in *The Burlington Magazine*,
June, 1958, pp. 212–13, fig. 33.

THE FINDING OF MOSES   Fig. 14
Canvas, 235 × 310 cm.; *c.* 1740–45.

This picture, with the attribution to Veronese, was one of a number of
very large canvases which Sir Bruce Ingram inherited from his father,
Sir Herbert Ingram, and had kept in store since his father's death. Sold
to the art market in London about 1930 (?) and bought by Mr. Francis
Stonor. Temporarily lent to the Bristol Gallery and then for some years
to the Italian Institute in London (Istituto Italiano di Cultura). Entered
the Museum in 1958 as a work by Sebastiano Ricci. As such, in fact, the
picture was lent and should have been exhibited at the Royal Academy
1954–55 but, because of its large size, it did not appear.
This large canvas is a misunderstood masterpiece by the hand of
Tiepolo, interpreting Veronese and partly inspired by the latter's
picture which was until 1747 in the Casa Grimani at Venice and is now
in the Dresden Gallery.
The present picture shows evident stylistic links with the copies after
Veronese which Tiepolo executed principally in the same period, that
is, *Christ and the Magdalen in the House of the Pharisee*, now in Dublin,
and the *Rape of Europa*, now in London. The style is the large one of
Tiepolo's maturity, so much appreciated by Algarotti, who considered
Tiepolo the greatest interpreter of Veronese. We know that Algarotti
asked the painter also to counterfeit Veronese, and to execute for his
collection works to be believed by Veronese himself (in the same way
that Consul Smith listed some Riccis of his collection as by Caliari).
F. Watson, in *Arte Veneta*, 1955, p. 260, as by Sebastiano and Marco
Ricci.
When I recognised the picture in London, 1959, as Tiepolo's original,
I found no agreement.

MERLENGO (Province of Treviso), Palazzo Cornaro di S. Maurizio

Frescoes in the main salon (6.5 × 15 m.):
TRIUMPH OF DIANA, on the ceiling, 500 × 220 cm.;
SACRIFICE OF IPHIGENIA, on the principal wall, 210 × 500 cm.;
DIANA FLYING TO TAURIS WITH IPHIGENIA and
FLIGHT OF IPHIGENIA AND ORESTES on the opposite wall
210 × 180 cm. each.

Bettinelli saw the frescoes in 1750 and praised them highly in a
panegyric on Tiepolo's works at the Villa Cornaro, published on the
occasion of the marriage of Andrea Cornaro with Maria Foscarini.
The frescoes were partly covered for reasons of prudery by Bishop
Soldati in the XIXth Century and completely whitened by his nephew,
Marchese Bandini. Only by the present owner, Signor Pavan, were
they restored to view (1930–35). Their state is, of course, not at all
good, the colour is fading and in some parts lacking; nevertheless, the
frescoes on the whole give quite a pleasing impression.
In the other ground-floor room, corresponding to the frescoed upper
salon, there were *feigned statues*, one of which is now in the Museo
Civico at Treviso (q.v.), while the remaining decoration of the room
no longer exists. The *modello* for the *Sacrifice of Iphigenia* in Paris,
Patino Coll. (q.v.); the *modello* for the ceiling in London, Dulwich
College (q.v.). In this connection can be mentioned the *Sacrifice of
Iphigenia* in the Giustiniani-Recanati Coll., Venice (q.v.) as the first
realisation of this theme.
In the other rooms, no traces now exist of decorations with Chinoiserie
subjects, mentioned by Bettinelli (1800). From a letter of Count Tessin,
25.5.1736, it transpires that Tiepolo was working at that time for the

N. H. Cornaro for five or six months. It is very likely that this indication refers to the present Villa, although because of the bad condition of the frescoes, a judgement on their dating is rather difficult. In any case, on general stylistic grounds, a date about 1735–40 is quite probable.
Bettinelli, 1800, XVII, p. 226, 231; Federici, 1803, p. 186; Crico, 1833, pp. 127–128; Siren, 1902, p. 109; Molmenti, p. 94; Sack, pp. 74, 172; Molmenti, 1911, p. 180; Pallucchini, *Emporium*, 1947, p. 236, fig. 6; Mazzotti, 1953, pp. 656–657.

MILAN, Brera

MADONNA DEL CARMELO WITH SAINTS   [1955, fig. 4]
Canvas, 210×650 cm.; *c.* 1720–22.

Originally painted for the Carmelite Chapel in the church of S. Apollinare in Venice; mentioned by da Canal 1732. Removed from there some years after the church was closed in 1810. Bought in Paris (where it was cut in two parts) for the Brera, 1925. Recently restored to one piece.
Zanetti, 1733, p. 268; Cochin, 1758; Zanetti, 1771, p. 467; Molmenti, p. 52, Sack, p. 130; Modigliani, 1933, pp. 129–133 with figs.; Morassi, p. 15, figs. 5, 6; Lorenzetti, p. 8, figs. 3, 4.
Very important early work.

THE TEMPTATION OF S. ANTHONY   [1955, pl. 11]
Canvas, 40×47 cm.; *c.* 1725.

Given to the Gallery in 1929 by Mr. Lederer of Vienna, who had bought it from a Milanese private coll.
Modigliani, 1933, p. 135 with fig.; Morassi, p. 17, fig. 9; Lorenzetti, p. 28, fig. 19.
An excellent early work, of the Udine period, very closely related to the *Venus with a Mirror* in the Count Gerli Coll., Milan.

BATTLE SCENE
Canvas, 52×70 cm.

By Domenico.
Wrongly (Catalogue of the Brera, 1931, p. 57) believed to be the sketch for one of the *Battles*, ex-Dolfin, now in the Castiglioni Coll., New York. Probably the first idea, suggested by Giambattista, for the fresco, executed by Domenico, with the battle scene of SS. Faustinus and Jovita in the church dedicated to them in Brescia (*c.* 1754–55).
Sack, p. 170, fig. 19; Morassi, *Burlington Magazine*, 1955, p. 8.
The pendant with the *Martyrdom* of these Saints was formerly in the Weisbach Coll., Berlin (q.v.).

MILAN, Ambrosiana

THE PRESENTATION IN THE TEMPLE
Canvas, 37×51 cm.

By Domenico.
Sack, p. 170, fig. 29, wrongly attributes it to Giambattista, as all guides also do. The composition is identical with the picture in Dresden, and that formerly in the Fischmann Coll., London.
Exh. Cat., Lucerne, 1946, p. 66; Galbiati, *Catalogue*, 1951, p. 187, both as by Giambattista.

HALF-LENGTH OF A BISHOP SAINT
Canvas, 43×33.5 cm.

By Domenico.
Molmenti, p. 149; Sack, p. 171; wrongly attributed by both to Giambattista, followed by *Exhib. Catalogue*, Lucerne, 1946, p. 65.

HEAD OF AN OLD MAN
Canvas, 47×40 cm.

By Domenico.
Engraved by Domenico in 'Raccolta di Teste', No. 11 (De Vesme, 127).
Sack, p. 171, wrongly attributes it to Giambattista, as the guides also do.

ALLEGORY WITH A FLYING ANGEL
Canvas, 65×53 cm.

Sketch for a circular ceiling, by a follower (possibly G. C. Ligari), wrongly attributed to Giambattista by Sack and by all guides and

Museum catalogues: it is a copy of the picture in the Talleyrand Coll., Paris.
Sack, p. 171, fig. 162.

ALLEGORY WITH AN ANGEL AND A HORSE
Canvas, 65×53 cm.

Sketch for a circular ceiling similar to the one in the Pal. Labia, Venice; by a follower, perhaps G. C. Ligari, and wrongly attributed to Giambattista by Sack and by all guides and Museum catalogues.
Sack, p. 170, fig. 120.

THE BRAZEN SERPENT
Canvas, 120×150 cm.

By G. C. Ligari.
Sack, pp. 66–67, 171, fig. 51, wrongly attributes it to Giambattista. It is in part copied from the frieze by Giambattista now in the Accademia, Venice. On the back is the inscription, certainly authentic, *Cesare Ligari figlio di Pietro dip. nel 1740.*
Riccoboni, 1953, p. 75, figs. 155–156.
Stylistically very close to Tiepolo but not of such high quality.

MILAN, Museo Civico

THE COMMUNION OF S. LUCY   Fig. 115
Canvas, 55×35 cm.; *c.* 1740–45.

Sketch for the altarpiece in SS. Apostoli, Venice.
Molmenti, p. 149; Sack, p. 171.
Rapidly sketched *modelletto* in a silver-grey tonality.

THE MARTYRDOM OF S. VICTOR
Canvas, *c.* 20×40 cm.

By a follower, perhaps Giambattista Raggi.
From the Beltrami Coll., Milan.
Another sketch, also by a pupil, in Rotterdam (q.v.).
Molmenti, p. 134, fig. p. 136; Sack, p. 168; fig. 159; both wrongly attribute it to Giambattista, believing it to be the sketch for the fresco in S. Ambrogio. Morassi, *Le Arti*, 1941, p. 253, as by a follower.

MILAN, Museo Poldi-Pezzoli

JOSHUA COMMANDING THE SUN TO STAND STILL   Fig. 17
Canvas, 29×71 cm.; monochrome on gold ground; *c.* 1725–30.

Acquired in 1898 from the painter Giuseppe Bertini.
Molmenti, p. 149; Sack, p. 170; Morassi, 1942, p. 266, fig. 23; Morassi, p. 20; Lorenzetti, p. 110, fig. 80; Russoli, Catalogue, 1955, p. 221.

MADONNA OF THE ROSARY   Fig. 92
Arched canvas, 180×102 cm.; *c.* 1730–35.

Acquired in 1855 from A. Cassani.
Probably painted for a private chapel. Rather conventional in composition and in a style recalling two pictures in the Museo Civico at Udine (*Guardian Angel* and *S. Francis of Sales*); it may be assumed, therefore, that this painting belongs to the same period. Sack (p. 57) states that it is signed and dated 1731, but there is no trace of the inscription.
Bertini, *Catalogo generale della Fondazione artistica Poldi-Pezzoli*, Milan, 1881, p. 31, as by Domenico; Sack, p. 170; Santangelo, *La critica d'arte*, 1935, I, p. 48, as workshop; Russoli, *Catalogue*, 1955, p. 221, as Domenico. No doubt by G.B.

THE DEATH OF S. JEROME   [1955, fig. 18]
Canvas, 35×45 cm.; 1732–33.

Acquired from the Magni Coll., Milan, in 1934.
Pendant to the *Communion of S. Jerome* in the Stuttgart Museum.
One of the most impressive and inspired small paintings of the Bergamasque period. Another similar subject, rather weak and of an earlier period, in Chicago (q.v.).
Modigliani, 1933, p. 138 with fig. dates it wrongly 1750–55; Morassi, 1942, p. 266, fig. 22; Morassi, p. 20; Lorenzetti, p. 46, fig. 34; Russoli, *Catalogue*, 1955, p. 219.

APOTHEOSIS OF SAINTS   Fig. 135
Canvas, 47×29 cm.; 1734.

Acquired from the painter Bertini in 1855.
Modelletto for the altarpiece at Rovetta (1734). Frizzoni, 1877, p. 69,
and by him identified as a *prima idea* for Rovetta; Molmenti, p. 149;
Sack, p. 170; Morassi, p. 22; Lorenzetti, p. 55, fig. 40; Russoli,
Catalogue, 1955, p. 218.
There are many remarkable differences between this sketch and the
finished altarpiece. Perhaps Tiepolo painted some other *modello* after
this (certainly the first) and closer to the large canvas.

SS. GAETANO, ANTONY ABBOT AND JOHN THE BAPTIST
Canvas, 51×29 cm.; c. 1740–50.   Fig. 134
Given to the Museum 1898 by the painter Bertini. Sketch for an
altarpiece either unknown or never executed.
Molmenti, p. 149; Sack, p. 170, fig. 161; Morassi, 1932, p. 7; Loren-
zetti, p. 77, fig. 57; Russoli, *Catalogue*, 1955, p. 220.
A very fluent sketch, light in colour, called also the *Vocation of S. Louis*.

FORTITUDE AND WISDOM   Fig. 343
Canvas, 36×30 cm.; c. 1740–45.

Acquired in 1885 from the painter Giuseppe Bertini.
Sketch related to the ceiling of Pal. Barbarigo, now in Ca' Rezzonico,
Venice, as well as to that formerly in the Pal. Caiselli, Udine, now in
the Museo Civico, Udine.
This very spirited sketch is one of the first known ideas by Tiepolo of
a composition which was often to be repeated or developed in his
ceilings.
Molmenti, p. 149; Sack, p. 170, fig. 160; Morassi, 1932, p. 7; Lorenzetti, p. 81, fig. 61; Russoli, *Catalogue*, 1955, p. 220.

MILAN, S. Ambrogio

THE MARTYRDOM OF S. VICTOR   Fig. 143
THE SHIPWRECK OF S. SATYRUS   Fig. 144
Frescoes, c. 2.50 metres square, executed for the Chapel of S. Victor in
1737. Damaged by damp and stripped from the walls about 1930.
Removed during the war and now replaced in the chapel. In very bad
condition.
There can be no doubt that the frescoes were painted in 1737 (and not
in 1731 as Sack affirms) as they are clearly documented by Lattuada.
They were executed during the last year of the episcopate of Cardinal
Erba-Odescalchi (1737).
Lattuada, *Descrizione*, 1738, IV, p. 302; Molmenti, p. 135; Sack, p. 168;
Morassi, in 'Le Arti', 1941, p. 253, Tav. XCIX; Morassi, p. 22.
The sketch for the *S. Victor* in Milan, Museo Civico, believed to be the
original *modello*, is a copy after the fresco or after the original, unknown,
modello.

In the Sacristy:
APOTHEOSIS OF S. BERNARD   Fig. 149
Fresco, 1737, destroyed during the war, in August, 1943.

This very impressive ceiling was much admired by contemporary
painters and writers, and had certainly a large influence on the ceiling-
painting of the Lombard school during the eighteenth century.
Lattuada, *Descrizione*, 1738, IV, p. 302; Molfese and Centelli, Turin,
1897; Molmenti, p. 134, fig. p. 134; Sack, p. 168, fig. 42a; Morassi,
p. 22. Documented by Lattuada, like the preceding.

MILAN, Palazzo Archinto

All the frescoes were destroyed by bombing in August, 1943.
TRIUMPH OF THE ARTS   Figs. 336, 337
Ceiling, 9×15 metres, fresco, dated 1731, in the principal saloon.

The *Allegory of the Arts* is in the middle of the ceiling. Around it is a
balustrade in perspective with feigned columns and statues. The date
1731 was on a label held by a King in the middle of the balustrade.
(Molfese-Centelli, Plates 1–3). A little fragment of the ceiling, bearing
this date, was saved after the bombing, and is now in the Museo Civico.

In the other four saloons, ceiling-frescoes:
PHAETHON AND APOLLO   [1955, pl. 12]
c. 7×9 m.   Fig. 239
Around the oval fresco, eight grisailles: the two larger representing
Apollo and Daphne and *Mercury appearing to Aeneas*; the smaller with
other scenes from the Phoebus legend (Molfese-Centelli, Plate 9).

PERSEUS AND ANDROMEDA   Fig. 252
c. 6×7 m.
Around the shaped fresco eight grisailles with mythological scenes
related to Perseus (Molfese-Centelli, Pl. 4).

JUNO WITH FORTUNA AND VENUS   Fig. 264
c. 6×7 m.
Zephyrus bore the arms of the Archinto and the Borromei.

NOBILITY
c. 3×4 m.
Nobility is sitting on the clouds, holding a lance in the left hand, a statue
of Minerva in the right. All the frescoes were executed in 1731.
Lattuada, *Descrizione*, 1737, III, p. 150; Bianconi, *Guida*, 1795, p. 214;
Molfese-Centelli, 1897, with large plates; Molmenti, pp. 125–128.
fig. p. 123; Sack, pp. 53–54, 169, figs. 37, 39, 40–42; Morassi, 'Le Arti',
1941, p. 265, figs. 18, 19; Morassi, pp. 18–19, figs. 36–39.
These frescoes are among the most important works of Tiepolo's early
maturity. Da Canal (1732) says that Tiepolo was working in Milan—
certainly in this Palace—in 1731, when he was thirty-five years old.
A sketch related to the *Triumph* is in Lisbon; two for the *Phaethon* are in
Barnard Castle and Vienna, Academy, and one, for *Perseus*, in the Frick
Coll., New York.

MILAN, Palazzo Clerici

THE COURSE OF THE SUN ON OLYMPUS   [1955, pls. 25–27]
Ceiling fresco, 22×5.40 m.; 1740.

In the middle of the feigned architecture of the smaller walls, two
grisailles with one scene of a *Sacrifice* each.
Celebrated in a series of poems, by an anonymous poet, in 1740 (Milan,
1740, Ed. Bolzini): *Poesie dedicate al merito . . . di G. B. Tiepolo*.
Mongeri, *L'Arte in Milano*, 1872, p. 442; Beltrami, 'Emporium',
Dec., 1896, p. 445; Molfese-Centelli, 1897, with large plates; Molmenti,
pp. 136–144, figs. p. 136; Sack, pp. 78, 168–169; Morassi, p. 24,
figs. 58–61.
One of the most important works in the whole of Tiepolo's career. It
has suffered from damp since the war.
A sketch related to it in Zürich, Hausammann Coll. (q.v.).

MILAN, Palazzo Dugnani, formerly Palazzo Casati

THE CONTINENCE OF SCIPIO   Fig. 304
5.20×6.50 m.

SCIPIO AND THE SLAVE   Fig. 305
5.20×4.50 m.

SOPHONISBA RECEIVING THE POISON FROM MASSINISSA
5.20×6.50 m.   [1955, fig. 13]
Frescoes on the walls in the principal saloon.

ALLEGORY OF MAGNANIMITY   Fig. 368
9.50×11.10 m.; painted in 1731.

Ceiling fresco in the same saloon. On the large frame around the
ceiling there are four grisailles painted in ochre with single female
figures. Below the frieze, six overdoors, also in ochre grisaille, with
smaller female figures. Between the windows, two female allegorical
statues painted in ochre.
The ceiling was already in very bad condition after the 1914–18 war;
the frescoes on the walls were a little damaged (especially the head of
Sophonisba) in 1943, and shortly afterwards transferred to canvas and
restored (Prof. O. Della Rotta). Exhibited in the Tiepolo Exhibition,
Venice, 1951. They are now replaced *in situ*.

Pirovano, *Nuova Guida*, 1857, p. 245; Beltrami, 'Emporium', Dec., 1896, p. 441 ff.; Molfese-Centelli, 1897, with large Plates; Molmenti, p. 144, figs. pp. 137–38; Sack, pp. 50–52, 169, figs. 34–36; Morassi, p. 19, figs. 40–41; Lorenzetti, p. 36, figs. 25–27.

The exact date of the beginning of this work is known from a letter by Tiepolo of the 14th April, 1731, published by G. Morazzoni in 1918 (see Bibliography).

These frescoes are among Tiepolo's finest creations of this period. No *modelli* are known for them, and Sack's reference is to a sketch for the *Scipio and the Slave*, recorded in the Gaifami Coll., Brescia, by Rodella, *Pitture e sculture di Brescia*, 1760, of which no other record exists.

MILAN, Palazzo Gallarati-Scotti

ALLEGORY OF VIRTUE AND FORTITUDE   Fig. 348
Circular fresco on the ceiling of a small room, *c.* 3 m. in diameter; *c.* 1740.

Removed (after being transferred to canvas) during the war, and now replaced *in situ*. The composition is very similar to the group in the Pal. Caiselli at Udine, or to that in the Pal. Barbarigo, Venice.
Morassi, p. 24.

MILAN, Palazzo Isimbardi

APOTHEOSIS OF FRANCESCO MOROSINI PELOPONNESIACO
See: Paris, formerly A. de Rothschild Coll.

MILAN, Palazzo Tanzi (later Poldi Pezzoli)

ALLEGORY
Ceiling fresco in the Yellow Room, attributed by Sack, p. 170, 236, to Tiepolo, was confused by him with a documented painting (*Nuova Guida di Milano*, 1795, p. 469) no longer existing in the Palace. The ceiling, assigned by Sack to Tiepolo, was in reality a work by Scrosati, destroyed in 1943.

MILAN, D. Anghileri Coll.

S. ROCH   Fig. 165
Canvas, 45 × 33 cm.; *c.* 1730–35.

Morassi, 1944, VI, p. and fig. 6; Lorenzetti, p. 56, fig. 40 *bis*.
Excellent example of the well-known series of devotional pictures painted for the members of the Scuola di S. Rocco, Venice.

MILAN, formerly Bertini Coll.

CHRIST HEALING THE BLIND
Canvas, 43 × 63 cm.
By Domenico.

Attributed by Molmenti, p. 149, fig. p. 147, to Giambattista; assigned by Sack rather to Domenico, p. 307.
Now in a Private Coll., Paris.

MILAN, A. Bolchini-Bonomi Coll.

TWO ROUNDELS WITH ALLEGORICAL FIGURES   Figs. 392–93
71 cm. diam.; *c.* 1745–50.

Painted on a gold ground.
Formerly decorated a room in the Pal. Labia, Venice. Recorded by Molmenti in the Oreffice Coll. in Venice; then in the Böhler Coll., Munich (1904); Silbermann, Vienna; Silbermann, New York.
The other two roundels in the Yale University, New Haven (q.v.).
Molmenti, p. 173, figs. pp. 69a, 69b reproducing six of these roundels; Sack, p. 152; Catton-Rich, 1938, p. 28.

RINALDO ABANDONING ARMIDA
Canvas, 39 cm. square; *c.* 1755–60.

A version hitherto unpublished, similar to that in the Cailleux Coll., Paris.

MILAN, Ing. L. Bonomi Coll.

THE SACRIFICE OF IPHIGENIA
Canvas, 81 × 98 cm.; *c.* 1720–25.

Morassi, 1934, II–III, p. 92, fig. C.
Very early work, and difficult to judge on account of its bad condition, but certainly autograph.

MILAN, Count Borletti Coll.

THE RAPE OF HELEN   Fig. 227
THE MADNESS OF ULYSSES   Fig. 228
Two canvases, 43 × 52 cm.; *c.* 1755–60.

Fiocco, 1929, p. 55; Morassi, p. 35, fig. 104 (*The Rape of Helen*); Lorenzetti, p. 126, figs. 89–90.
Excellent sketches in his late style, light in colour. So far as we know, never executed on a large scale.

MILAN, formerly G. Botta Coll.

RINALDO AND THE WARRIORS
RINALDO ABANDONING ARMIDA
Two canvases, 79 × 134 cm. each.

By a follower of Tiepolo (Menescardi).
Exhibited as originals by Tiepolo in Florence, 1922 (Coll. Besozzi, Turin); sold in Milan, 1934, also as Giambattista Tiepolo.
M. Nugent, *Alla Mostra della Pittura It. del '600 e '700*, San Casciano 1925, pp. 94–96, figs. p. 95; *Cat.* of the Botta Sale, Scopinich, Milan, 9–11.4.1934, p. 18, Tavv. XVII–XIX.

MILAN, formerly A. Chiesa Coll.

A BISHOP READING PRAYERS   Fig. 133
Canvas, 59 × 33 cm.; *c.* 1735–40.

Chiesa Sale, American Art Assoc., New York, 27.11.1925 (47).
Identical with Sack, p. 226, fig. 219, recorded in Dudley Coll., London.

THE COMMUNION OF S. LUCY
Canvas, 92 × 62 cm.

Good old copy of the central part of the altarpiece in SS. Apostoli, Venice.
Chiesa Sale, American Art Assoc., New York, 22–23.11.1927 (60) with ill., as Giambattista. Later in the De Angeli-Frua Coll., Milan.

MILAN, Count Cicogna Coll.

S. ROCH   Fig. 156
S. ROCH   Fig. 158
Two canvases, 45 × 33 cm.; *c.* 1730–35.

Formerly in Private Coll., Florence.
Morassi, 1950, XI, p. 202, figs. 10–11.
They belong to the series of devotional paintings for the members of the Scuola di S. Rocco, Venice.

MILAN, Senator M. Crespi Coll.

A HUNTER KILLING A STAG   [1955, fig. 19]
Canvas, 262 × 143 cm.; *c.* 1730–35.

A HUNTER ON HORSEBACK   [1955, fig. 19]
Canvas, 262 × 148 cm.; *c.* 1730–35.

These two canvases belonged to a triptych, together with the *Scene from Roman History* (or, *Founding of Rome*), now in the National Gallery, Washington, and originally in the Villa Grimani-Valmarana, at Noventa Padovana near Vicenza. It has also been suggested that they represent *Hercules and the Stag* and *Hercules and the Horses of Diomedes*. Lorenzetti, 1935, August, p. 152 with figs.; Morassi, p. 20.
Bought with the central scene by Mr. Ladyard Blair in Venice, 1909, from Count Barozzi (who had acquired them shortly before from the

Villa Grimani-Valmarana) and taken to New Jersey. Blair Sale, Parke-Bernet, New York, 10.6.1950. Excellent paintings, very free and strong in brushwork, recalling the style of the pictures in Sant' Alvise, Venice.

S. Dominic Instituting the Rosary   Fig. 89
Canvas, 108×51.5 cm.; c. 1737-39.

One of the sketches for the ceiling of the Gesuati, Venice.
Catalogue of the Pasquinelli Coll., Milan (n.d., c. 1933), p. 258, pl. XXXIX (colour plate).
The other sketch is in Berlin, Gemäldegalerie (q.v.). An old copy after this painting is in Chicago, Art Institute. This sketch is closer to the ceiling fresco in Venice than the Berlin one.

The Family of Darius before Alexander   Fig. 281
Canvas, 56×41 cm.; 1743.

Sketch for the fresco in the Villa Cordellina, Montecchio Maggiore, near Vicenza, and pendant to the *Continence of Scipio* in Stockholm.
Ex coll. Gompertz, Vienna; Heimann, Beverly Hills, Calif.
Molmenti, pp. 97, 281, fig. p. 281; Sack, pp. 174, 206; Morassi, p. 26; Lorenzetti, p. 72, fig. 54; Venturi, 1952, colour plate 77.
One of the finest *modelli* of that period, in light and transparent colours, and certainly identical with the painting recorded after Algarotti's death as in his collection—*cf.* Sack, p. 231.

Juno and the Peacock on Clouds   Fig. 263
Fresco, oval, transferred to canvas, 350×210 cm.; c. 1750.

Originally in the Sagredo Palace in Venice, taken to Paris before 1910 (Cléry Coll.) and returned to Italy in 1949. The two grisailles belonging originally to the same room are in a Private Coll., Bergamo (q.v.).
Sack, p. 64; Molmenti, 1911, p. 198.

The Arms of the Barbarigo-Sagredo Family
See Venice, formerly Donà dalle Rose Coll.

The Angel Appearing to Abraham and Sarah
See Vaduz, formerly Liechtenstein Gallery.

Apotheosis of Spain
Paper on canvas, 65×49 cm.

Published by Molmenti as the sketch for the central part of the Throne Room ceiling in Madrid. It is a copy after the *modello* now in Washington (q.v.).
Molmenti, in *Dedalo*, 1925, pp. 475-479, fig. p. 477; Cailleux, *Catalogue*, 1952, p. 51, as an original.

MILAN, formerly B. Crespi Gallery

Beata Laduina   Fig. 425
Canvas, 65×48 cm.; old inscription on the back: 1741: *Fu fatta dal Sig . . . Batta Tiepolli Insigne Pittore Veneziano, La Beata Laduina.*

Later in the Welsh Sale, Parke-Bernet, New York, 25-27.5.1938 (256); Kelley Sale, Parke-Bernet, New York, 17.2.1944.
A. Venturi, 1900, p. 186, fig. p. 185; Molmenti, p. 147; Sack, p. 172.
Certainly autograph. Present whereabouts unknown.

MILAN, formerly De Angeli-Frua Coll.

Martyrdom of a Female Saint
Canvas, 104×75 cm.

The Saint kneeling, the executioner standing behind her.
Wrongly ascribed to Tiepolo, it is certainly by F. Zugno. (Photograph in the Berenson Library, Florence.)

The Communion of S. Lucy
See: Formerly Chiesa Coll., Milan.

MILAN, G. Falck Coll.

The Martyrdom of S. Theodora   Fig. 153
Canvas, 61×35 cm.; c. 1740-50.

Bought at the Lurati Sale, Galleria Pesaro, Milan, 22.4.1928.
There are many copies of this excellent sketch, including one in Ca' Rezzonico, Venice, and others in Paris etc. Perhaps identical with the painting once in the Benfatto Coll., Venice, recorded by F. Zanotto, in *Pinacoteca di Valentino Benfatto*, Venice, 1856, which differs only in the height (*cf.* Sack, p. 232). Hitherto unpublished, it is not known whether this sketch was ever executed on a large scale.

MILAN, Count P. Gerli Coll.

Venus with a Mirror   [1955, p. 1]
Canvas, 38×48 cm.; c. 1725.

Formerly regarded as a school work, it was not identified as by Tiepolo until 1949. An excellent painting, very closely related to the *Temptation of S. Anthony* in the Brera, Milan. Identical with the painting in the Mniszech Sale, Petit, Paris, 1902; Strauss Sale, Charpentier, Paris, 27.5.1949, No. 39, as *atelier des Tiepolo*.
Morassi, 1949, p. 76, figs. 67-69; Lorenzetti, p. 31, fig. 21; *Exhib. Cat.*, Petit Palais, Paris, 1960-61, No. 388.

MILAN, formerly Antonio Grandi Coll.

Martyrdom of a Female Saint
Two sketches on canvas, 29.5×18 cm. each, rounded.

Sack, p. 172. No reproduction of them existing, it is quite uncertain if they belonged to Tiepolo.
Missing.

MILAN, F. Marinotti Coll.

Jugurtha before the Roman Consul   [1955, fig. 8]
Canvas, 27×54 cm.; c. 1720-25.

Sketch for the picture in Baltimore.
Morassi, 1935, p. 144, with fig., first recognizing it as by Tiepolo; Morassi, 1941, p. 89 with fig.; Morassi, p. 15, fig. II; Lorenzetti, p. 12, fig. 5; *Exhib. Cat.*, Petit Palais, Paris, 1960-61, No. 387.
Formerly on the market in Paris, ascribed to Pittoni. Excellent sketch, certainly the original *modello* for the large canvas in Baltimore. Another sketch of the same theme, of an earlier period, in London, Clifford Smith Coll.

S. Roch   Fig. 164
Canvas, 44×33 cm.; c. 1730-35.

Perhaps identical with that formerly in the Liphart Coll., Leningrad, mentioned by Molmenti, p. 283. Hitherto unpublished. Belongs to the series painted for the members of the Scuola di S. Rocco.

MILAN, Count O. Miani Coll.

S. Francis of Paola   Fig. 181
Canvas, 44.5×33 cm.; c. 1725-30.

Morassi, 1944, VI, p. 6, fig. 5.
Modello for the altarpiece in S. Nicolò at Piove di Sacco (q.v.).

MILAN, E. Moizzi Coll.

Moses Saved from the Waters   Fig. 19
Moses Threatened   Fig. 22

Two canvases, 58×76 cm. each, c. 1720-22.

The first is signed on the back: *G. B. Tiepolo.*
Morassi, 1950, XI, pp. 197-99, figs. 4-7.
Stylistically related to the four mythological scenes in the Accademia, Venice, but certainly a little earlier.

MILAN, Private Coll.

Allegory (of the Sciences?)
See Vicenza, Palazzo Trento-Valmarana.

MILAN, Private Coll.

ALLEGORY OF AGE AND DEATH   Fig. 408
Oval on copper, 11 × 8 cm.; *c.* 1718–1720.

The smallest painting by Giambattista known.
Morassi, 1942, XII-1, p. 89, fig. 4; Morassi, p. 14.
A very unusual theme in the work of Tiepolo, perhaps inspired by
some engraving. There is a certain relationship to Magnasco. A similar
subject, after a drawing by Tiepolo, was engraved by F. Zucchi (1742)
for his illustrations to Milton's 'Paradise Lost'.

MILAN, Private Coll.

MADONNA AND CHILD WITH S. CATHERINE, S. CHARLES
BORROMEO AND S. JOHN BISHOP OF BERGAMO   Fig. 100
Canvas, 53 × 29 cm.; 1731.

Modello for an altarpiece (certainly projected for a church in Lombardy),
which was probably never painted on a large scale. An old *cartellino*
on the back states that it was executed in 1731, a date which seems, for
stylistic reasons, to be certain. A good autograph replica was in the
Nemes Coll., Munich (q.v.); sold at U. Helbig, 1933. Another one was
on the market in Germany (photo in the Kunsthistorisches Institut,
Florence, No. 101025) and one (76 × 40 cm.) in the Simonetti Sale,
Tavazzi, Rome, 25.4–6.5.1932. Hitherto unpublished.

MILAN, Private Coll.

MADONNA AND CHILD ENTHRONED, WITH A CAPUCHIN MONK
PRESENTED BY A BISHOP SAINT
Canvas, *c.* 50 × 40 cm. ; *c.* 1730–35.

The Bishop is probably S. John, Bishop of Bergamo.
Small devotional painting or a *modello* for a never executed altarpiece.
The heads of the Virgin and of the Child badly repainted.

MILAN, Private Coll.

HOMER AS KING OF POETRY
Canvas, 73 × 178 cm.

Attributed to Tiepolo, but it is of an earlier period and obviously not
by him.
Mostra del Settecento Italiano, with Preface by G. Fiocco, Galleria Asta,
Milan, 1941, p. 19, with repr., as by Giambattista.

MILAN, Private Coll.

TWO HEADS OF ORIENTALS
Two canvases, 54 × 45 cm. each.

Attributed to Giambattista, but they are by a pupil of his, close to
Domenico.
Morandotti, *Catalogue*, 1941, pp. 40–41, fig. 35–36.

MILAN, Private Coll.

TIME RAVISHING BEAUTY (Two figures over clouds)
Canvas, 49 × 39 cm.

A late work by F. Fontebasso, and wrongly attributed to Tiepolo.

MILAN, formerly Private Coll.

SCENE FROM ROMAN HISTORY   Fig. 291
Canvas, *c.* 60 × 90 cm.; 1718–20.

Morassi, 1944, p. 4, fig. 3.
Very early work, rather confused in composition; not in very good
condition.
Present whereabouts unknown.

MILAN, formerly Private Coll.

THE PROCESSION TO CALVARY
See: Lugano, Thyssen Coll.

MILAN, formerly Private Coll.

MUCIUS SCAEVOLA BEFORE PORSENNA
Canvas, 110 × 140 cm.

A free copy by Antonio Guardi after the painting by Tiepolo in
Leningrad, listed by Goering, *ad vocem*, as by Tiepolo.
Scerbaciova, 1941, p. 15, Pl. 1, fig. 6, as by Tiepolo; Morassi, *Arte
Veneta*, 1952, pp. 88–89, figs. 86–87, as by A. Guardi.
Present whereabouts unknown.

MILAN, formerly Ranieri Coll.

THE HOLY FAMILY WITH A BISHOP SAINT
Canvas, medium size (?).

Attributed to Tiepolo by A. Venturi in *L'Arte*, 1932, p. 476, fig.
p. 477, it is a typical work by Giambattista Cignaroli.

MILAN, Count G. Rasini Coll.

THE REPUDIATION OF HAGAR   [1955, fig. 2]
Canvas, 96 × 136 cm.; signed and dated *G. B. Tiepolo. F. A.* 1717 (*or*
1719).

Morassi, 1937, p. 53 with pl.; Morandotti, 1941, pp. 38–39, figs. 34 and
34 *bis*; Morassi, p. 13, fig. 3; Lorenzetti, p. 7, fig. 2.
This is the earliest autograph signed and dated work known, but it is
not clear if the final figure of the date is 7 or 9.

S. JOSEPH WITH THE CHRIST CHILD
Canvas, 58 × 42 cm.; *c.* 1720.

Ex coll. Mancinelli-Scotti, Sale at Scopinich Gall., Milan, 29.5.1931,
No. 31.
Morassi, 1934, II–III, p. 91, pl. 11A.
A very early work, close to Piazzetta in style.

HEAD OF AN ORIENTAL   [1955, pl. 38]
Canvas, 43 × 35 cm.; *c.* 1750–60.

One of the many canvases from the series of 'Heads'.
Morandotti, 1941, p. 42, fig. 37; Lorenzetti, p. 99, fig. 74.

MILAN, M. Rossello Coll.

JUDITH SHOWING THE HEAD OF HOLOFERNES TO THE PEOPLE
Canvas, 37 × 48 cm.; *c.* 1732–33.   Fig. 25

Lancaster Sale, Christie, London, 21.12.1923, No. 49.
Fiocco, 1929, p. 70 (attributed to Ligari); Morassi, 1942, p. 265, fig. 20;
Morassi, p. 20, fig. 43; Lorenzetti, 1935, p. 391; Lorenzetti, p. 50, fig. 37.
Excellent small painting in very vivid colours, perhaps a *modello* for
some unknown larger composition.

MILAN, L. Scotti Coll.

S. ANTHONY OF PADUA
Canvas, arched, 118 × 59.5 cm.; *c.* 1720–30.

Ex coll. Giuseppe Beltrami, Milan.
Molmenti, p. 341, fig. p. 341, wrongly attributed to Domenico. A
rather early work, dark in tone, probably painted as a private altarpiece.

MILAN, Senator G. Treccani Coll.

S. JOHN THE BAPTIST PREACHING   [1955, fig. 14]
Canvas, 32 × 45 cm.; *c.* 1732–33.

Bought from the dealer Grassi in Florence, about 1920.
Sketch for the fresco in the Colleoni Chapel, Bergamo. Copies after
this sketch in Madrid, Casa Torres Coll., and in Besançon. Pendant
to the *Decollation of the Baptist* in Stockholm.
Fiocco, 1929, p. 55; Morassi, in *Le Arti*, 1941, p. 253; Morassi, p. 18;
Lorenzetti, p. 48, fig. 35.

MILAN, O. Venier Coll.

S. VINCENT FERRER   Fig. 173
Canvas, 34×26 cm.; *c.* 1730–35.

Certainly to be identified with the painting once in the Cantoni Coll.,
Milan, mentioned by Sack, p. 172, as iconographically related to one of
the series of Saints drawn in red chalk in Stuttgart (Sack, p. 241,
fig. 246).
Very similar in style to the S. Gaetano in Rio de Janeiro and to many
devotional paintings of S. Roch.
L. Coletti and T. Spini, *Collezione Ottaviano Venier*, Bergamo 1954,
pp. 35, 57, Pl. 49, attributing it wrongly to the Spanish period.

MINNEAPOLIS, Art Institute

THE MARTYRDOM OF S. LAWRENCE
Canvas, 56×44 cm.

By Domenico.
Sketch for a circular ceiling.
Ex coll. Grandi-Baslini, Milan.
Sack, p. 172, fig. 163, as Giambattista, and also exhibited with this
attribution in the Museum.
A light and sketchy *modello* for a ceiling which may never have been
executed.

HEAD OF AN OLD MAN
Canvas, 69×57 cm.

By Domenico.
Engraved by Domenico in the series of 'Heads'.
Ex coll. Manfrin, Venice; Rudolph Kann, Paris.
In the Alte Pinakothek, Munich, is a similar head, which Molmenti,
p. 285, n. II, records as a copy.
Molmenti, p. 285; Catton Rich, 1938, p. 33; *Exhib. Cat.*, Bordeaux
1956, No. 60, all as Giambattista.

MIRA (on the Brenta, near Dolo), Villa Contarini

Frescoes now removed to the Musée Jacquemart-André, Paris (q.v.).

MIRANO, Parish Church

A MIRACLE OF S. ANTHONY OF PADUA   Fig. 132
Arched canvas, 270×180 cm.; *c.* 1754–60.

The sketch for this altarpiece is in Bologna, Modiano Coll.
Molmenti, p. 112, fig. 110b; Sack, p. 173, fig. 164; Fiocco, 1929,
pp. 55–56; Modigliani, 1933, p. 133, fig. p. 140; Pallucchini, 1945,
p. 128.
Engraved by Lorenzo Tiepolo (De Vesme, 2). The superintendent of
the galleries in Venice, Edwards (Documents in the Seminario Patriarcale in Venice), stated that Domenico helped his father in painting this
altarpiece (Fiocco, 1929, p. 56) and that the figure of S. Anthony is by
Domenico: which is confirmed on stylistic grounds.

MODENA, formerly L. Giusti Coll.

JULIUS CAESAR CONTEMPLATING THE SEVERED HEAD OF
POMPEY   Fig. 309
Canvas, 55×72 cm.; 1743.

Reproduced in the Catalogue of the auction at the A. Geri Gallery,
Florence, 18.5.1914, No. 176.
Judging from the small reproduction, certainly by Giambattista. The
same subject was commissioned by Algarotti from Tiepolo in 1743
(Algarotti *Opere*, VIII, pp. 375–388). (See Amsterdam.) This was the
modello.
M. Precerutti-Garberi, in *Commentari*, April–June, 1958, pp. 114–116,
Pl. XLVI.
Present whereabouts unknown.

MONTAUBAN, Musée Ingres

THE ASSUMPTION OF THE VIRGIN
Canvas, 79×36 cm.; sketch for a ceiling.

Catalogued in the old *Guide* of the Museum (1885) as by Giambattista,
while it is clearly derived from the fresco in the Purità at Udine, and
must be assigned to Domenico or to a follower of his.

APOLLO AND THE MUSES
Canvas, 43×38 cm.

Attributed to Tiepolo in the *Catalogue* of the Museum (1885), but it is
a characteristic work by G. A. Pellegrini.

ALEXANDER AND THE FAMILY OF DARIUS
ALEXANDER AND THE DEAD BODY OF DARIUS

Two canvases, 48×68 cm. each.

Considered wrongly to be by Giambattista in the old *Guide* of the
Museum, they are undoubtedly works by Giambattista Piazzetta,
painted as *modelli* (the second for the large canvas in Pal. Pisani-
Moretta, the first for an unknown painting).

MONTBELIARD, Musée

THE SUPPER AT EMMAUS
Canvas, 115×168 cm.

Ex Campana Coll.
Attributed to Giambattista by De Chennevières, p. 115, and mentioned
by Sack, p. 212; doubted by Molmenti, pp. 309–10; it is not by Tiepolo
but possibly by a master of the Piazzetta circle (judging from the
photograph).

MONTECCHIO MAGGIORE (Vicenza), Villa Cordellina

Frescoes in the Saloon:

On the walls:
THE FAMILY OF DARIUS BEFORE ALEXANDER   Fig. 280

THE CONTINENCE OF SCIPIO; signed: *G. Batta. Tiepolo.*
490×550 cm. each; 1743.   Fig. 307

Over the doors:
THE QUARTERS OF THE WORLD
Four grisaille decorations.

Round the ceiling:
Six medallions, also in grisaille, of *Allegorical Figures*. The ceiling fresco
itself, *Nobility and Virtue*, removed (1917) to the Museo Civico,
Vicenza, and badly repainted. (In this Museum there is a further ceiling
on canvas, coming from the same villa, representing an allegory of
Time discovering Truth.)
Recently the ceiling was replaced in the Villa Cordellina, which is
going to be restored (together with its frescoes) by the present owner,
Dr. Lombardi.   Fig. 347
Molmenti, pp. 96–98, figs. on pp. 96–98; Sack, pp. 173–174; Molmenti,
1927, pp. 42, 43, with fig.; Morassi, p. 26.
The sketches for the frescoes on the walls exist: the *Continence of Scipio*
in the National Museum, Stockholm; the *Family of Darius before
Alexander* in the Senator Crespi Coll., Milan. A sketch related to the
ceiling is in the Dulwich College Gall., London. The date of this cycle
can be fixed with precision by the letters from Tiepolo to Algarotti
(see Chronological Table).

MONTREAL, Museum of Fine Arts

ALEXANDER AND CAMPASPE IN THE STUDIO OF APELLES
Canvas, 54×74 cm.; *c.* 1725.   [1955, col. pl. II]

Formerly in the Museum at Sigmaringen, Germany; Schwitzer Coll.,
Berlin; Colnaghi, London; Van Horne Coll., Montreal, 1911; Adaline
van Horne bequest, 1945.
Molmenti, p. 272, fig. p. 271; Sack, p. 193, fig. 186; L. Venturi, 1933,

v. III, p. 585 pl.; Morassi, p. 17; Pignatti, 1951, p. 31, fig. 28; Lorenzetti, p. 33, fig. 23; *Exhib. Cat.*, Bordeaux, 1956, No. 52, fig. 20.
The painter Apelles is probably the self-portrait of Giambattista, Campaspe the portrait of his wife Cecilia Guardi. It is an interesting glimpse of the interior of a painter's studio in Tiepolo's time.
Another, later, version of the same subject is in the Louvre, Paris.

MOSCOW, Pushkin Museum of Fine Arts

TWO SAINTS (probably SS. MAXIMUS AND OSWALD)   Fig. 142
Canvas, 61 × 36 cm.; *c.* 1740–45.

Inscribed on the back: *Regalo fatto dal padre a Giovanni Dom. Tiepolo.*
Sketch related to the altarpiece in S. Massimo at Padua, comparable with the other versions of the subject in Bergamo, Carrara Gall. and London, Nat. Gall. (q.v.). This is the only sketch in the series to show S. Oswald standing.
Ex coll. Ostrouchov, Moscow; entered the Museum 1931.
O. I. Lavrova, in *Bulletin of the Pushkin Museum*, 1960, with repr.
Not seen by me.

MADONNA WITH THREE SAINTS (Antony of Padua, Francis and Louis of Toulouse)
Canvas, 161 × 118 cm.; *c.* 1730–35.

Excellent small altarpiece related in style to the one in Chicago, Art Institute, and another once in S. Prosdocimo, Padua, now in the Accademia at Venice.
The *modello* for the present altarpiece in Bergamo, formerly Piccinelli Coll. (fig. 83). Another *modello* also related to the same altarpiece formerly in Zürich, Private Coll. (fig. 84).
(I owe the knowledge of this painting to the courtesy of Mrs. Lavrova of the Fine Arts Museum in Moscow.)
Not seen by me, but, judging from the reproduction, undoubtedly by Giambattista. Perhaps identical with the altarpiece once in S. Provolo, Venice (q.v.).

MADONNA WITH THREE SAINTS
Canvas, 49 × 30 cm.

A replica (?) with slight variations of the above altarpiece.
Probably also this an autograph by Tiepolo, but the poor reproduction in my possession does not permit a final judgement.

THE DEATH OF DIDO   Fig. 234
Canvas, 40 × 63 cm.; *c.* 1750–60 (?).

Acquired by Prince N. B. Jusupov in Italy, 1783–89; entered the Hermitage, Leningrad, 1920, and passed later to the Pushkin Museum. A weak copy of this canvas is in the Museum at Berlin (q.v.).
P. Weiner, *Les anciennes écoles*, Brussels, 1910, p. III; Molmenti, fig. p. 304; Sack, p. 207; Catalogue of the Jusupov Coll., 1920, no. 238, as by Domenico; Catalogue of the Museum, Moscow, 1948, no. 1605; O. I. Lavrova, in *Bulletin of the Institute of History of Art*, No. 13–14, 1960, with repr.
Judging from the reproduction the authenticity of the painting does not seem convincing.
Not seen by me.

MADONNA AND CHILD
Canvas, oval, 34 × 29 cm.

By Domenico.
Ex coll. Jusupov.
Starye Gody, 1908, no. 201; Molmenti, p. 284, rightly called 'among the best works by Domenico'; Sack, p. 207, wrongly as by Giambattista; *Catalogue* of the Jusupov Coll., S. Petersburg, 1920, p. 11, no. 187.
Not seen by me.

THE PRODIGAL SON
Canvas, 49 × 59 cm.

By Domenico.
Correctly attributed in the Museum to Domenico, but wrongly called

the pendant to *Alexander and Diogenes* (which is a studio copy) in the Hermitage, Leningrad.
Ex coll. Jusupov; entered the Museum in 1924.
Also attributed wrongly to G.B.
Catalogue of the Jusupov Coll., 1920, p. 12, no. 196.
Not seen by me.

S. CECILY
Arched altarpiece, signed and dated: *Gio. Batta Tiepolo f.* 1743.
The signature certainly false, the altarpiece being undoubtedly a work by Francesco Zugno.

MOTTA DI LIVENZA, Duomo

APPARITION OF THE VIRGIN
Canvas, *c.* 3 × 1.60 m., at the third altar.

By a weak follower of Tiepolo.
Attributed to Tiepolo by some local guides (e.g., *Veneto*, Touring Club Italiano, Milan, 1932, p. 569).

MUNICH, Alte Pinakothek

POPE S. CLEMENT ADORING THE HOLY TRINITY   Fig. 126
Canvas shaped at the bottom; 488 × 256 cm.; *c.* 1734–37.

Formerly in the Convent of the Schloss Nymphenburg. This great altarpiece, although standing in an accessible church (Nymphenburg), on the High Altar, was unknown to the Tiepolo literature until it was published by Goering. The canvas was apparently commissioned by the Elector Clemens August of Cologne, the brother of Elector-Regent Karl Albrecht of Bavaria, for the High Altar in the Chapel of the Nuns of Notre-Dame at Nymphenburg. The Chapel was consecrated in 1739 and the painting by Tiepolo may have been executed before this date. The style points to the years about 1735.
Goering, *ad vocem*; Goering, 1944, pp. 98–100, with fig.; A. Morassi, in *Arte Veneta*, 1957, pp. 173 ff., 186, 188.
The *modello* for this altarpiece is in London, National Gallery (q.v.).

THE ADORATION OF THE MAGI   [1955, pls. 50, 52, 53]
Arched canvas, 425 × 211 cm.; signed and dated on the stone at the bottom: *GIO. B. TIEPOLO F. A.* 1753.

Altarpiece painted for the church of the Benedictines, Schwarzach, for which Tiepolo received 432 florins. In the Hofgartengalerie, 1804.
A sketch of the same subject, but certainly of a later period, is in the Metropolitan Museum, New York.
Meusel, *Miscellaneen artistischen Inhaltes*, Erfurt, 1779, I. p. 46; Molmenti, p. 178, fig. p. 178; Sack, p. 190, fig. 91; Morassi, p. 32, figs. 91–93; Lorenzetti, p. 101, fig. 75.
Masterpiece of his Würzburg period in religious painting, to which the stylistic parallel in secular painting is the *Death of Hyacinth* in the Thyssen Coll., Lugano.
Another *Adoration* is said to have been painted by Tiepolo for the church of Aranjuez (Nagler, 1835–52; De Vesme, 1906, p. 382; Molmenti, p. 192), but Sack (p. 295) says that Tiepolo never painted this altarpiece and that he made only an engraving (Molmenti, fig. p. 197) of this subject which is signed 'Tipeolo' without other indications.

RINALDO AND ARMIDA IN THE GARDEN   Fig. 271
RINALDO ABANDONS ARMIDA   Fig. 272

Two canvases, 105 × 140 cm.; *c.* 1751–53, both signed, bottom left, *B. Tiepolo.*

Entered the Museum 1919 from the Gallery of the Residenz in Würzburg, painted there. Engraved by Lorenzo Tiepolo (De Vesme, 4, 6).
Molmenti, p. 181, figs. p. 142; Sack, p. 197, figs. 93–94; Morassi, p. 32; Freeden, Catalogue, 1951, p. 14.
A sketch related to the first painting is in Berlin, Kaiser Friedrich Museum. Another sketch related to the second (but with the composition in reverse) is in Paris, Cailleux Coll.

THE SACRIFICE OF IPHIGENIA
Two canvases, 58 × 45 cm. each.

Attributed to Giambattista by Meissner, 1897, fig. 66; by Molmenti, p. 267, to an imitator of Tiepolo. The pictures are by F. Zugno, as Sack rightly notes (p. 240).

MUNICH, Böhler

HEAD OF AN OLD ORIENTAL
Canvas, 45 × 35 cm.; c. 1750–60.

Related to the series of 'Heads' engraved by Domenico.
Lorenzetti, p. 99, fig. 72.

MUNICH, formerly Böhler

S. FRANCIS OF PAOLA   Fig. 172
Canvas, 46 × 39 cm.; c. 1730–35.

Not seen by me, but, judging from the photograph, certainly autograph work by Giambattista.
Present whereabouts unknown.

FORTITUDE AND PEACE   Fig. 217
Canvas, 33 × 43 cm.; c. 1754.

Excellent modello for an unknown fresco engraved by Domenico (De Vesme 81).
Until 1915 with Böhler; later in the Dr. Anschütz-Kaempe Coll., Munich.
Certainly identical with the oval mentioned by Sack, p. 233, as in the Sellar Coll., London, Sale, London, 1889. Mireur 1912, VII ad locum.
Present whereabouts unknown.
Hitherto unpublished.

HEAD OF AN OLD WHITE-BEARDED MAN WITH A BARRET
Canvas, 46 × 37 cm.

By Domenico.
Sold to the G. Müller Coll., Berlin, 1917.
Also attributed to Giambattista.
Present whereabouts unknown.

S. JOSEPH WITH THE CHRIST CHILD
MADONNA IN PRAYER

Two canvases, 39.5 × 30 cm. each.

By Domenico.
The two pictures, formerly in Venice, once formed pendants. Present whereabouts of the first is now unknown; the second was later in the Lederer Coll., Budapest, and now in the Sarkany Coll., Budapest.
Both are mentioned by Sack, p. 192, figs. 183–84, with slightly different measurements (30 × 24 cm.), as by Giambattista.
The Madonna was exhibited in Budapest Museum in 1952 as by Giambattista, Catalogue of the 'Exhibition of the Italian XVIII Century', No. 27.

THE ASSUMPTION
Circular canvas, 53 cm. diam.

Traditionally attributed to Giambattista, this sketch is a typical work by Domenico. Perhaps a modello for a circular ceiling.
Later in the Talleyrand Coll., Paris.
Present whereabouts unknown.

MUNICH, formerly Caspari Coll.

THE SUMMONS TO CINCINNATUS   Fig. 293
Canvas, 58 × 39 cm.; c. 1725–30.

Sold 9–10.6.1937 at Böhler ('Kunstwerke aus dem Besitz der Staatlichen Museen, Berlin', Catalogue No. 671, Pl. 62, as being after 1902 in the Dr. Wassermann Coll., Munich). Sketch for the canvas painted for Ca' Dolfin, and now in Leningrad.

Morassi, 1934, II–III, p. 126, fig. IIB; Morassi, p. 10; Scerbaciova, 1941, p. 26, with repr.
An excellent early modello, present whereabouts unknown. Another canvas, a copy after this modello, was at the Dorotheum, Vienna, about 1951; another in Kiew, Museum (q.v.).

A CHERUB WITH A CROWN OF LILIES AND TWO HEADS OF
CHERUBIM   Fig. 199
Canvas, c. 65 × 104 cm., c. 1767–69.

Fragment of the S. Joseph painted for Aranjuez. This fragment belonged to Caspari till 1930; it was later cut in two parts, one of which is now in the Prado, the other was in New York, French (q.v.). This latter had palm-branches behind the cherubim, which disappeared in cleaning.
Hitherto unpublished.

MUNICH, formerly Drey Coll.

THE BRAZEN SERPENT   Fig. 16
Canvas, 17 × 69 cm., c. 1730–35.

Bossi Sale, Helbing, Munich, 29.9.1917; Wollenberg Sale, Lepke, Berlin, 17.3.1932, No. 206 (with three det. repr.).
A first idea for the frieze now in the Accademia, Venice.
Sack, p. 196, fig. 59; Morassi, p. 21.
Formerly in the Beyerlen-Di Bossi Coll., Stuttgart, where it is mentioned by Sack. This family was descended from the miniaturist Domenico Di Bossi, who was a friend of Tiepolo, and who bought some paintings and drawings from the two Tiepolos.
Present whereabouts unknown.

MUNICH (Tegernsee), formerly Gulbransson Coll.

ESTHER AND AHASUERUS   Fig. 24
Canvas, 86 × 106 cm.; c. 1751–53.

Goering, 1944, p. 110, with fig.
Bought in 1843 from the descendants of the Princes of Würzburg in Würzburg by the von Pollnitz family. Bequeathed by them to the wife of the painter Gulbransson.
The painting certainly belongs stylistically to the Würzburg period, and was probably executed there. Closely related to the Family of Darius before Alexander in the Würzburg University Museum. Pendant to the painting in Fürth.
Now in the Bührle Coll., Zurich.

MUNICH, formerly Haberstock Coll.

TARQUIN AND LUCRETIA: See Augsburg, Museum.

MUNICH, formerly Heinemann Coll.

PARIS SEATED IN A LANDSCAPE HOLDING THE APPLE IN HIS
RIGHT HAND
Canvas, 33.8 × 24.8 cm.;

By Domenico (judging from the photograph). Probably a fragment of a Judgement of Paris recorded by Sack, p. 208, as in the Paul Delaroff Coll., Leningrad (as work by G.B.). Present whereabouts unknown.

MUNICH, formerly von Nemes Coll.

CHRIST HEALING A MAN POSSESSED
Canvas, 48 × 57 cm.

By Domenico.
Catalogue of the v. Nemes Sale, Müller-Cassirer-Helbing, Berlin, 16.6.1931 (42) with repr.; M. Precerutti-Garberi, in Commentari, No. 3–4, 1960, p. 278, fig. 15, as by Domenico.
Belongs to the series of pictures, one in the Fodor Coll., Paris, the others formerly in the Strauss Coll. and in the Sedelmeyer Coll., Paris, attributed to Giambattista. (Another scene of Christ and the Centurion, also by Domenico, here not catalogued, in a Private Coll., Lausanne.)

MADONNA AND CHILD WITH S. CATHERINE, S. CHARLES
BORROMEO AND S. JOHN BISHOP OF BERGAMO
Canvas, 69×39 cm.; c. 1731.

Ex Cassirer, Berlin.
One of various existing replicas intended as a *modello* for an altarpiece
probably never executed.
Very good in quality, to judge from the reproduction.
A replica dated 1731 on the back is in Milan, Priv. Coll. (q.v.); another
(76×40 cm.) was once in Rome, Simonetti Sale, Tavazzi, 25.4–6.5.1932;
another one on the German market.
Present whereabouts unknown.
Catalogue of the v. Nemes Sale, Helbing, 2–4.11.1933, No. 150, fig. XVII.

MUNICH, formerly Schnackenberg Coll.

MADONNA AND CHILD WITH A BIRD
Canvas, 52×44 cm.

By Domenico.
Later in the Oppenheimer Coll.; Davies Sale, Parke-Bernet Gall., New
York, 14.11.1951.
Venturi, *Studi dal vero*, 1927, p. 401, fig. 277, wrongly as Giambattista.

MUNICH, formerly Prof. Otto Seitz Coll. (sold 1904)

THE FINDING OF MOSES
Canvas, 65×75 cm.

Sack, p. 233.
No reproduction or documentations existing, it is questionable if it
was by Tiepolo.
Missing.

MUNICH, formerly Schloss Nymphenburg, Convent

POPE S. CLEMENT ADORING THE HOLY TRINITY
See Munich, Alte Pinakothek.

NANCY, Musée des Beaux-Arts

TWO CARNIVAL SCENES
Two canvases, 77×97 cm. each.

Wrongly attributed to Tiepolo by Galetti-Camesasca, 1950, *ad vocem*,
they are works by the Roman school of the XVII Century, and have
nothing to do with Tiepolo.

NANTES, Musée des Beaux-Arts

THE TRIUMPH
THE FUNERAL
Two canvases, the first 140×191.5 cm., the second 103×172.5 cm.

Attributed by M. Nicolle to the school of Tiepolo, later to Amigoni
(by R. Longhi), they are certainly by Gaetano Zompini.
Catalogue du Musée, Nantes, 1953, p. 41, as by Amigoni.

HEAD OF A WOMAN WITH A YELLOW RIBBON
Canvas, 30×22 cm.

Attributed in the *Catalogue* of the Museum (1953, p. 197) to Tiepolo
following the opinion of Clément de Ris and confirmed by R. Longhi,
it has nothing in common with Tiepolo's style and belongs probably
to the Spanish School.

NAPLES, Lauro Coll.

THE PENITENT MAGDALEN   Fig. 151
Canvas, 72×55 cm.; c. 1723–24.

Ex coll. Raffaldini, Mantua; Ventura, Florence.
Morassi, 1944, p. 5, fig. 14; Longhi, 1946, p. 70, with fig.; Lorenzetti,
p. 30, fig. 20; Benesch, 1952, p. 58, fig. 2.
One of Tiepolo's strangest early works, with echoes of Crespi in the
strong chiaroscuro and livid nocturnal lights.

NERVESA, Villa Soderini

All the frescoes were destroyed during the bombardments of 1917.
The photos were taken before.
Frescoes in the Saloon:
On the walls:
ENTRY INTO FLORENCE OF THE GONFALONIERE PIER SODERINI
                                                    Fig. 318b
NICOLA SODERINI SENT BY THE REPUBLIC OF FLORENCE AS
A DELEGATE TO THE ROMAN SENATE   Fig. 318a

On the ceiling:
APOTHEOSIS OF THE SODERINI FAMILY   [1955, fig. 44]
This ceiling was one of the most spectacular of Tiepolo's works on
account of its light effects. Above a first vault some windows were cut
which lighted the ceiling, giving to it more atmosphere and trans-
parence.
In the *Entry* the self-portrait of Tiepolo may be seen at the extreme left
near the frame.

In another room:
CROWNING OF THE POET SODERINI (?)
No photograph or other record of this last fresco exists and the icono-
graphy of it is unknown. Perhaps the sketch, formerly in the Fauchier-
Magnan Coll., Paris, represents the composition of the *Crowning*.

In the neighbouring room:
JUNO AND THE PEACOCK
All the frescoes were executed c. 1754 when Tiepolo was painting in the
Palazzo Volpato Panigai at Nervesa (a monochrome fresco from this
cycle, now in Berlin, is dated 1754, see Molmenti, p. 92). Boucher
dated the Soderini frescoes between 1725–30, but they were certainly
not executed before 1737, since they are not mentioned by Silvano
Razzi (*Vita di Pier Soderini*, Padua, 1737). Molmenti (1911, p. 78 ff.)
rightly assumes that the execution must have taken place at the same
period as the decorations in the Pal. Panigai. For stylistic reasons this
date must be considered the right one. The whole Villa was painted
with the collaboration of Mengozzi-Colonna for the perspective and
ornamental part, and perhaps with the assistance of Domenico and of
some pupil, probably Zugno. In the same Villa there were also frescoes
by Domenico Tiepolo, F. Battaglioli, F. Zugno, G. Mengozzi-Colonna
and A. Canal (Caccianiga, 1874, pp. 330–331; Mazzotti, 1953, p. 629).
A fragment of the frescoes was on the art market in Rome in 1933 and
was recorded by A. Colasanti in *Cose*, 1933.
Federici, 1803, II, p. 226; Crico, 1833, p. 129; Boucher, 1901, IX,
p. 367; Battistella, 1903; Molmenti, p. 90, figs. pp. 91–93; Sack, p. 74,
figs. 102–103; Fiocco in 'Enciclopedia Italiana Treccani', 1934, vol.
XXIV, p. 608; Morassi, p. 33, fig. 108.

NERVESA, formerly Villa Volpato Panigai

TWENTY-TWO MONOCHROME FRESCOES
Now in Berlin, Kaiser Friedrich Museum (q.v.).

NEW HAVEN, Yale University, Gallery

TWO ROUNDELS WITH ALLEGORICAL FIGURES   Figs. 394, 395
71 cm. diam.; c. 1745–50.

Painted on gold ground.
Formerly decorated a room in the Pal. Labia, Venice. Recorded by
Molmenti in the Oreffice Coll., Venice; then in the Böhler Coll.,
Munich (1904); Silbermann, Vienna; Silbermann, New York.
The other two in the Bonomi-Bolchini Coll., Milan (q.v.).
Molmenti, p. 73, figs. pp. 69a, 69b reproducing six of these roundels;
Sack, p. 152; Catton-Rich, 1938, p. 28.

S. ROCH CARRIED TO HEAVEN BY TWO ANGELS   Fig. 146
Canvas, 41×35 cm.; c. 1750–60.

Sketch for a small oval ceiling.
Ex coll. Kaulbach, Munich; Drey, Munich and New York.
S. De Vito Battaglia, 1930, pp. 115–120, with repr.; Catton Rich,
1938, p. 28.

NEW ORLEANS, Isaac Delgado Museum of Art

PORTRAIT OF A BOY HOLDING A BOOK   Fig. 417
Canvas, 48 × 39 cm.; *c.* 1740–50.

Ex coll. Visconti di Modrone, Milan; Kress Coll., New York, 1932; National Gall., Washington, until 1952; then on loan to the New Orleans Museum; Gift of the S. H. Kress Foundation, 1961.
This is the best version of the subject known to me. Another version, probably from Tiepolo's shop, was published by Fiocco in *Dedalo*, 1932, p. 474 and fig. p. 475 (now in a Private Coll., Strasbourg). A copy, attributed to Domenico, was exhibited in Paris, Cailleux, 1952; another was published by Goering, 1936.
Catalogue of the Nat. Gall., Washington, 1941, p. 193; Cailleux, 1952, p. 53; Catalogue of the S. H. Kress Collection in the Isaac Delgado Museum, New Orleans, 1953, pp. 60–61, with repr.

THE MINUET
Canvas, 78 × 108 cm.

Old copy of Domenico's painting, now in the Louvre.
Listed in the Catalogue of the S. H. Kress Collection in the Isaac Delgado Museum, New Orleans, 1953, p. 52, as 'Studio of G. B. Tiepolo'.

NEW YORK, Metropolitan Museum

APOTHEOSIS OF FRANCESCO BARBARO   [1955, fig. 27]
Canvas, shaped for a ceiling, 250 × 465 cm.; *c.* 1745–50.

Originally a ceiling in the Pal. Barbaro, Venice; where it remained *in situ* until about 1870. Gift to the Museum 1923. A related sketch is in a private coll., Paris.
Engraved by Domenico (De Vesme, 104).
Probably to be identified with the picture sold, 9.2.1875, Sale X, Paris, for 25,000 fr.; ex coll. Camondo, Paris, sold 1893 for 30,000 fr.; Groult Coll., Paris.
Mireur, 1912, VII, *ad locum*; Molmenti, p. 258; Sack, p. 150, fig. 101; Cat. Exhib. 'Tiepolo', New York, 1938, No. 14 with fig.; Wehle, Catalogue, 1940, p. 282 with fig.; Morassi, p. 26.

THE INVESTITURE OF BISHOP HAROLD   Fig. 316
Canvas, 71.7 × 51.4 cm.; *c.* 1751–52.

Sketch related to the Kaisersaal at Würzburg, but with many variations, and probably the first idea for the fresco. Perhaps the pendant to the sketch in the Gardner Museum, Boston.
Wrongly known, at one time, as the *Triumph of Ferdinand III*.
From a French Coll.; to the Museum in 1871.
Sack, p. 227; Catton Rich, 1938, p. 24; Wehle Catalogue, 1940, p. 282 with fig.; Goering, 1944, p. 102 with fig.; Freeden u. Lamb, 1956, pp. 47–48, fig. 32.

THE ADORATION OF THE MAGI   [1955, fig. 40]
Canvas, 60.4 × 47.6 cm.; *c.* 1753 or later.

Sketch perhaps related to the altarpiece from Schwarzach, now in the Alte Pinakothek, Munich, but more probably of a later period.
Ex coll. Sedelmeyer, Paris; Marquis de Biron, Paris. Entered the Museum in 1937.
Sack, p. 106, 219, fig. 92; Cat. Exhib. 'Tiepolo', New York, 1938, No. 12; Wehle, Catalogue, 1940, pp. 283–284 with fig.; Goering, 1944, p. 102 with fig.; Morassi, p. 32, fig. 90.
A very fluent and light coloured *modello* for an *Adoration*, but it is not certain if, as most critics believe, it is for the altarpiece once in Schwarzach, or later. This sketch seems also rather close to the engraving signed *Tiepolo* at the left corner (see Molmenti, fig. p. 197), which is said to be based on an altarpiece executed for Aranjuez.

A MIRACLE OF S. THECLA   [1955, col. pl. VIII]
Canvas, 80 × 45 cm.; *c.* 1758–59.

Sketch for the altarpiece at Este (1759).
Ex coll. Infanta Maria Amelia of Naples, Prince Pierre de Bourbon (sale Drouot, 1890); Schiff Coll., Paris; Marquis de Biron, Paris. Entered the Museum in 1937.
Engraved by Lorenzo (De Vesme, 3).

Molmenti, p. 260; Sack, pp. 167, 216; Cat. Exhib. 'Tiepolo', New York, 1938, No. 16 with fig.; Wehle, Catalogue, 1940, p. 285 with fig.; Lorenzetti, p. 129, fig. 92.
One of the most beautiful and impressive *modelli* of Tiepolo's late Italian period. The background with the view of Este and the small figures show many variations from the finished altarpiece.
Another sketch (79 × 44 cm.), by an imitator, was in the Broglio Coll., Paris (ex coll. Felix Bois, Madrid; Kleinberger, New York; Böhler, Munich) and was published by A. Canal in *Pantheon*, July, 1932, p. 224, fig. 226, with a wrong attribution to Giambattista.

APOTHEOSIS OF THE SPANISH MONARCHY   Fig. 320
Canvas, 81.6 × 66.4 cm.; *c.* 1764.

Sketch for the ceiling of the 'Saleta' in the Royal Palace, Madrid (1764–66).
Ex coll. Guillaume Dubufe, Paris; Marquis de Biron, Paris. Entered the Museum in 1937.
Sack, p. 218; Catton Rich, 1938, p. 30; Cat. Exhib. 'Tiepolo', New York, 1938, No. 18 with fig.; Wehle, 1940, Catalogue, p. 286, with fig.
This excellent sketch is stylistically related to the sketches formerly in the Baroness de Becker-Rothschild Coll., New York.

NEPTUNE AND THE ZEPHYRS   Fig. 255
Canvas, 62.2 × 62.2 cm.; *c.* 1762–70.

Ex coll. Madrazo, Madrid; Marquis de Biron, Paris. Entered the Museum in 1937.
Goering, *ad vocem*; Wehle, Catalogue, 1940, p. 284, with fig.
Sketch for a circular ceiling which, so far as we know, was never executed. Certainly of the Spanish period.

A DECORATIVE COMPLEX said to come from a Villa on the Brenta, bought about 1914–15 by Durr Freedley for Mrs. Rogers, and bequeathed by Mrs. Grace Rainey Rogers to the Museum in 1943:

1. FOUR ALLEGORICAL FIGURES as feigned statues inscribed on the base: ARITMETICA, GRAMMATICA, METAFISICA, GEOMETRIA. Each represented between two feigned Doric columns.   Figs. 375–378
Frescoes transferred to canvas, each 365 × 135 cm., *c.* 1750–60 (?).
Similar to the four feigned statues once in the Palazzo Trento-Valmarana in Vicenza, destroyed in 1945, and to the sole remaining figure once in the Villa Cornaro, now in the Museum of Treviso.

2. ALLEGORY OF TRUTH AND ABUNDANCE   Fig. 406
Circular fresco, in grisaille, transferred to canvas, 285 cm. diam.; *c.* 1750–60 (?).
Originally, perhaps, an overdoor.

3. FOUR ALLEGORICAL FIGURES, as feigned bas-reliefs, representing EUROPE, ASIA, AFRICA and AMERICA. Frescoes on pinkish ground, transferred to canvas, each 81 × 103 cm.; *c.* 1750–60 (?).

4. FOUR SINGLE ALLEGORICAL STANDING FIGURES, in ovals. Frescoes transferred to canvas, grisailles, 122 × 92 cm.; *c.* 1750–60 (?). Originally probably overdoors.

All these frescoes are hitherto unpublished, save for a brief mention of them in an article on the newly installed galleries of decorative arts, where they are hanging at present (1956). It can be assumed that all these frescoes were executed by Domenico and possibly other assistants for the solely ornamental parts, after *modelli* or drawings by Giambattista and under his direction.
There is no information about the exact provenance of the frescoes.

VIRTUE AND WISDOM
Canvas, 53.3 × 40 cm.

By Domenico.
Gift of Pierpont Morgan, 1906.
Wehle, Catalogue, 1940, p. 286, with fig., attributes it to the workshop of Giambattista, but it is certainly by his son, as suggested by Goering, *ad vocem*.

The Crowning with Thorns
Canvas, 77 × 87 cm.

Listed by Berenson, 1897, p. 128 and Sack (p. 227) as by Tiepolo, it is a copy from the original by Tiepolo in Hamburg, perhaps by Guarana, whose supposed abbreviated signature appears upon the canvas, or by some other follower of Tiepolo.
Wehle, *Catalogue*, 1940, p. 290 with fig., as by Guarana.

Esther and Ahasuerus
Canvas, 45.7 × 129.5 cm.

Mentioned by Sack (p. 227) as by Giambattista, it is by a follower, probably Menescardi.
Wehle, *Catalogue*, 1940, p. 278 with fig., as by Menescardi.

S. James
Canvas, 27.9 × 63.5 cm., sketch.

Believed by Sack (p. 227) to be related to the painting in Budapest, it is not by Tiepolo or his circle, but perhaps by a Central Italian painter.
Wehle, *Catalogue*, 1940, p. 267 with fig., as by an unknown Italian painter.

NEW YORK, Museum for the Arts of Decoration
(Cooper Union Museum)

The Immaculate Conception
Canvas, 183 × 108 cm.

By Domenico.
Wrongly attributed to Giambattista.
De Chennevières, p. 109; Sack, p. 221 (both as Giambattista).

NEW YORK, Brooklyn Museum

S. Benedict and Other Saints
Canvas, small size, sketch for an altarpiece, attributed in the Museum to Giambattista Tiepolo and as such published in the 'Quarterly' of the Museum 1923, X, 4, p. 140; not by the Master, but by some other painter (probably Bellotti).

NEW YORK, Frick Collection

Perseus Rescuing Andromeda   Fig. 251
Canvas, 51.5 × 41 cm. 1730–31.

Ex coll. Trotti-Nicolle, Paris; Sale, Drouot, Paris, 20–22.11.1911; Parissot Coll. (1918).
Modelletto for the ceiling of the Pal. Archinto, Milan (1731) (q.v.).
An excellent painting, notable for its fluid touch, certainly the preparatory sketch for the ceiling fresco, because it differs in many ways from the executed work. Perhaps identical with the sketch mentioned by Sack, p. 233, No. 603 in the Sedelmeyer sale, Vienna and Paris, 1872, and afterwards in the Coll. of the Marquis de la Rochebousseau, sold in 1873 for 1,520 fr. (Mireur, 1912, VII, *ad locum*).
Illustrated Cat. of the Coll. of H. C. Frick, Pittsburgh, 1949, I, pp. 250–52, No. 126, II, Pl. CXXVI.

NEW YORK, formerly American Art Association

Head of an Old Oriental (with barret and large collar, holding a book)
Canvas, c. 55 × 45 cm.

By Domenico.
The original by Giambattista, from which the present was copied, in Paris, formerly Orloff Coll. (q.v.), now in Prague.
Pepoli Sale in the *Catalogue* as Domenico.
Like the engraving in Molmenti, *Acqueforti*, 1896, p. 159 r. with the inscription 'Joannes Batta Tiepolo inv.' Another 'Head' like this in Baltimore and another one in Trieste, formerly Opuich-Fontana Coll.
Repr. in *Art News*, 1929.

NEW YORK, Anderson Sale, 15.4.1926

The Virgin Appearing to a Kneeling Bishop Saint
Canvas, arched at the top, 58 × 31.5 cm.; *c.* 1740–50.

Not in good condition. Judging from the photograph in the Witt Library it seems an autograph work.
Present whereabouts unknown.

NEW YORK, Mme Balsan Coll.

Allegorical Female Figure
See: New York, formerly de Becker–Rothschild Coll.

NEW YORK, formerly Baroness de Becker-Rothschild Coll.

Allegorical Female Figure
Canvas, oval, 82 × 65 cm.; *c.* 1740–50.

Grisaille on gold background.
This belonged to the series mentioned by Waagen, Art Treasures, 1857, IV, p. 173, as in the Cheney Coll. Pendant to the figures in Zurich, private coll., and in the Rijksmuseum, Amsterdam.
Now in the Mme. Balsan Coll., New York.

Two Bearded Orientals
Rinaldo Looking at his Reflection in his Shield
Two Turbaned Turks
A Seated Man and a Young Woman with a Vessel
See: London National Gallery.

Apotheosis of the Spanish Monarchy
See: Wrightsman Coll., New York.

Allegory with Venus and Apollo
See: Heinemann Coll., New York.

Triumph of Hercules
See: Manchester, Currier Gall. of Art.

NEW YORK, formerly Böhler-Steinmeyer

Christ and the Adulteress
Canvas, 68 × 113 cm.

By Domenico.
Pendant to the *Miracle of the Pool of Bethesda*, now in Philadelphia. Both paintings originally given by some Venetian patrician families to the Genoese advocate Marcantonio Bono.
Sedelmeyer Coll., Paris; Rudolph Kann Coll., Paris; Fritz von Gans Coll., Frankfurt; Duveen, London; sold 1938 by Steinmeyer to the Almas Gallery, and from this probably to Hitler.
Present whereabouts unknown.
Molmenti, p. 260, fig. p. 256, attributing to Giambattista; Sack, p. 234, as Giambattista, p. 306, as Domenico; L. Venturi, 1933, Plate CCCCXXVI, as Domenico; Morassi, 1941, p. 279, fig. p. 275, as Domenico.

NEW YORK, formerly C. Castiglioni Coll.

The Triumph of Marius   Fig. 294
Canvas, 510 × 330 cm.; *c.* 1725–30.

The Battle of Vercellae   [1955, fig. 15]
The Capture of Carthage   Fig. 306
Two canvases, 480 × 370 cm.; *c.* 1725–30.

Originally all in the Pal. Dolfin, Venice; ex coll. Miller von Aicholz, Vienna; Castiglioni, Vienna. The other pictures belonging to this cycle are: two in Vienna, Kunsthistorisches Museum, and five in Leningrad, Hermitage (q.v.).
Da Canal, 1732; Bergeret et Fragonard, 1773–74, p. 386; Moschini, 1806, III, p. 75; Molmenti, p. 274; Sack, p. 251, figs. 18–20; Morassi, in *Le Arti*, 1942, pp. 261 ff., figs. 2–4, 12–15; Morassi, p. 16, figs. 30–31. Masterpieces of Tiepolo's early period. Present whereabouts unknown.

NEW YORK, Mrs. Crane Coll.

APOLLO RECEIVING HOMAGE   Fig. 235
Canvas, 68.5 × 94 cm.; *c.* 1740–45.

Related in style to, but earlier than, the Rinaldo and Armida scenes in the Art Inst., Chicago.
Ex coll. Marquise de Salza and Count von Berchtold, Vienna; Lilienfeld Coll., New York; Dieterich Sale, Anderson, 8–9.4.1920.
Recalling in style the *Triumph of Flora* in San Francisco (q.v.) and perhaps identical with the canvas mentioned by Sack, p. 220 as in the C. Rogier Coll., Paris, sold May, 1876, in Paris.

NEW YORK, Drey Coll.

S. PROCULUS, BISHOP OF VERONA, VISITING SS. FERMUS
AND RUSTICUS   Fig. 139
Canvas, 57 × 35 cm.; *c.* 1740–45.

Replica of the painting in London, National Gallery, of which there is another replica in Bergamo, Galleria Carrara and many copies.
From the Collections Earl Egerton of Sallos; Duchess of Buckingham; F. Cavendish-Bentinck.

NEW YORK, formerly Duveen

'EX VOTO'
Canvas, 37 × 45 cm.

By Domenico.
Published by Fiocco in *Art in America*, XXVI, October 4, 1938, p. 157, as by Giambattista. Restored to Domenico by Morassi, 1941, p. 279.

NEW YORK, formerly French

A ROMAN TRIAL BY FIRE
Canvas, 70 × 100 cm.; *c.* 1715–20.

A very early work similar in style to the *Last Supper* of the Dal Zotto Coll., Venice, and to the *Incident from Roman History* formerly in a Private Coll., Milan.

TWO HEADS OF CHERUBIM   Fig. 199
Canvas, 65 × 56 cm.; *c.* 1767–69.

Fragment of the *S. Joseph* executed for Aranjuez. It formed part, together with the *Cherub with a Crown of Lilies* in the Prado, of a larger fragment once with Caspari, Munich (q.v.).
Formerly Heimann Coll., New York.
Hitherto unpublished.

PORTRAIT OF A BOY IN FANCY DRESS
Canvas, 64 × 46 cm.

By Domenico.
Exhibited at the Tiepolo Exhib. in Chicago, 1938, No. 18 as by Giambattista.
Similar to the boy by Domenico in the Uffizi, Florence (here not catalogued).
Catton-Rich, *Catalogue*, 1938, p. 24.

NEW YORK, formerly Heimann

S. ROCH
See Cambridge, Fogg Art Museum.

HEAD OF AN OLD ORIENTAL
See San Diego, Fine Arts Gallery.

NEW YORK, Mr. and Mrs. Heinemann Coll.

ALLEGORY OF VENUS AND APOLLO   Fig. 253
Canvas, 88.5 × 70.7 cm.; *c.* 1762–70.

Ex coll. Baron von Stumm, German Ambassador at Madrid; Van Diemen Gallery, Berlin; Jacob Goldschmidt, Berlin and New York; Baroness de Becker-Rothschild, New York.

Excellent sketch of the late period, *modello* for ceiling but it is not known if it was ever carried out.
Morassi, p. 39, fig. 124.

NEW YORK, formerly Knoedler

S. JOHN NEPOMUK WITH A CHORISTER
Canvas, 83 × 74 cm.

By a follower of Tiepolo, perhaps Menescardi.
Ex coll. Freiherr von Stamora, Berlin.
Exhibited in Chicago, 1938, as by Giambattista Tiepolo.
Catton Rich, Catalogue, 1938, p. 28.

THE CHARIOT OF AURORA
See Williamstown Sterling and Francine Clark Art Institute.

NEW YORK, formerly C. Lambert Coll.

MADONNA AND CHILD WITH S. ANTHONY OF PADUA, S. PETER
AND AN ANGEL
Canvas, 61 × 41 cm.

Sold at the American Art Association, Feb., 1916.
Certainly painted by some pupil very close to Giambattista in the style of his thirties. (Compare with the *Madonna and Saints* in Zurich, Private Coll.)
Not seen by me. Photo in the Kunsth. Institut, Florence, No. 95627.
Present whereabouts unknown.

NEW YORK, Lilienfeld Coll.

MADONNA WITH S. GIUSTINA AND THE LITTLE S. JOHN
Canvas, 48 × 28 cm.; *c.* 1755–60.   Fig. 101

Excellent sketch, fluently painted for an unknown or never executed altarpiece. Stylistically related to the two pictures in Milan, Borletti Coll.
Hitherto unpublished.

PORTRAIT OF AN OLD MAN IN ORIENTAL COSTUME
Canvas, 60 × 51 cm.

By a follower of Giambattista.
Another almost identical painting in the Museum at Lyons, there attributed to Lorenzo Tiepolo.
Acquired from the Hermitage of St. Petersburg.

NEW YORK, E. Mayer Coll.

THE MINUET
PERFORMING DOGS
Two canvases, 33 × 49 cm.

By Domenico.
Ex coll. H. Bendixon, London; Wildenstein, New York; Maurice de Rothschild, Paris.
Lorenzetti, Catalogue, 1937, pp. 51–52, figs. 29, 30; and others attribute it to Giambattista; Morassi, 1941, VII, p. 271 ff., fig. 273, to Domenico.
Another canvas with *Performing Dogs*, similar to the present, and a pendant (*The Charlatan*), published by Sanchez-Canton, 1953, f. 26, 27, fig. 42, in the Marquesa de Balboa Coll., Madrid, as by Giambattista, are also by Domenico.

NEW YORK, Parke-Bernet Galleries, *c.* 1951
(Auction of the Speyer Coll.)

RINALDO AND ARMIDA
Two canvases, 67 × 91 cm.

Believed to be by Tiepolo, they are by the same hand (Menescardi) as the three scenes of Rinaldo and Armida in a Private Coll., Paris (q.v.). The photograph of the drawing for one of these canvases is in the Witt Library, London.

NEW YORK, Private Coll.

REBECCA AT THE WELL   Fig. 10
Canvas, 80×125 cm.; *c.* 1720–25.

Ex Camondo Coll., Paris, sold in 1893 (Mireur, 1912, VII, *ad locum*);
Melzi Sale, Kende, New York, 8.12.1951 (23). Morassi, 1950, XI,
p. 200, fig. 6.
Very similar to the same subject in the Museum of Athens, but from an
earlier period and darker in tonality. Another canvas of the same subject
(121 × 104 cm.) is mentioned (Molmenti, 1911, p. 210) as in the Coll. of
Baron Alphonse de Rothschild in Vienna.

NEW YORK, Private Coll.

THE ASCENSION   Fig. 64
Canvas, 75×89.5 cm.; *c.* 1745–50.

Formerly Brunner Coll., Paris.
Belongs to the series of scenes from the Passion of Christ, among which
are the *Last Supper* in the Louvre, the *Crowning with Thorns* and *Agony
in the Garden*, in the Kunsthalle, Hamburg, etc. One of the most
impressive examples of the cycle.
A copy was sold in Munich, 17–18.10.1903, Sparr Sale, Helbing (Cat.
No. 494).
Morassi, *Burlington Magazine*, 1955, pp. 11–12, fig. 13.

NEW YORK, Private Coll.

S. FRANCIS OF PAOLA, S. JOHN NEPOMUK AND S. ANTHONY
OF PADUA WITH THE CHRIST CHILD
Canvas, *c.* 35×25 cm.; *c.* 1730–35.

Small devotional painting (or sketch for an unknown or never executed
altarpiece) in the style of the many similar others of the same period.
Hitherto unpublished.

NEW YORK, Private Coll.

THE FLIGHT INTO EGYPT
See Berlin, formerly Private Coll.

NEW YORK, Private Coll.

GLORY OF S. CATHERINA OF SIENA (carried by two angels and
a putto with a crozier)
Canvas attributed to Tiepolo but is certainly by G. Diziani.

NEW YORK, Private Coll.

THE DEATH OF S. JOSEPH
Canvas, 49×43 cm.

Assigned to Tiepolo, it is a work by his school, certainly by G. Diziani.

NEW YORK, formerly Maurice de Rothschild Coll.

DIANA AND ACTAEON   Fig. 246
Canvas, 79×90 cm.; *c.* 1750–60.

Originally belonged to Count Algarotti and described, with measure-
ments, in his Catalogue, 1779.
Molmenti, p. 236; Sack, p. 231 ('Lost Works'); Sammlung E. O.
Bührle, *Exhib. Cat.*, Zürich, 1958, pp. 73–74; E. Huttinger, in *Arte
Veneta*, 1958, p. 218 ff., figs. 247–248.
Painted in a very classical style, perhaps influenced by Algarotti's
theories, and possibly with the collaboration of Domenico.
Now in the Bührle Coll., Zürich.

NEW YORK, formerly Schaeffer

SUSANNA AND THE ELDERS
See Hartford, Wadsworth Atheneum.

NEW YORK, Seligmann

MADONNA WITH THE GOLDFINCH   Fig. 77
Canvas, 62×49.5 cm.; *c.* 1760–70.

Another version, but certainly by Domenico, is in the National Gallery,
Washington.
Ex coll. Marques de Castrillo, Madrid; Wadsworth Sale, Parke-Bernet,
New York, XI–XII, 1948 (38); Col. Repr. in 'Studio', Christmas, 1929.
Catton Rich, 1938, p. 23, fig. p. 65; Morassi, p. 39, fig. 129.

NEW YORK, formerly Silbermann

FOUR ROUNDELS WITH ALLEGORICAL FIGURES   Figs. 392–5
See: Milan, Bolchini-Bonomi Coll.
See: New Haven, Yale University.

NEW YORK, Stillman Sale, 3.2.1927

MADONNA AND CHILD
Canvas, 58×43 cm.

By Domenico, wrongly attributed to Giambattista.
Photograph in the Witt Library.
Present whereabouts unknown.

NEW YORK, Stout Sale, Parke-Bernet, 3.12.1942

A SAINT IN GLORY
Canvas, oval, 41×33.5 cm.; *c.* 1750–60.

Exhibited at the Opening Exhib., Springfield Museum of Fine Arts,
1933, Cat. No. 33.
Photograph in the Witt Library.
Present whereabouts unknown.

NEW YORK, Timken Coll.

JUNO AND LUNA   Fig. 266
BACCHUS AND ARIADNE   Fig. 260
Two canvases, 213×231 cm. each.; *c.* 1740.

Originally in the Villa Girola on the lake of Como, together with the
Triumph of Amphitrite, now in Dresden (q.v.); all formerly in the
Artaria Coll., Vienna.
Modern, in *Gazette des Beaux-Arts*, 1902, pp. 239–241 with figs.;
Molmenti, p. 277, figs. pp. 279–280; Sack, p. 203, figs. pp. 201–202;
L. Venturi, 1933, III, pls. 586–587; Morassi, p. 23, figs. 52–53.
Whereas the *Bacchus and Ariadne* is one of the most beautiful of Tiepolo's
mythological creations and seems to have been inspired by the
Bacchanals of Titian, the *Juno and Luna* is not very well balanced in
composition and seems to have been rather restored.

NEW YORK, Wildenstein

TIME DISCOVERING TRUTH   Fig. 329
Canvas, oval, 46×64 cm.; *c.* 1745–50.

Ex coll. Poloutzoff, St. Petersburg.
A very rapid, light sketch in a nervous style, for a ceiling which was
probably never executed.
Earlier versions of the same composition are in Vicenza, Museo Civico;
Venice, Pal. Barbarigo, and elsewhere. The pendant—*Apotheosis of
Francesco Barbaro*—is in a private coll. in Paris.

ALLEGORY OF A QUEEN CRUSHING VICE   Fig. 405
Canvas, 54×34 cm.; *c.* 1760–70.

Ex coll. Beurnonville, Paris; Monteaux, Paris; coll. Cassirer, Berlin;
Thors Sale, Drouot, Paris, 10–11.6.1929 (31); Heimann, New York.
Brownish monochrome sketch. Said to have been for a large allegory
of the Empress Catherine of Russia, but it is not known if it was ever
executed on a large scale.
Exhib. Amsterdam, 'Italiaansche Kunst', 1934, Cat. No. 364; Exhib.
Wiesbaden, 1935 (Cat. No. 185).
Sack, p. 218; L. Venturi in *L'Arte*, 1934, 37, p. 499.

NEW YORK, formerly Wildenstein

HEAD OF AN OLD MAN   Fig. 413
Canvas, 47.5×39 cm.; *c.* 1745–50.

Formerly Rudolph Kann Coll., Paris.

Closely related to the head of the old man in the *Banquet of Cleopatra* (1744) in Melbourne.
Engraved in the 'Raccolta di Teste', P. I, No. 9 (Molmenti, *Acqueforti*, 1896, p. 155 r.; De Vesme, 125).
Gazette des Beaux-Arts, 1901, p. 494; *Catalogue of the R. Kann Coll.: Pictures*, Paris, 1907, II, 40, No. 132, Pl. 132; Catton-Rich, *Catalogue*, 1938, p. 33, No. 45.
Now in a private collection in South America.

NEW YORK, Mr. and Mrs. Wrightsman Coll.

OLYMPUS, THE QUARTERS OF THE GLOBE AND OTHER ALLEGORIES   [1955, fig. 35]
Canvas, 184×132 cm.; 1752.

Modello for the large ceiling fresco (1753) over the Great Staircase at Würzburg. It must have been painted in the previous year, since Tiepolo showed the sketch to the Prince-Bishop Greiffenklau in April, 1752. This sketch differs in several respects from the executed fresco, and lacks all the portraits of Court personages. One of the most splendid large *modelli* by Tiepolo.
Discovered in the Hendon Hotel, Hendon (London), in 1954, and noticed in *The Times*, 31.3.1954. To the present owners in 1956.
Morassi, *Burlington Magazine*, May 1, 1955, p. 4, n. 1; von Freeden und Lamb, 1956, p. 53, figs. 35–40.

ARMIDA CROWNING THE SLEEPING RINALDO WITH FLOWERS
ARMIDA AND RINALDO WITH A MIRROR   [1955, fig. 39]
Two canvases, 134×72.5 cm. each; *c.* 1750–55.

From the coll. of Baron A. de Rothschild, who lived in Naples; later Château Pregny, Geneva.
Excellent works of the time and style of the Chicago pictures and the four paintings in London, National Gallery (q.v.).

APOTHEOSIS OF THE SPANISH MONARCHY   Fig. 321
Canvas, 88×67.8 cm.; *c.* 1764.

Ex coll. Baron von Stumm, German Ambassador at Madrid; Van Diemen Gallery, Berlin; Jacob Goldschmidt, Berlin and New York; Baroness de Becker-Rothschild Coll., New York.
Modello for the 'Saleta' of the Royal Palace in Madrid, like the similar sketch in the Metropolitan Museum, New York (q.v.).
Morassi, p. 39, fig. 125.

THE DEPARTURE IN THE GONDOLA
Canvas, 37×73 cm.

By Domenico.
Considered by Fiocco, in *Nuova Antologia*, 1938, p. 333 (and also by other critics), as by Giambattista, it is clearly an enchanting masterpiece by Domenico and bears his signature on the left column (Morassi, 1941, p. 275).
From the Count de Quintanilla Coll., Madrid.

NICE, Musée des Beaux-Arts

OLYMPUS
Canvas, 72×54 cm.

Wrongly attributed to Tiepolo and labelled as such, but it is a rather late work, probably French, with only some weak echoes of Tiepolo's style.

NOVENTA VICENTINA, Parish Church

SS. ROCH AND SEBASTIAN   Fig. 145
Arched canvas, 321×164 cm.; *c.* 1758–60. Signed: G. B. TIEPOLO.

Altarpiece, perhaps commissioned by Cardinal Carlo Rezzonico (from 1758, Pope Clement XIII), who was then buying a Palace in Noventa Vicentina. At this time Tiepolo was also in touch with the Rezzonico family, for whom he painted the frescoes in Pal. Rezzonico, Venice.
Molmenti, p. 107, fig. p. 106; Sack, p. 175, fig. 167; Lorenzetti, p. 119, fig. 84.

OMAHA, Nebraska, Joslyn Art Museum

ALLEGORY OF A NAVAL BATTLE
Canvas, 230×280 cm.

Attributed to Tiepolo, but certainly a work by Giambattista Raggi. It probably formed part of a series of canvases originally in the Palazzo Priuli in Venice, representing scenes, and especially battles, celebrating Priuli's deeds, which are now in a private coll. in Venice.

ORANIENBAUM, near Leningrad, Castle, Chinese Pavilion (formerly)

MARS AND THE GRACES
Canvas, shaped for a ceiling, 8×4.50 metres; *c.* 1762–70.

Engraved by Lorenzo.
Molmenti, p. 282; Sack, p. 206, fig. 131, after the engraving; Morassi, p. 39.
One of the four paintings furnished by Tiepolo and his son for St. Petersburg in the last years of his life, entitled: *The Chariot of Venus, The Triumph of Hercules, The Magnificence of the Princes*, and *Mars and the Graces*. All were engraved by Lorenzo, except the *Hercules*, painted and engraved by Domenico (De Vesme, 7, 8, 9. III). Domenico mentions all four ceilings in his Catalogue of Engravings, but we do not know where the other three are now. The present one was looted by the Germans in 1942–43 and is said to have appeared later in a sale in the U.S.A. (communication from Mrs. M. Scerbaciova of the Hermitage).

OTTAWA, National Gallery of Canada

THE ADORATION OF THE MAGI
Canvas, 59×46 cm.

Always attributed to Giambattista Tiepolo, but is clearly a work by a follower, certainly Menescardi.
Formerly (till about 1920) in the Thiem Coll., San Remo; art market, New York.
Reproduced in colour in *Canadian Art*, X, 1953, p. 74.
Exhibited Toronto, Art Gallery, European Masters, 1954, No. 25.

OTTOBEUREN (Bavaria), Benedictine Abbey

GIFTS OFFERED TO CLEOPATRA
Canvas, 70×54 cm.

Contemporary copy after the overdoor once in the Palazzo Barbaro, Venice, now in the Necchi Coll., Pavia.
Signed: 'Tepolo pt 1746'.
Goering, *ad vocem*, mentions it with a question mark as a *bozzetto* (?) or replica (?).

OXFORD, Ashmolean Museum

PORTRAIT OF A LADY WITH A PARROT   Fig. 416
Canvas, 72×53.5 cm.; *c.* 1750–60.

Brocklebank Sale, Christie's, 8.7.1938; Durlacher Coll., London; later in New York; Ashmolean Museum, Oxford, bequeathed 1955 by Mr. E. E. Cook to the National Art Coll. Fund.
The original painting from which one of the two pastels (by Lorenzo) in Washington was copied. Nothing is known about the second original representing a *Portrait of a Lady with a Fur*.
Paintings selected . . . in the Ashmolean Museum, Oxford (n.d.), fig. 21.

THE GATHERING OF THE MANNA
Canvas, 94×70 cm.

By a follower of Tiepolo. Wrongly attributed to Giambattista.
Coll. von Goldammer, Schloss Plausdorf bei Kirchheim; Cook Coll., Richmond. Italian Exhibition, R.A., London, 1930.
Sack, pp. 43, 192, fig. 16, confusing it with the ex-Maccari sketch, now in Buenos Aires (q.v.), which is the original.
This sketch is not the preparatory study or *modello* for Verolanuova, as Molmenti, Sack and others believe, but painted after the original sketch.
Another copy in Bressanone (Brixen) (q.v.).

PADUA, Museo Civico

MIRACLE OF S. PATRICK OF IRELAND   Fig. 152
Arched canvas, 347 × 173 cm.; signed: GIO. BATTA. TIEPOLO F.

Altarpiece painted in 1746 for the Jesuit Monastery in Padua. Engraved by Domenico (De Vesme, 69), with the inscription *Joannes Baptista Tiepolo pinx. in Eccl. S. Joannes de Verdara Patavij* and called *S. Paolino Vescovo e Patriarca d'Aquileja*. To the Museum 1866 from the Church of S. Giovanni di Verdara.
Brandolese, 1795, p. 195; Molmenti, p. 110, fig. p. 110; Sack, p. 176, fig. 168; A. Moschetti, *Il Museo Civico di Padova*, Padua, 1938, pp.191–193, pl. XLII; Grossato, *Catalogue*, 1957, p. 162.
A sketch for this altarpiece (46 × 35 cm.) is recorded in the Cat. of the Vianelli Coll. in Chioggia (Venice, 1790).

MUCIUS SCAEVOLA
Canvas, 44.5 × 28.6 cm.

By a follower of Tiepolo.
A. Moschetti, *ibid.*, p. 464, fig. 350, attributes it to Giambattista, but it is a very poor old copy of the large canvas now in Leningrad, Hermitage (q.v.); Scerbaciova, 1941, p. 15 with repr. as an original by Tiepolo. (The other sketch, reproduced by Scerbaciova as on the art-market in Milan, is a free copy of the same subject, painted by Antonio Guardi. Cf. Morassi, in *Arte Veneta*, 1952, p. 89, fig. 87.)

PADUA, Basilica del Santo

THE MARTYRDOM OF S. AGATHA   Fig. 124
Canvas, 350 × 170 cm.; *c.* 1735–36.

Altarpiece commissioned in December, 1734, and put in position in January, 1737. Damaged by restorations. Two sketches are in the Broglio Coll., Paris; another in Venice, Ca' Rezzonico, is by a follower.
Brandolese, 1795, p. 32; Molmenti, p. 108; Sack, p. 176; Arslan, *Inventario*, 1936, p. 10, fig. 13; Morassi, p. 21.

PADUA, S. Gregorio

S. GREGORY WITH SS. FRANCIS AND BOVO
Arched canvas, 228 × 127 cm.

By F. Zugno.
Sack, p. 176, wrongly attributes this altarpiece to Tiepolo; Arslan, *Inventario*, 1936, pp. 181–182, fig. p. 181, restoring it to Zugno

PADUA, S. Lucia

S. LUKE   Fig. 189
Canvas, monochrome on gold ground; 90 × 90 cm.; *c.* 1730–35; a half-length figure over a door.
Brandolese, 1795, p. 205; Moschini, *Guida . . . di Padova*, 1817, p. 141; Molmenti. p. 110; Sack, p. 176; Fiocco in *Dedalo*, 1932, XII, p. 470, fig. p. 471; Arslan, *Inventario*, 1936, p. 3.
One of a series of sacred figures all painted as overdoors in fresco by Jacopo Ceruti around the walls of the church, except this *Evangelist*. Sack, p. 176, wrongly mentions it as a fresco.

PADUA, S. Massimo

SS. MAXIMUS AND OSWALD   Fig. 141
Canvas, 270 × 200 cm.; *c.* 1742–45.

Altarpiece of the high altar. The sketch is in the Ruzicka Coll., Zurich. Another related sketch in Moscow, Pushkin Museum (q.v.).

THE REST ON THE FLIGHT INTO EGYPT   Fig. 33
Canvas, 240 × 150 cm.; *c.* 1742–45.

Altarpiece of the altar on the left: damaged by retouches.
Engraved by Bart. Crivellari.

S. JOHN THE BAPTIST   Fig. 45
Canvas, 240 × 150 cm.; *c.* 1742–45.

Altarpiece of the altar on the right; damaged, badly restored in the 19th century; cleaned some years ago and newly restored.

A stone slab on the floor before the High Altar records that the three paintings were commissioned by the parish priest, Giuseppe Cogolo of Thiene (died 1745). According to Perli (*La parrocchia d'Ognissanti . . . Padova*, 1885, ms. BP2305 in the Biblioteca Comunale, carta 16 V) the altars were rebuilt about 1742 and the Chapel of the *Rest of the Flight into Egypt* was restored in that year.
Brandolese, 1795, pp. 232–233; Moschini, *Guida . . . di Padova*, 1817, p. 149; Molmenti, pp. 109–110; Sack, pp. 78–79, 176, figs. 60–62; Arslan, *Inventario*, 1936, pp. 139–140, figs. pp. 140–141.
The cycle in S. Massimo marks the peak of Tiepolo's classical style in religious painting.

PALERMO, Chiaramonte-Bordonaro Coll.

TWO PROPHETS
Canvas, medium size.

By an imitator of Tiepolo.
Said by Sack to be a sketch for the Scuola dei Carmini, Venice.
Molmenti, p. 312, fig. p. 317, as a work of an imitator; Sack, p. 176, fig. 13b, as an autograph work of the artist's youth.
The signature is false. The painting is undoubtedly not by Tiepolo, but probably by Giustino Menescardi, who painted similar figures in the Scuola dei Carmini.

PARIS, Louvre

ALEXANDER AND CAMPASPE IN THE STUDIO OF APELLES
Canvas, 42 × 54 cm.; *c.* 1735–40.   Fig. 284

Ex coll. Salem, Paris; exhibited at the Sedelmeyer Gall., Paris, 1913, Cat. No. 63; ex Trotti Coll., Paris.
Unknown to the Tiepolo literature, this small painting is a very charming version of the subject Tiepolo had already painted ten years earlier (picture now in Montreal). It is very interesting to observe how his conception has changed from an almost baroque to a classic one. The types of the figures and the style in general are very close to the *Danäe* in Stockholm, of 1736.

APOLLO AND DAPHNE   Fig. 237
Canvas, 96 × 79 cm.; *c.* 1740.

Bequeathed by Baron Schlichting, 1915.
Fogolari, *Emporium*, 1911, I, pp. 77–79, fig. p. 77; Goering, *ad vocem*. Engraved at the end of the 18th century, by Ferdinando Gregori. There is also an engraving by G. Zocchi of this subject in the *Raccolta di ottanta Stampe rappresentanti i quadri più scelti de' Sig.ri March.si Gerini di Firenze*, Florence, 1786, and probably the painting once in the Gerini Coll. (until 1825) is identical with the present in the Louvre.
Excellent painting, sometimes unjustly doubted (cf. Catton Rich, 1938, p. 24).
An old copy is in the Hamill Coll., Lake Forest; another one was on the market in Milan about 1940.

THE LAST SUPPER   [1955, fig. 24]
Canvas, 78 × 88 cm.; *c.* 1745–50.

Originally in the collection of the Comte d'Angiviller, Directeur-Général des Bâtiments under Louis XVI. It is one of a group which includes two paintings in the Kunsthalle, Hamburg, the *Crucifixion* in S. Louis, and several others. An old copy of this picture is in the Prince Torre e Tasso Coll. (ex Hohenlohe), Duino Castle, near Trieste; another one is in the Museum of Warsaw.
Molmenti, p. 248, fig. p. 250; Sack, p. 213, fig. 209; Lorenzetti, p. 108, fig. 79.

THE QUACK DOCTOR
THE MINUET

Two canvases, 79 × 110 cm. each.

By Domenico.
Ex coll. Count Algarotti; Princesse Mathilde; in the Louvre since 1903.
Molmenti, p. 206, figs. p. 203; Sack, p. 214, figs. 109–110, both attributing the pictures to Giambattista Tiepolo. Sack adds that one of them is

signed and dated 1754, but there is no trace now of the date and only part of the signature exists.

Morassi, *Emporium*, 1941, VI, p. 271, first restoring them to Domenico; Lorenzetti, pp. 168–169, figs. 119–120, also as by Domenico; *Exhib. Cat.*, Petit Palais, Paris, 1960–61, No. 440–441.

Engraved by Leonardis, 1765.

There are many copies of these paintings; one of the *Minuet* is in the Isaac Delgado Museum, New Orleans.

The fact that the two paintings have been listed by Algarotti as works by Giambattista is not a real evidence of their authenticity, as we know that Algarotti made in some cases no difference between Giambattista and Domenico.

THE TRIUMPH OF FAITH
Canvas, oval, 95 × 69 cm.

By Domenico.
Goering, *ad vocem*.
Modello for a ceiling never executed or no longer extant.

THE VIRGIN APPEARING TO S. JEROME
Canvas, 29–22 cm.

Once attributed to Giambattista (Sack, p. 213) or to Domenico (Molmenti, p. 323, fig. p. 326); it is by F. Fontebasso.

MADONNA AND CHILD WITH S. JOHN THE BAPTIST
S. MARTIN SAYING MASS

Double-sided banner, attributed in the old Guides to Giambattista Tiepolo and now to Domenico, it is a work by a contemporary imitator.
In the depot.

MEEKNESS AND HUMILITY
Canvas, 120 × 86 cm.

From the Schlichting Coll., Paris.

Once believed to be a sketch by Giambattista. Recently assigned to Zugno, but it is probably by Menescardi, a copy after one compartment by Tiepolo in the Scuola dei Carmini, Venice, where Menescardi painted in the adjacent room.

PARIS, Musée des Arts Décoratifs

APOTHEOSIS OF A HERO (Francesco Barbaro?)
Canvas, oval, 45 × 65 cm.

By a follower of Tiepolo, copy of the sketch in a private collection in Paris mentioned below; another copy is mentioned by Sack in Berlin, E. Schweitzer Coll.
Sack, p. 213; Goering, *ad vocem*.

THE NEW WORLD
Canvas, *c.* 30 × 60 cm.

By Domenico.
Sometimes attributed to Giambattista.
Sack, p. 214, as by Domenico.

PARIS, Musée Cognacq-Jay

BANQUET OF ANTHONY AND CLEOPATRA (called *Nabal and Abigail*) Fig. 310
Canvas, 51 × 69 cm., shortly before the spring of 1743.

Engraved by Pietro Monaco, with caption describing it as property of 'Signor Giuseppe Smith' and called *Nabal and Abigail*. From this dedication it is clear that the painting was executed before Smith was appointed Consul in Venice (1744).
Ex coll. Princesse Mathilde; Gronkowski Sale, 17–22.5.1904 (68).
Molmenti, p. 260, fig. p. 73, after the engraving; Sack, p. 214, fig. 82, after the engraving; Catalogue du Musée Cognacq-Jay, 1930, no. 104 with repr.; Cailleux, Catalogue, 1952, p. 41; F. Haskell, in *The Burlington Magazine*, June, 1958, pp. 212–213, fig. 35.

Molmenti (p. 75) is wrong in saying that the engraving was derived from a picture in the Correr Museum, Venice, recently attributed to F. Zugno (see Lorenzetti, *Ca' Rezzonico*, 1951, p. 47).

This splendid small picture is certainly the *modello* for the large *Banquet* in Melbourne; and to be considered the best of all the many versions of the Pal. Labia type of *Banquet*.

PARIS, Musée Jacquemart-André

RECEPTION OF THE EMPEROR HENRY III AT THE VILLA CONTARINI ALLA MIRA (1574) Fig. 317
Fresco, removed from the Villa Contarini at Mira, between Venice and Padua, in 1893, and transferred to canvas.
Present measurements: 402 × 729 cm.; original size 330 × 740 cm.

A sketch for the *Reception*, said to be by Giambattista Tiepolo, and perhaps the one which belonged to Algarotti, was in the Rothschild Coll., Frankfurt (and its present whereabouts is unknown), the small picture in the Museum at Berlin is certainly an old copy.

The following frescoes were also removed from the walls and transferred to canvas at the same time:

SPECTATORS ON A BALCONY, two decorations flanking the preceding one, 300 × 113 cm. Fig. 389–390

FAME ANNOUNCING TO THE SPECTATORS THE ARRIVAL OF THE EMPEROR Fig. 391
Canvas, 10 × 4 m.; ceiling of the saloon. One of the most beautiful creations of the Master, with many portraits of the Contarini family and with his selfportrait. A clue to the dating of the frescoes is given in a letter from the Marquis de Vandières, Surintendant des Bâtiments du Roi, written at Versailles on 21.5.1754, to the painter Natoire, Director of the French Academy in Rome. Vandières, who saw Tiepolo's frescoes during his stay in Italy, suggests in his letter to send some 'pensionnaires' from the French Academy for the express purpose of copying them. As Vandières left Rome on 3.3.1751, he must have seen the Contarini frescoes on his way back to France. The frescoes must therefore be dated from before Tiepolo's departure for Würzburg (November, 1750), perhaps in that summer (cf. Byam-Shaw, in *The Burlington Magazine*, December, 1960, pp. 529–531). The frescoes were executed with the assistance of G. Mengozzi-Colonna in the illusionistic parts and of Domenico in the less important figures. They are somewhat damaged and faded. There is a selfportrait of Tiepolo at the left, behind a column, in the *Reception*.
De Chennevières in *Gaz. des Beaux-Arts*, 1896; Molmenti, p. 252–254, figs. pp. 246, 248, 252; Sack, pp. 214–215; *Catalogue* of the Museum, Paris, n.d. (*c.* 1920), pp. 104, 158; Morassi, p. 33.

APOTHEOSIS OF A HERO
Fresco with large figures, shaped for a ceiling and transferred to canvas.

Very damaged; *c.* 1730–40. The central part (an oval) is original, the remaining part is a modern addition.
Ex coll., Grandi, Milan; acquired for the Museum in 1893.
Sack, p. 215, fig. 226; Catalogue du Musée J.-A., Paris, n.d. (*c.* 1920), p. 30. Original provenance unknown.

PEACE AND JUSTICE Fig. 398
Fresco transferred to canvas, oval 242 × 200 cm.; *c.* 1735–40.

Acquired from Grandi, Milan, in 1893.
Sack, p. 215; Catalogue du Musée J.-A., Paris, n.d. (*c.* 1920), No. 318, p. 43. Original provenance unknown.

PARIS, Petit Palais

ALEXANDER AND BUCEPHALUS Fig. 292
Canvas, 59 × 35 cm.; *c.* 1755–60.

Ex coll., Signol, Paris, sold 1878 for 3,000 fr.; Dutuis, Paris, by whom bequeathed to the Petit Palais.
Molmenti, p. 248, fig. p. 252; Sack, p. 219; Mireur, 1912, VII, *ad locum*; Morassi, p. 35; Lorenzetti, p. 125, fig. 88; Cailleux, Catalogue, 1952, p. 48, fig. 36; *Exhib. Cat.*, Petit Palais, Paris, 1960–61, No. 397.

Very fresh and sketchy small canvas, perhaps a *modello* for a larger picture or simply an independent work in itself. Stylistically related to the *Rape of Helen* in the Guerlain coll., Paris.

PARIS, formerly Albert Besnard Coll.

PULCINELLI (*Le Polichinelle coupable*)   Fig. 421
Canvas, 101 × 169 cm.; *c.* 1760–70.

Pendant to the *Pulchinellos' Kitchen* in the Cailleux Coll., Paris (q.v.). Formerly in the coll. of the Duc de Trévise; Albert Besnard Sale, Paris, 1.6.1934 (54). Engraved by Antoine Cardon (1772–1813) with the inscription *Gio. Bata Tiepolo inv. et del.*
Catton Rich, Catalogue, 1938, p. 31.

PARIS, Birtschansky

ZEPHYR AND FLORA   Fig. 334
Canvas, 42 × 37 cm.; *c.* 1745–50.

Sketch for an oval ceiling.
Reproduced in *The Burlington Mag.*, Dec., 1938 (Plate IV), when it was on the art market in London (Mr. H. D. Gronau).
Related to the ceiling in Venice, Palazzo Labia.

PARIS, Comte de Boisrouvray Coll.

TEN ALLEGORIES
Single figures in grisaille transferred to canvas, ovals of different sizes.
From a Villa in the Veneto.
Once in the Brass Coll., Venice; later in the Fauchier-Magnan Coll., Paris.
Painted in the main part by Domenico and collaborators.

PARIS, Broglio Coll.

THE MARTYRDOM OF S. AGATHA   Fig. 125
Canvas, 48 × 29 cm.; *c.* 1735–36.

Sketch for the altarpiece in the Santo, Padua.
Ex private coll., Vienna; exhibited at the Gall. St. Lucas, Vienna, 1937, Cat. no. 125, fig. 125.

THE MARTYRDOM OF S. AGATHA   Fig. 123
Canvas, 50 × 32 cm.; *c.* 1735–36.

Another sketch for the altarpiece in the Santo, Padua.
Ex coll., Sedelmeyer, Paris, sold 1897; private coll., Vienna; exhibited at the Gall. St. Lucas, Vienna, 1937.

ARIADNE WITH PUTTI AMID CLOUDS
Canvas, 24 × 30 cm.; *c.* 1730–35.

Fragment of a *Bacchus and Ariadne* of which there was another complete version, formerly in the Kleinberger Coll., Paris, reproduced by Sack, p. 216, fig. 211.
Another sketch was in the Eckstein Coll., London (q.v.), now Hasson Coll., London.

PARIS, formerly Broglio Coll.

GROUP OF PULCHINELLOS
Canvas, 31 × 55 cm.

By Domenico.
Ex coll. Duc de Trévise, Paris. Exhibited as by Giambattista in Chicago, 1938, no. 41. Sold at the Hôtel Drouot, 8.12.1947, no. 71.
Catton-Rich, *Catalogue*, 1938, p. 32, as Giambattista.

PARIS, Cailleux Coll.

RINALDO ABANDONS ARMIDA   [1955, fig. 38]
Canvas, 39 × 61 cm.; *c.* 1755–60.

Gentili di Giuseppe Coll., Paris, until 1941.
Lorenzetti, p. 106, fig. 78; Cailleux, Catalogue 1952, p. 48; Cat. Exhib. R.A., London, 1954–55, No. 481.

Pendant to the *Rinaldo and Armida* in Berlin. The style of this picture is close to the same subjects painted in fresco at the Villa Valmarana (1757). Iconographically related, but with the composition in reverse, to the painting in Munich.

THE PULCHINELLOS' KITCHEN   Fig. 420
Canvas, 104 × 165 cm.; *c.* 1760–70.

Lorenzetti, *Feste e Maschere*, 1937, No. 7, fig. 31; Catton Rich, 1938, No. 40 with repr; Lorenzetti, p. 147, fig. 105 *bis*; Cailleux, 1952, p. 51, fig. 28.
Brunet made a lithograph after a drawing of the same subject; the drawing was in the Denon Coll. in Paris (Sack, p. 279).
The pendant to this painting was in the Besnard Coll., Paris (q.v.).

PARIS, formerly Camondo Coll.

REBECCA AND ELIEZAR
MOSES SAVED FROM THE WATERS
Two canvases, 72 × 185 cm. each.

Sold February, 1893, for 2,400 francs.
Sack, p. 221, mentions them as overdoors, with a detailed description; Mireur, 1912, VII, *ad vocem.*
The first could be perhaps identified with the picture now in a Private Coll. in New York (q.v.); the second is missing.

PARIS, formerly Cotnareanu Coll.

TIME ABDUCTING BEAUTY   Fig. 324
Canvas, 230 × 166 cm.; *c.* 1745–50.

Ex coll. Baron de Schwiter, sold Paris 3.5.1886, Cat. No. 38 for 20,000 fr.; Blumenthal Coll.; sold at Charpentier, Paris, 29.11.1935, Cat. No. 65; sold at Charpentier, 14.10.1960, Cat. No. 14.
Molmenti, p. 255, fig. p. 254; Sack, p. 221; Mireur, 1912, VII, *ad locum*; Morassi, p. 26; Lorenzetti, p. 84, with the history of the picture, fig. 62.
After the cleaning the picture has revealed its very high standard and the beauty of its colours. Now in a Private Coll., New York.

PARIS, formerly Guillaume Dubufe Coll.

PUTTI PLAYING WITH A PIGEON
Canvas, 50 × 60 cm.

Sale Drouot, Paris, 10.2.1873, p. 43 (54 × 60 cm.).
Sack, p. 218, describing it as a fine but slightly repainted overdoor.
Present whereabouts unknown.

PARIS, formerly Fauchier-Magnan Coll.

ALLEGORY OF THE POET SODERINI (?)   Fig. 328
Canvas, oval, 51 × 33.5 cm.; *c.* 1754.

From the Meazza Coll., Milan (sold 1884, No. 26); then Grandi-Baslini Coll., Milan; Marczell von Nemes Coll., Budapest; Fauchier-Magnan Sale, Sotheby, London, 4.12.1935, No. 55 with repr.
Exhibited in Dusseldorf, 1912, Cat. No. 20.
Sketch for a ceiling, probably for the Villa Soderini at Nervesa (q.v.). Another version, of inferior quality, is in the Museum at St. Louis (q.v.).
Sack, p. 172, fig. 166 (repr. in reverse); *Cat.* of the Coll. von Nemes, Paris, 1913, No. 82 with repr.
Present whereabouts unknown.

HALBERDIER
See London, M. Tree Coll.

PARIS, formerly Flameng Coll.

ALLEGORY WITH MARS AND VENUS   Fig. 258
Canvas, oval, 41 × 72 cm.; *c.* 1740–45.

Excellent *modello* for the ceiling in the Pal. Pisani-Moretta, Venice (q.v.). Paris: Sale, Gal. Georges Petit, 26–27.5.1919 (37). Now in a private coll., Paris.
Molmenti, p. 258, fig. p. 254.

PARIS, Fodor Coll.

CHRIST CALMING THE TEMPEST
Canvas, 50 × 58 cm.

By Domenico.
Ex coll. Nemes, Munich; Matthiesen, London.
Cat. Detroit Exhibition, 1938, no. 27; Morassi, p. 40; Lorenzetti, p. 144, fig. 102; Cailleux, 1952, p. 52, fig. 27. Always as by Giambattista. In *Pantheon*, 1933, XXI, 5, May, p. 141; M. Precerutti-Garberi, in *Commentari*, No. 3–4, 1960, p. 278, fig. 14, both as Domenico. One of the most impressive masterpieces by him.
The pendant, *Christ on the Lake of Tiberias*, was formerly in the Strauss Coll., Paris (q.v.), and another picture from the same series, *Christ Healing the Man Possessed*, was once in the Nemes Coll., Munich (q.v.).

PARIS, formerly Groult Coll.

OLYMPUS
See Zurich, Hausammann Coll.

DEATH OF SOPHONISBA
See Paris, Patino Coll.

GOD THE FATHER ACCOMPANIED BY ANGELS (one bearing the seven-branched candelabra, and below the Birth of the Virgin or Christ)
Octagonal canvas, 78 × 40 cm.

Sketch for a ceiling.
By Domenico.
Attributed to Giambattista in the Sale Catalogues.
Ex coll. Rochefort, Paris, Kleinberger Sale, New York, 23.1.1918, p. 38 with repr.; Caspari, Munich, 1930; Berlin Museum Sale, Böhler, Munich, 9–10.6.1937, p. 671, Pl. 61.

PARIS, Guerlain Coll.

THE RAPE OF HELEN   Fig. 229
Canvas, 59 × 34 cm.; *c.* 1755–60.

Cailleux, 1952, p. 49, fig. 26, *Exhib. Cat.*, Bordeaux, 1956, No. 55.
The subject is very closely related to the fresco in the Villa Valmarana. Excellent sketch, stylistically related to the *Alexander and Bucephalus* in the Petit Palais, Paris.

PARIS, Haviland Sale (Hôtel Drouot, 14–15.12.1922, No. 59)

ZEPHYR AND AURORA (?)
Canvas, 74 × 46 cm.; *c.* 1730–40 (?)

Sketch for a ceiling, attributed in the Catalogue of the Sale to Domenico, whereas it seems, judging from the reproduction, to be a rather early work by Giambattista.
Not seen by me; present whereabouts unknown.

PARIS, formerly Kann Coll.

THE DEPOSITION
See London, National Gallery.

PARIS, formerly Kleinberger Coll.

BACCHUS AND ARIADNE WITH PUTTI
Canvas, 46 × 32 cm.; *c.* 1730–35.

Sketch for a ceiling in the style of the frescoes of the Palazzo Archinto, Milan (1731), probably autograph. Another one was formerly in the Eckstein Coll., London (q.v.). A fragment of a similar sketch in the Broglio Coll., Paris.
Not seen by me.
Present whereabouts unknown.
Sack, p. 216, fig. 211.

CHRIST CROWNED WITH THORNS
Canvas, 76 × 86 cm.

Old copy of the painting in Hamburg.
Sack, p. 184, note on No. 304, as Giambattista.

PARIS, formerly Lamoy Coll.

TRIUMPH OF FAITH
Canvas, oval, 150 × 110 cm.

Sketch for a ceiling. Christ and the Virgin in a glory on the clouds, with angels and cherubs; behind a parapet, on the lower part, monks and figures with candles, flags, etc.
Sack, p. 218, with a description; Mireur, 1912, VII, *ad locum*.
No photograph exists. According to Sack's description, certainly related to the painting by Domenico, now in the Louvre.

PARIS, M.L.C. Coll. Sale

TRIUMPH OF FAITH AND RELIGION OVER HERESY
Ceiling canvas, 52 × 82 cm.

Listed by Sack, p. 221 (sold in the auction 1901).
Perhaps related to the ceiling of the Palazzo Trento-Valmarana in Vicenza.
No reproduction exists; present whereabouts unknown.

PARIS, formerly M.P.M. Coll.

THE BAPTISM OF CHRIST
Canvas, 124 × 163 cm.

Wrongly said to be Tiepolo's autograph sketch for the fresco in the Colleoni Chapel in Bergamo, but it seems to be a copy by Antonio Guardi after a lost original by Tiepolo.
Catalogue des Tableaux Anciens . . . composant la collection de M.P.M., Petit, Paris, 28.5.1909, No. 93, with rep. as by G.B. (Isolami Coll., Bologna).
Later in the Agalbato Coll., Milan.

PARIS, formerly Orloff Coll.

HEAD OF AN OLD MAN (with a barret and a large collar, holding a book)   Fig. 411
Canvas, 59 × 50 cm.; *c.* 1750–60.

Engraved by Domenico with the inscription: *Joannes Batta. Tiepolo inv.* (Molmenti, *Acqueforti*, 1896, p. 159 r.).
Certainly the original from which the copies by Domenico in Baltimore, Museum of Art, and in New York, Am. Art Ass. (q.v.) were derived. Another copy was formerly in the Opuich-Fontana Coll., Trieste.
The same passed later in a Private Coll., Prague and is now in the National Gallery at Prague.
Not seen by me.
Catalogue of the Orloff Coll., Petit Palais, Paris, 29–30.4.1920 (61), with repr.

HAGAR AND ISHMAEL
Canvas, 38 × 21 cm.

By Domenico, wrongly attributed to Giambattista.
From the Orloff Coll. to Agnew, London, in 1926; Féral Coll., Paris, 1935. Present whereabouts unknown.
It reflects Giambattista's last style.
Catalogue of the Orloff Coll., Petit Palais, Paris, 29–30.4.1920 (62), as Giambattista with repr.

PARIS, Patino Coll.

THE DEATH OF SOPHONISBA   Fig. 290
Canvas, 46.5 × 36 cm.; *c.* 1755–60.

Ex coll. Groult, Paris; sale Charpentier, 21.3.1952, No. 96.
Sack, p. 215, fig. 210, wrongly reproduces an old copy formerly in the Kleinberger Coll., now in a private coll. in Milan as the original; Molmenti, 1911, p. 197; Cailleux, p. 47, fig. 29.
Excellent and very well preserved work.
De Vesme (*Paralipomeni tiepoleschi*, Turin, 1911, pp. 309–29), mentions a *Death of Sophonisba* in the Maurizio Baudi di Selve Coll., Turin. This picture, exhibited in Turin in 1880, is dated about 1730–35 by De Vesme, who says that the sketch for it was in the Kleinberger Coll.,

Paris (this *modello* is certainly to be identified with the old copy mentioned above). The Turin picture, concerning which there is no further information, was perhaps the realization on a large scale of the Patino sketch (?).

THE SACRIFICE OF IPHIGENIA   Fig. 233
Canvas, 39×62.5 cm.; *c.* 1735–40.

Henry de Rothschild Coll., Paris, till 1951.
Lorenzetti, p. 116, fig. 82; Cailleux, 1952, p. 48, pl. 21.
Very fine work, related to the fresco of the same subject in the Villa Valmarana at Vicenza and still more to the fresco, very damaged, of Palazzo Cornaro di S. Maurizio in Merlengo (for which it is possibly the *modello*, or a record of it). An autograph replica is in Hamburg, Kunsthalle (q.v.).

PARIS, Private Coll.

STUDY OF A NUDE MAN FROM THE BACK   Fig. 429
Canvas, 39×45 cm.; *c.* 1718–20.

Very interesting sketchy study from Tiepolo's beginnings, painted probably under the influence of the Bolognese Crespi and of Piazzetta. Hitherto unpublished.

PARIS, Private Coll.

TWO FLYING ANGELS   Fig. 225
Canvas, *c.* 80×70 cm.; *c.* 1720–25.

Fragment of a larger canvas, stylistically very close to the frescoes of the Udinese period.
Hitherto unpublished.

PARIS, Private Coll.

S. NORBERT, ARCHBISHOP OF MAGDEBURG   Fig. 180
Canvas, 32×23 cm.; *c.* 1730–35.

Represented sitting with a spider in the lower left corner. Probably a *modelletto* for an unknown or never executed altarpiece.
Hitherto unpublished.

PARIS, Private Coll.

MADONNA ENTHRONED   Fig. 424
Canvas, 31×23 cm.; *c.* 1730–35.

The Madonna enthroned on a platform, with the Child in her arms, is holding a missal in the right hand.
Believed to be by Domenico, it is by the hand of Giambattista.
Anonim. Sale, 17.2.1879, Paris; ex coll. heirs E. Borton (*Cat.* of the Borthon Coll., Dijon, 1890, No. 99).

PARIS, Private Coll.

APOTHEOSIS OF FRANCESCO BARBARO   Fig. 332
Canvas, oval, 45×63 cm.; *c.* 1745–50.

Ex coll. Poloutzoff, St. Petersburg, where there was also a pendant to it.
Cailleux, 1952, p. 40, fig. 8.
Excellent sketch, related to the ceiling of the *Apotheosis of Francesco Barbaro*, in the Metropolitan Museum, New York (q.v.). An old, rather weak copy (50×62 cm.) was once in a Viennese private coll. The pendant is in the Wildenstein Coll., New York (q.v.).

PARIS, Private Coll.

THE DEPOSITION (Christ lying in the foreground, the Virgin standing near the cross and other spectators)
Canvas, 41×31 cm.

Attributed to Tiepolo, but it is by F. Fontebasso.

PARIS, Private Coll.

RINALDO ON THE ISLAND
ARMIDA THE ENCHANTRESS
RINALDO AND ARMIDA
Three canvases, 51×97 cm. each; shaped.

From Pal. Guarnieri, Feltre; Corrèr Coll., Venice; Saint Marceaux, Paris.

Believed to be by Tiepolo, but are by a follower, Giustino Menescardi.
Molmenti, 1911, p. 197; Sack, p. 219; Cailleux, 1952, p. 38; *Exh. Cat.*, Zürich, 1955, Nos. 304–305; *Exh. Cat.*, Bordeaux, 1956, Nos. 61, 62; in every case as Giambattista. See also New York, Parke-Bernet.

PARIS, formerly Private Coll.

CHRIST AND THE ADULTERESS
CHRIST AT THE POOL OF BETHESDA
Two canvases, 113×180 cm.

By Domenico.
From the Valentino Benfatto Coll., Venice; Prince Don Jaime de Bourbon, Duke of Madrid, Schloss Frohsdorf, Austria, until *c.* 1920.
Zanotto, Catalogue of the Benfatto Coll., 1856, p. 232; Molmenti in *Dedalo*, 1927–28, p. 43 ff., with figs.; Sack, pp. 131, 232, in every case as by Giambattista. Undoubtedly Domenico's style.
Present whereabouts unknown.

PARIS, formerly Camille Rogier Coll.

MADONNA WITH A GREYHOUND
Canvas, 45×36 cm.; signed *J. B. Tiepolo*.

Sale May, 1876, fetched 1,200 francs.
De Chennevières, p. 56, with description; Sack, p. 220.
No photograph exists of the painting, now missing.

CALVARY
Canvas, 73×84 cm.

Mentioned in the Catalogue of the Collection Rogier (sold in Paris, May, 1876) as an important work (fetched 1,000 francs).
Sack, p. 220.
Probably identical with the painting now in Vierhouten (q.v.).

VISION OF S. FRANCIS OF ASSISI
Canvas, 74×54 cm.

Sold at the same auction for 250 francs.
De Chennevières, p. 58; Sack, p. 221.
No reproduction exists. Missing.

S. JEROME WITH THE ANGEL
Grisaille on canvas, 42×30 cm.

De Chennevières, p. 58; Sack, p. 221.
No reproduction exists. Missing.

PARIS, formerly Henry Rochefort Coll.

PORTRAIT OF A PATRICIAN BOY WITH A MANDOLINE
Described as belonging to this Collection in *Les Arts*, June, 1905, with the attribution to Giambattista. (Perhaps by Domenico?)
Sack, p. 216. No reproduction exists; present whereabouts unknown.

PARIS, formerly Baron A. de Rothschild Coll.

APOTHEOSIS OF FRANCESCO MOROSINI PELOPONNESIACO
Canvas, rectangular, shaped at the corners, 6×9 m.; *c.* 1750–60.

A ceiling originally in Pal. Morosini a Santo Stefano, Venice; then Count Szapary (one of Countess Morosini-Gatterbourg's heirs), Budapest, until the First World War; A. de Rothschild Coll., Chateau Ferrières, near Paris, till 1953.
In bad condition, much damaged by old restorations and recently restored again.
De Chennevières, 1898, p. 56, fig. p. 37; Molmenti, p. 282; Sack, p. 2201; Mireur, 1912, VII, *ad locum* (probably identical with the *Apotheosis of Morosini*, sold in Paris, 1894, for 8,100 fr. from the Palazzo Morosini-Gatterbourg in Venice.
Difficult to judge because of its bad condition; in any case, largely due to collaboration of Tiepolo's assistants.
Now in Milan, Pal. Isimbardi.

PARIS, Baroness Elly de Rothschild Coll.

ALLEGORY OF RICHES AND STRENGTH
Oval canvas with large figures, *c.* 5 × 3 m.; *c.* 1740–50.

Also known as *The Wealth of Venice*. A sketch believed to be original is
in the Ferdinandeum, Innsbruck, but it is certainly a copy.
Leroi, *L'Art*, 1876, IV, p. 299, repr. the engraving by Boetzel; De
Chennevières, fig. p. 33; Molmenti, p. 255, repr. of the engraving
on p. 253; Sack, p. 220, fig. 213, rightly says that the sketch in Innsbruck
is a copy.
Very well preserved, and vivid in colour.

PARIS, formerly Baron H. de Rothschild Coll. (?)

TIME ABDUCTING BEAUTY
Circular canvas with large figures, intended for a ceiling; *c.* 1740–50 (?).

Ex coll. Nathaniel de Rothschild.
P. Leroi in *L'Art*, 1876, vol. IV, p. 320, with an engraving by Ch.
Waltner; Sack, p. 220.
Not seen by me. Present whereabouts unknown; probably destroyed
in the war.

PARIS, Baron Ph. de Rothschild Coll.

THE MEETING OF ANTONY AND CLEOPATRA   [1955, fig. 30]
Canvas, 47 × 67 cm.; *c.* 1747.

Sketch for the picture in Archangel.
Ex Fourau Coll. (1869); ex coll. Nathaniel de Rothschild; H. de
Rothschild Coll.
Molmenti, p. 225, fig. p. 72; Sack, p. 127; Morassi, p. 39; Lorenzetti,
p. 89, fig. 66; Cailleux, 1952, p. 46, fig. 19; *Exh. Cat.*, Bordeaux, 1956,
No. 54, fig. 25.
One of the best *modelli* of this period, fresh in handling and splendid
in colour.

PARIS, formerly Schiff Coll.

A MEETING OF MONKS (some represented praying, others reading)
De Chennevières, p. 113, adds that this painting looks like a Subleyras;
Sack, p. 216.
No reproduction exists, present whereabouts unknown.

S. PETER DELIVERED FROM PRISON
On paper.
De Chennevières, p. 113, as a very strange sketch, almost a 'prima idea';
Sack, p. 216.
No reproduction exists. Missing.

PARIS, formerly Schloss Coll.

THE ANGEL APPEARING TO ABRAHAM AND SARAH
Canvas, 54 × 43 cm.

By Domenico, wrongly attributed to Giambattista.
Catalogue of the Schloss Sale, Charpentier, Paris, 1951.
Now in Chicago, Everett Graff Coll.
Another almost identical version of the subject was formerly in Vaduz,
Liechtenstein Coll. (q.v.).

PARIS, formerly de Schwiter Coll.

APOTHEOSIS OF S. GAETANO DA THIENE
Canvas, 48 × 26 cm.; *c.* 1757.

Sketch for the altarpiece in Rampazzo (q.v.). Passed to the Blumenthal
Coll., Paris, 1886.
De Chennevières, p. 190 fig. p. 93, as *Glorification of S. Antony of Padua*;
Sack, p. 221.
Present whereabouts unknown.

PARIS, formerly Sedelmeyer Coll.

MADONNA OF THE ROSARY.
See London, J. B. Robinson Coll.

CHRIST AND THE ADULTERESS
CHRIST AND THE BLIND
Two canvases, 48 × 57 cm. each.

By Domenico.
Assigned to Giambattista by Berenson, 1894; rightly catalogued by
Sack, p. 314, figs. 334, 336 as by Domenico; M. Precerutti-Garberi, in
Commentari, No. 3–4, 1960, p. 279, as by Domenico.
Belong to the series in Paris, Fodor Coll.; Munich, von Nemes Coll.
(q.v.) etc.

THE FALL OF THE REBEL ANGELS
Canvas, 73.5 × 45 cm.

Exactly corresponding to the Würzburg altarpiece; believed by Sack
(p. 219) to be the *modello* for it, but no reproduction exists to judge.
Probably identical with a painting by Domenico on the art-market in
London about 1955.

THE GATHERING OF THE MANNA
Canvas, 46.5 × 59.5 cm.

Claimed as a sketch for one of the two large canvases in Verolanuova,
it is, judging from the reproduction, a copy by a pupil like the
sketch in Oxford. The original *modello* in Buenos Aires.
Sack, p. 219, fig. 15.
Not seen by me. Present whereabouts unknown.

PARIS, Sedelmeyer Sale, 1872

THE FAMILY OF DARIUS BEFORE ALEXANDER
Canvas, 56 × 41 cm.

Mentioned by Sack, p. 233 and compared to the sketch for the Villa
Cordellina, once in the Algarotti Coll., now in the Crespi Coll., Milan.
The measurements of the two sketches are identical.
Probably a replica of the M. Crespi sketch.
Present whereabouts unknown.

PARIS, formerly Strauss Coll.

CHRIST ON THE LAKE OF TIBERIAS
Canvas, 48 × 58 cm.

By Domenico.
Probably one of the series including the *Christ Calming the Tempest*, in
the Fodor Coll., Paris, and the *Christ Healing a Man Possessed*, formerly
in the von Nemes Coll., Munich (q.v.).
Catalogue of Exhibition, Paris, 1935, no. 438, as by Giambattista;
M. Precerutti-Garberi, in *Commentari*, No. 3–4, p. 278, rightly as
Domenico.

PARIS, Duc de Talleyrand Coll.

PUTTO WITH GRAPES   Figs. 403–404
PUTTO WITH EARS OF CORN

Two canvases, 104 × 75 cm.; *c.* 1740–50.

Allegories of Autumn and Summer, of high quality.
Ex coll. Viscomte de Schwitter, sold 1886 for 3,700 fr.; at Mme.
Gauchez Sale, Paris, 1892, for 1,950 fr.; Marquis de Biron.
Molmenti, p. 247; Sack, p. 211; Mireur, 1912, VII, *ad locum*; Cailleux,
1952, pp. 47–48.
It is reasonable to assume that two other canvases, *Winter* and *Spring*
(lost, or present whereabouts unknown), formed a series with these, of
the Seasons. The two panels with *Vases and Heads of Putti*, formerly
with Agnew, London, certainly formed part of this decoration. Related
to the canvas in Leningrad (q.v.).

APOTHEOSIS OF A HERO   Fig. 333
Circular canvas, 38 cm. diam.; *c.* 1750–60.

Ex coll. Marquis de Biron, Paris.
Said to be connected with the fresco in Pal. Rezzonico, Venice, but
there seems to be no evidence for this.
Cat. Exhib. R.A., London, 1954–55, no. 509; Morassi, 1956, *Emporium*,
Jan., fig. 3.
A fresh sketch in dazzling colours and in good condition. There is a
copy in Milan, Ambrosiana.

BACCHIC HEAD ON SIMULATED MARBLE BACKGROUND
Canvas, 44.5 × 53 cm.

Ex coll. Simonetti, Rome, sold at Tavazzi, Rome, 1932, no. 542, as
Giambattista. Formed part, in a Vicentine Villa, of a decorative cycle to
which the three frescoes exhibited in Venice, 1929 also belonged. One,
ex-Simonetti Coll., Rome, is now in Sarasota, the whereabouts of the
two others are now unknown. Painted in fresco heightened with oil-
paint; originally a wall-decoration, from Tiepolo's shop.
Cat. Exhib. R.A., London, 1954–55, no. 493.

PARIS, formerly Trotti-Nicolle Coll.

TRIUMPH OF AMOR   Fig. 342
A ceiling on canvas, oval, *c.* 3 × 2 m. (?); *c.* 1740–45.

By Molmenti, p. 310, fig. p. 314, assigned to the French School; by
Sack, p. 314, to Domenico, but judging from the photograph it seems
to be undoubtedly by Giambattista.
Present whereabouts unknown.

PARMA, Pinacoteca

S. FIDELIS OF SIGMARINGEN CRUSHING HERESY   Fig. 120
Canvas, 247 × 171 cm.; *c.* 1752–58.

This altarpiece is not mentioned in Ruta's *Guida* of 1752, but the Parma
Academy conferred the title of *Amatore* upon Tiepolo in 1758, probably
on account of this picture. It was formerly in the church of the Capu-
chins, and was transferred to the Pinacoteca in 1810. The sketch is in
Turin (q.v.).
Affò, *Parmigian servitor di Piazza*, Parma, 1796 (stating that the picture
was placed in the first chapel left of the church of the Capuchins);
Ricci, 1896, p. 14; Molmenti, p. 154, fig. p. 154; Sack, p. 177, fig. 125;
Quintavalle, *La R. Galleria di Parma*, Rome, 1932, pp. 141–42, fig. 216.
Emphatic in composition; close to the style of the Würzburg period.

PAVIA, Museo Civico Malaspina

HEAD OF AN OLD MAN
HEAD OF AN ORIENTAL

Two canvases, 45 × 39 cm. each.
By Domenico.
Gift of Francesco Reale.
In the Museum 1894 with the attribution to Domenico (*Catalogue Ms.*
by Maiocchi, 1900). Later listed as Giambattista and attributed by
various critics also to Ligari, Nogari, or to Tiepolo's workshop.
Published in the Catalogue 'Italienische Kunst aus der Ambrosiana von
Mailand' Kunstmuseum, Lucerne, 1946, p. 66, rightly as Domenico.
One of the two *Heads* is very similar to that by Giambattista in Munich,
formerly Böhler, and the other to that in Philadelphia, Johnson Coll.

PAVIA, Necchi Coll.

GIFTS OFFERED TO CLEOPATRA   Fig. 288
Canvas, oval, 138 × 107 cm.; signed G. B. TIEPOLO; *c.* 1745–50.

Formerly in the Palazzo Barbaro, Venice; ex Coll. Thedy, Weimar;
Colonna Coll., Turin.
Replica in the Museum of Atlanta, Georgia. A copy in Ottobeuren,
another old copy (143 × 110 cm.) was on the art-market in Paris,
c. 1958.
This was one of the four overdoors of a saloon; the other three ovals

are now in Washington, National Gallery (q.v.); Augsburg, Museum
(q.v.), and Copenhagen, Museum (q.v.).
Engraved by Domenico (De Vesme, 89).
Molmenti, p. 271, fig. p. 268 (of the engraving); Sack, p. 150; Morassi,
p. 26, fig. 68.

PHILADELPHIA Museum of Art (Johnson Collection)

S. ROCH   Fig. 160
Canvas, 45 × 34 cm.; *c.* 1730–35.

One of the many small pictures for the confraternity of the Scuola di
S. Rocco, Venice. From the Spiridon Coll., bought 1910.
Berenson, *Catalogue of the Johnson Coll.*, 1913; Goering *ad vocem*.
Another *S. Roch* attributed to Tiepolo was in the John McIlhenny
Coll., Philadelphia (sold 1946, present whereabouts unknown).

VENUS AND VULCAN   Fig. 245
Canvas, 66.5 × 85 cm.; *c.* 1755–60.

Ex coll. Gsell, Vienna (Sale, 1873); De Beurnonville Sale, Paris, 1881,
sold for 1,200 fr. (Mireur, 1912, VII, *ad locum*).
Sack, p. 233, lists among the missing works by Tiepolo, together with
this one, a companion composition entitled *Apollo and Daphne* (to be
identified with the picture now in Washington), and calls them
'overdoors'; Berenson, Catalogue of the Johnson Coll., 1913, p. 190;
Venturi, 1933, III, p. 593, considers this painting wrongly as a sketch
for the lower part of the ceiling fresco of the Guardroom in the Royal
Palace in Madrid and dates it about 1762; Morassi, p. 23; Catton Rich,
1938, p. 10, fig. p. 67.

SCENE FROM ROMAN HISTORY
See Washington, Nat. Gall of Art.

COURT OF A PALACE
Canvas, 37 × 57 cm.; *c.* 1730–35.

In this painting by Michele Marieschi, the little figures ('macchiette')
were added by G. B. Tiepolo. Pendant to the painting in Saint Louis.
O. Benesch, in *Art Quarterly*, winter, 1947, p. 13 ff., with repr.,
attributing the architecture and the 'macchiette' to Domenico Tiepolo;
A. Morassi, in *Arte Veneta*, 1953, p. 60, fig. 54; A. Morassi, in *The
Burlington Magazine*, June, 1959, p. 227 ff., fig. 28.

GLORY OF S. DOMINIC
Canvas, 38 × 52 cm.; *c.* 1737.

Possibly sketch for the lower part of the ceiling fresco in the church of
the Gesuati, Venice.
Pendant to the picture in a private coll. lent to the Fogg Museum,
Cambridge, Mass., 1923 (q.v.).
Goering, *ad vocem*; Berenson, Catalogue of the Johnson Coll., 1913,
no. 286. Other sketches, but of the central fresco, in Berlin and Milan.
Ex coll. Sellar, London, sold 1889 for 885 fr. (Mireur, 1912, VII,
ad locum). Present whereabouts unknown. Not seen by me.

HEAD OF AN OLD WHITE-BEARDED MAN
Canvas, 47 × 38 cm.

By Domenico.
Wrongly attributed to Giambattista in the Catalogue of the Johnson
Coll., 1913. Similar to that of Pavia (q.v.).
From Durlacher Brothers, 1910.

PHILADELPHIA, Museum of Art (Elkins Coll.)

THE MARTYRDOM OF S. AGATHA
Canvas, 60 × 34 cm.

A contemporary copy after the painting by Giambattista Tiepolo in
Padua, very close to the sketch of the same subject in the Broglio Coll.,
Paris.
Molmenti, 1911, p. 198, as by Giambattista.

PHILADELPHIA, Museum of Art (Wilstach Coll.)

MIRACLE OF THE POOL AT BETHESDA
Canvas, 68 × 113 cm.

By Domenico.
Given with its pendant of *Christ and the Adultress* (here catalogued under New York, Böhler-Steinmeyer), by some patrician Venetian families to the Genoese advocate Marcantonio Bono; Sedelmeyer Coll., Paris; in the Museum, 1902: always attributed to Giambattista.
Sedelmeyer Catalogue, 1902, no. 65; Molmenti, 1911, p. 198 (both as Giambattista); Sack, p. 307 as *Christ Healing the Sick*, rightly attributing it to Domenico; L. Venturi, 1933, Plate CCCCXXVII, also as by Domenico.

THE LAST SUPPER
Canvas, 59 × 108 cm.

In the Museum attributed to Giambattista, but certainly by Corrado Giaquinto.

PIOVE di SACCO (Padua), S. Martino

MADONNA DEL CARMELO WITH S. CATHERINE AND THE ARCH-
ANGEL MICHAEL   Fig. 98
Arched canvas, 262 × 128 cm.; *c.* 1735–40.
Altarpiece with large figures; restored in 1896 for the Tiepolo Exhibition in Venice, after being completely neglected.
Molmenti, p. 110, fig. p. 108; Sack, p. 177, fig. 169.
A fine work in vivid colour, stylistically close to the two pictures in Udine, Museo Civico.

PIOVE DI SACCO (Padua) S. Nicolò

S. FRANCIS OF PAOLA   Fig. 182
Canvas, 229 × 114 cm.; *c.* 1725–30.
Altarpiece.
Molmenti, p. 110; Sack, p. 177.
Exhibited in the Tiepolo Exhibition, Venice, 1896.
On a large label at the lower right is an inscription in capitals: QUESTO QUADRO FU FATTO FAR DA FRAN.CO RUBELLI/ET SUOI EREDI PER SUA DIVOTIONE.
The *modello* in Milan, Miani Coll.

PIRANO (Istria), S. Maria della Consolazione

MADONNA WITH THE GIRDLE   Fig. 112
Arched canvas, 190 × 100 cm.; *c.* 1725–30.
Altarpiece; the figure of the Virgin is somewhat damaged by bad restoration. There is a self-portrait of Tiepolo at the right of the Virgin.
First attributed to Tiepolo by Riccoboni, confirmed by Morassi (*Era Nuova*, Trieste, 1.4.1922).
Santangelo-Moschini-Morassi, *Provincia di Pola, Inventario*, Rome, 1935, p. 157, fig. p. 157; Santangelo, *La Critica d'Arte*, 1935, p. 48, figs. 2, 4–6.

PORTOGRUARO, Count G. Marzotto Coll.

HOMAGE TO THE SPANISH MONARCHY
Circular painting on a rectangular canvas, 52.5 × 51 cm.

By Domenico.
Sketch for the ceiling fresco of the 'Saleta' to the 'Anticamara de la Reyna' in the Royal Palace, Madrid, certainly executed by Domenico. There are very few differences between this sketch and the ceiling fresco; and this excellent sketch, wrongly attributed to Giambattista, is to be dated shortly before the fresco (1763–67).

PRAGUE, National Gallery
HEAD OF AN OLD MAN
See: Paris, formerly Orloff Coll.

PROVIDENCE, Rhode Island, School of Design
THE ANGEL OF FAME   Fig. 358
Shaped canvas with large figures, 332 × 198 cm.; *c.* 1750–60.

Ex coll. Gonse, Paris; acquired by the Museum in 1932. Originally a ceiling fresco of unknown provenance.
Molmenti, p. 259, fig. p. 254; Rhode Island Bulletin, 1933, XXI, 4, p. 58.

RAMPAZZO (Vicenza), Parish Church

APOTHEOSIS OF S. GAETANO OF THIENE   Fig. 184
Canvas, 210 × 119 cm.; 1757.

The altar on which this painting stands was built in 1756, as a commission of Vicenzo, Count of Thiene, and his wife Elisabetta.
Pallucchini, 1945, p. 129; Mariacher, 1950, p. 153; Mazzariol-Pignatti, 1951, p. 70 with repr.; Lorenzetti, p. 117, fig. 80.
This excellent altarpiece was painted during Tiepolo's stay in Vicenza, while he was working on the frescoes in the Villa Valmarana. Engraved by Domenico (De Vesme, no. 62). A sketch (48 × 26 cm.), certainly the original one for the altarpiece, with many differences in the poses of the Saints, was until 1886 in the Baron de Schwiter Coll., Paris, and later in the Blumenthal Coll., Paris. (See Paris, Schwiter Coll.)

RAVENNA, Cathedral

FEMALE SAINTS IN GLORY
De Chennevières, p. 91, followed by Sack, p. 177, mentions two panels by Tiepolo in a little chapel of this church. It was certainly a mistake, for no trace exists of them.

REGGIO EMILIA, Galleria Parmeggiani

MOSES SAVED FROM THE WATERS
Wrongly attributed to Tiepolo, is clearly a work by Andrea Celesti.
A. Fulloni, *La Galleria Parmeggiani*, in 'Le Vie d'Italia', May, 1932, with repr., as Giambattista.

RENNES, Musée des Beaux-Arts

S. PROCULUS, BISHOP OF VERONA, VISITING SS. FERMUS AND RUSTICUS
S. AUGUSTINE AND OTHER SAINTS

Two canvases, 58 × 34 cm. each.

Old copies after the original sketches by Tiepolo in the National Gallery, London.
Formerly in the Trotti Coll., Paris, till 1941; later in Dusseldorf; after 1945, as 'Restitutionsgut' to the French Government and allotted to the Museum of Rennes.
In storage.

RICHMOND, Virginia, Virginia Museum of Fine Arts

THE HOLY TRINITY IN A GLORY OF MUSICIAN ANGELS
Canvas, 99 × 69 cm.

Sketch for a ceiling, believed to be related to the Pietà in Venice.
By a follower or copyist of Domenico.

RIO DE JANEIRO, Museu Nacional de Belas Artes

S. CAJETAN   Fig. 174
Canvas, 98.5 × 78 cm.; *c.* 1730–35.

Not seen by me; but judging from the photograph certainly a good early work by Giambattista.
Brought by Cezar Lanciani in 1862 and bought from the Italian Consul, Dr. Alfonso Gonella, 1874.

ROME, Galleria Nazionale
SATYR WITH FAUN   Fig. 267
Canvas, 59 × 97 cm.; *c.* 1740.

Acquired in 1911 from Julius Böhler, Munich.
Hermanin, 1912, p. 369 ff.; Cat. *Mostra del '700*, Venice, 1929, p. 61, no. 13; Goering, *ad vocem*.
A very fine work, grey-blue in tonality. A copy, on the market in Paris, has been wrongly attributed to Tiepolo himself.

ROME, Albertini-Carandini Coll.

THE MEETING OF ABRAHAM AND LOT
THE PARTING OF ABRAHAM AND LOT
Two canvases, 75 × 118 cm.

By Domenico; wrongly attributed to Giambattista.
Modigliani, *Dedalo*, 1924, as by Giambattista; exhibited Venice, *Mostra del' 700*, 1929, as Giambattista; Fiocco, *Rivista di Venezia*, 1929, pp. 55–56, as Domenico; Morassi, *Emporium*, VI, 1941, p. 270 ff., fig. p. 267 as by Domenico, with stylistic reasons; Modigliani, *La Coll. di Luigi Albertini*, Rome, 1942, XVIII and XIX as Giambattista; Lorenzetti, p. 103, figs. 76–77, as by Giambattista.

ROME, formerly Principe d'Assia Coll.

SS. GAETANO, ANTONY ABBOT AND JOHN THE BAPTIST
Small canvas, shaped at the top. Old copy, wrongly attributed to Tiepolo, of the picture of the same subject in the Museo Poldi-Pezzoli, Milan.
Cat. *Mostra del' 700*, Venice, 1929, p. 61, no. 16, wrongly as Giambattista.

THE CONTINENCE OF SCIPIO
Small canvas, exhibited in Venice, 'Settecento Italiano', 1929 (*Catalogue*, p. 54, fig. 6), as Tiepolo, but by a pupil of his, i.e. F. Zugno.

ROME, formerly Marchese Campana Gallery

THE SUPPER AT EMMAUS
Canvas, 165 × 104 cm.

Sack, p. 233, under 'Lost Works,' by Tiepolo.
Present whereabouts unknown. No reproduction exists.

ROME, formerly Paoletti Coll.

ABRAHAM VISITED BY THE ANGELS
Canvas, 34 × 48 cm.

Weak copy after an early work by Tiepolo, similar in composition to the drawing by Tiepolo in the Museo Civico at Bassano. (Cf. Morassi, *L'Arte*, 1944, Pl. 8–9.)
Photograph in the Berenson Library.

ROME, Private Coll.

S. SEBASTIAN   Fig. 175
Canvas, 108 × 76 cm.; *c.* 1718–20.

The martyr is bound to a tree in an almost sitting pose, with arms upraised. A young woman withdraws the arrow from his belly.
Very close in style to the *S. Bartholomew* in Venice, S. Stae, but slightly earlier. Hitherto unpublished, this impressive picture, strong in chiaroscuro, is quite different from the celebrated composition in Diessen.

ROME, Private Coll.

THE FAMILY OF DARIUS BEFORE ALEXANDER (?)   Fig. 279
ARCHIMEDES IN THE SERAPEION OF ALEXANDRIA   Fig. 278
Two canvases, 211 × 146 cm. each; *c.* 1720.

The painted architecture is very probably by Gerolamo Mengozzi-Colonna, whereas the little figures ('macchiette') are without doubt by Giambattista Tiepolo. If by Mengozzi-Colonna, this is the first known example of the collaboration of the two artists.
A. Morassi, in *The Burlington Magazine*, June, 1959, p. 227 ff., figs. 17, 18, 20–23.

ROME, Private Coll.

MADONNA AND CHILD WITH S. ANTHONY OF PADUA
Canvas, 31.5 × 23.5 cm.; *c.* 1725–30.

Similar to the same subject in Venice, Congregazione di Carità and Cini Coll.
Not seen by me.

Present whereabouts unknown.
S. De Vito-Battaglia, in *Vita Artistica*, Rome, March-April, 1932, pp. 69–74, fig. 1.

ROME, Private Coll.

S. MARK THE EVANGELIST   Fig. 188
Oval canvas, 33 × 26.5 cm.; *c.* 1730–35.

Formerly in the Marches; about 1930 in Rome.
Good in quality. Stylistically similar to the small devotional paintings of S. Roch.
C. Lorenzetti, *Un' opera di G. B. Tiepolo proveniente dalle Marche*. 'Rassegna Marchigiana', 1933, nos. 3–4, pp. 110–113, with repr. p. III.

ROME, formerly Simonetti Coll.

TWO ALLEGORICAL FIGURES WITH AN OBELISK
See: Sarasota, Ringling Museum.

ROME, Spalletti-Trivelli Coll.

MADONNA WITH SS. GEORGE AND ANTONY ABBOT   Fig. 99
Canvas, 204 × 105 cm.; *c.* 1750–55. Signed on the pedestal and dated 17–5. (?), but the inscription is not certainly entirely original.
Altarpiece, engraved by Domenico (De Vesme, 55).
Catalogue of the *Mostra d'Arte Italiana*, Pal. Venezia, Rome, 1945, p. 91, fig. 91; Sack, p. 228, repr. of the engraving fig. 221.
An excellent work of Tiepolo's maturity, light grey in tone, but somewhat damaged by restoration.

ROME, formerly Stroganoff Coll.

THE BANQUET OF CLEOPATRA
Canvas, 32 × 47 cm.

Attributed to Tiepolo by Muñoz, *Catalogue de la Coll. Stroganoff*, vol. II, Rome, 1911, p. 32, fig. 28, but it is an old copy after the *Banquet* in the Cognacq-Jay Coll., Paris. Later Venice, Asta Coll.; exhibited in Venice, 1929, as by Giambattista.

ROTTERDAM, Boymans Museum

THE MARTYRDOM OF S. VICTOR
Canvas, 33 × 47.5 cm.

Acquired by the Museum in 1921.
Wrongly attributed to Tiepolo; it is by a follower and similar to the canvas in the Museo Civico, Milan (q.v.).

ROUEN, Musée des Beaux-Arts

THE CARD-PLAYERS
Canvas, 92 × 131 cm.

Attributed to Tiepolo by De Chennevières (p. 115); doubted by Molmenti (p. 310) and by Sack (p. 222), who both believe it to be by Longhi or his circle. It is a work by Traversi.

ROVETTA, near Bergamo, Parish Church

THE VIRGIN IN GLORY, ADORED BY APOSTLES AND SAINTS
                                              [1955, pls. 17, 19, 20]
Known also as the *Glory of the Saints*.
Canvas, 378 × 134 cm.; 1734.

Altarpiece placed in position in 1736. The sketch is in the Museo Poldi-Pezzoli, Milan. The frame of this picture is a splendid work by the woodcarver Andrea Fantoni of Rovetta.
Frizzoni, *L'Arte in Bergamo e l'Accademia Carrara*; Bergamo, 1877, p. 69; Molmenti, p. 133, fig. p. 135; Sack, p. 177, fig. 227; Pinetti, 1931, p. 386, fig. p. 385; Fiocco, 1938, p. 148 with repr.; Morassi, p. 22; Lorenzetti, p. 53, fig. 39; Exhib. Cat., Petit Palais, Paris 1960–61, No. 390, fig. 49.
One of the most important altarpieces of Tiepolo's first maturity.

ROVIGO, Accademia dei Concordi

PORTRAIT OF ANTONIO RICCOBONO [1955, pl. 34]
Canvas, 120×90 cm.; *c.* 1745.

Commissioned from Tiepolo by the Academy along with other portraits of famous men of Rovigo by other painters. Neglected by the old guides and rediscovered by Fogolari.
Fogolari, *Bolletino d'Arte*, Rome, 1908, IV, p. 115; Molmenti, pp. 107–108, fig. p. 108; Sack, p. 99; Morassi, p. 27, fig. 70; Lorenzetti, p. 80, fig. 59.
It is interesting to learn from a letter by Tiepolo to Count Algarotti of April 4th, 1761, that he was supposed to have painted Algarotti as well, but, in spite of the clear reference in the letter, nothing else is known of such a portrait.

SAINT LOUIS, Missouri, City Museum of Art

VENETIAN INTERIOR
Canvas, 37×57 cm.; *c.* 1730–35.

In this painting by Michele Marieschi, the little figures ('macchiette') were added by Giambattista Tiepolo.
Pendant to the painting in the Johnson Collection at Philadelphia.
A. Morassi, in *Arte Veneta*, 1953, p. 60; A. Morassi, in The *Burlington Magazine*, June 1959, p. 227 ff., fig. 29.
(The painting is on definitive loan at the City Art Museum and it is the property of the Washington University, Saint Louis—Parsons Coll.)

THE CRUCIFIXION [1955, fig. 25]
Canvas, 79×88 cm.; *c.* 1745–50.

Formerly part of a series similar to that of which two pictures in Hamburg formed part.
Ex coll. Brentano, Frankfurt, until 1870; Weber, Hamburg; Kress Coll., New York; Knoedler, New York.
Molmenti, 1910, p. 208–209; Sack, p. 189, fig. 177; Catton Rich, 1938, p. 29, fig. p. 61; Lorenzetti, p. 127; fig. 91.

ALLEGORY OF THE POET SODERINI (?)
Canvas, oval, 51×33.5 cm.

Warneck Coll., Paris; Kleinberger Sale, American Art Ass., New York, 18.11.1932, No. 12.
Sketch for a ceiling, wrongly attributed to Giambattista. It is the work of a pupil, probably Fabio Canal, after the sketch formerly in the Fauchier Magnan Coll., Paris (q.v.).
F. Lugt, *Coll. Warneck*, Paris, 1926, No. 112, with repr.

S. DANIELE DEL FRIULI, Duomo, Sacristy

THE ASSUMPTION OF THE VIRGIN Fig. 105
THE DECOLLATION OF S. JOHN THE BAPTIST Fig. 40
S. JOHN DISTRIBUTING ALMS Fig. 41

Canvases; the first 72×58 cm.; the two others 38×46 cm.; *c.* 1730–35.
Three sketches which, according to Molmenti, may have been intended to be executed as frescoes in the Church. Some documents in the Civica Biblioteca at San Daniele, made known to me by the kindness of the Bibliotecario Don Patriarca, show them to have been *modelli* for projected ceiling frescoes in the church of Madre di Dio della Fratta. Cavalcaselle, in his Ms. (in Biblioteca Civica of Udine, Udine, 1876) *Vite ed opere dei Pittori Friulani*, mentions these three sketches as works with the stylistic characteristics of Tiepolo, which were to have been carried out for the ceiling of this Cathedral. But Tiepolo never executed the frescoes. These *modelli* were used by an imitator for frescoes, still existing, in the church of S. John the Baptist in Spilimbergo before 1746, the year in which they were restored. (I am indebted to the courtesy of Prof. C. Someda de Marco for this notice.)
Molmenti, p. 123, as doubtful works; Goering, *ad vocem*, mentions only the *Alms*, as by Domenico; Morassi, *Burlington Mag.*, I, 1955, pp. 7–8, figs. 8–10, as by Giambattista.
Excellent works, previously neglected in the literature. Stylistically related to the sketch in Ascott (q.v.), and to the sketches of the Bergamo period.
A copy of the *Decollation* was on the market in Paris some years ago.

SAN DIEGO, Calif., Fine Arts Gallery

THE FLIGHT INTO EGYPT Fig. 39
Canvas, 65×50 cm.; *c.* 1718–20.

Engraved by Berardi.
Ex coll. Speranza, Bergamo; Heimann, New York.
Caversazzi, *Emporium*, 1924, p. 135, with repr. of both picture and engraving; Morassi, *Burlington Magazine*, 1934, p. 86, pl. IIIA; Catalogue of the Gallery, 1947, p. 63, with repr.; Exhib. Cat., Bordeaux 1956, No. 48.

HEAD OF AN OLD ORIENTAL Fig. 412
Canvas, 38×30 cm.; *c.* 1760–70.

Related to the series of 'Heads' engraved by Domenico.
From the Heimann Coll., New York to the Museum.
Hitherto unpublished.

ECCE HOMO
Canvas, 42×34 cm.

By Domenico.
Ex coll. Beltrami, Milan; given anonymously to the Museum, 1947.
Catalogue of the Gallery, p. 64, with repr., wrongly attributed to Giambattista.

SAN FRANCISCO, M. H. de Young Memorial Museum

TRIUMPH OF FLORA Fig. 354
Canvas, 72×89 cm.; 1743–beginning of 1744.

Commissioned by Algarotti, together with the *Maecenas* in Leningrad, for Count Brühl in July, 1743.
Sent to Dresden (probably in March, 1744), together with other pictures acquired in Venice by Algarotti for Augustus III, among them the *Banquet* now in Melbourne.
Probably presented by Brühl to his secretary, Baron Heinecken, who sold it in 1757 for 1,200 fr. when Dresden was occupied by Frederick of Prussia; Beurnonville Sale, Paris, 1881, No. 699, with repr. in the Catalogue after the engraving by Felix Milius (sold for 7,000 fr.); Georges Coll., Paris; Private Coll., New York; S. H. Kress Collection 1952; given to the Museum by the S. H. Kress Foundation in 1954.
A record of this picture, in watercolour, belonged to Count Algarotti (*Catalogue . . . du feu Comte Algarotti*, n.d. (1766?), p. 54), and was engraved by G. Leonardis in 1766. It was still in the Algarotti Coll. in 1854 (noted in the *Galleria Particolare* of Lauro Bernardino Corniani de' Conti Algarotti, 1854, p. 8).
This composition, clearly influenced by Algarotti's artistic theories, is certainly not one of the best creations by Tiepolo.
Sack, p. 121, 218, fig. 112 after the engraving; Molmenti, 1911, p. 190; Mireur, 1912, VII, *ad locum*; H. Posse, Prussian Jahrbuch, 1931, p. 49; *The Samuel Kress Collection*, Catalogue, S. Francisco, 1955, p. 18, with col. plate; Levey, in *Burlington Magazine*, March, 1957, pp. 89–91.

SAN MARINO, Calif., Huntington Library and Art Gallery

S. ROCH Fig. 157
Canvas, 43×32 cm.; *c.* 1730–35.

One of the series of many similar works executed for the members of the Confraternity of the Scuola di S. Rocco in Venice.
Morassi, *Emporium*, 1950, XI, p. 202, fig. 9.

S. REMO, formerly Thiem Coll.

S. PROCULUS VISITING SS. FERMUS AND RUSTICUS
Canvas, *c.* 60×30 cm. (?).

Similar to the examples in the National Gallery, London, and the Galleria Carrara, Bergamo. Not seen by me. Present whereabouts unknown.
Molmenti, p. 262.

SARASOTA, Florida, Ringling Museum

AURORA AND FLYING PUTTI   Fig. 357
Shaped ceiling, fresco transferred to canvas, 295 × 135 cm.; *c.* 1750–60.

Originally in the Palazzo Onigo a S. Andrea, Treviso. The decoration
of this Palace represented *Aurora* and *Night*.
Both frescoes were detached and bought by Grandi of Milan (about
1900), but nothing is now known of the *Night*. Stylistically closely
related to the fresco in Providence.
Ex coll. Pozzi, Paris; sold Petit, Paris, 23–24.6.1919 (25); Canessa Sale,
American Art Assoc., New York, 25–26.1.1924; then Böhler, Munich.
Molmenti, p. 117, note 10, believes the fresco to be by an imitator;
Cat. of the Museum, 1949, p. 184, fig. 155.

TWO ALLEGORICAL FIGURES WITH AN OBELISK (the standing
female figure represents Beauty, dominating Strength, symbolized by
the sitting warrior)   Fig. 372
Fresco in grisaille, transferred to canvas, 380 × 192 cm.; *c.* 1755–60.

Formerly in a Vicentine Villa; later Baron Franchetti Coll., Venice;
Simonetti Coll., Rome.
Catalogue of the Simonetti Sale, Rome, Tavazzi, 1932, No. 541 (with
repr.); Cat. *Mostra del Settecento*, Venice, 1929, p. 68, No. 2.
There were exhibited in Venice, together with this one, two other
frescoes from the same cycle: *Mars* (No. 1) and *Venus* (No. 2), whose
present whereabouts is unknown.
The *Bacchic Head*, now in the Talleyrand Coll., Paris, was also part of
the same decorative cycle.

SEATTLE, Washington, Art Museum

APOTHEOSIS OF ORAZIO PORTO   Fig. 331
Ceiling fresco transferred to canvas, 508 × 300 cm.; *c.* 1755–60.

This ceiling was executed for the Palazzo Porto in Vicenza (q.v.),
where there were also the six monochromes now in the National
Museum, Stockholm.
Ex coll. Simon, Berlin; Drey Coll., Munich-New York; S. H. Kress
Coll., 1951. Gift of the S. H. Kress Foundation to the Seattle Museum,
1961.
F. Vendramin Mosca, *Descrizione delle Architetture, Pitture e Sculture
di Vicenza*, Vicenza, 1779, p. 86, and Molmenti, p. 271, fig. p. 268,
both believe that the ceiling and the monochromes were in separate
rooms in Pal. Porto; Sack, p. 182, and later writers assume that the six
monochromes originally decorated the walls beneath the ceiling fresco;
M. Friedländer, *Sammlung Dr. Ed. Simon, Gemälde*, I, Berlin, 1929,
p. 40, repr. XII–XIV; A. Scharf, in *Cicerone*, XXI, 1929, p. 457; S. De
Vito Battaglia, II, 1930, pp. 115–120; Goering, 1939, p. 152; Cat. of the
S. H. Kress Coll. in the Seattle Museum, Seattle, 1954, p. 78.

APOTHEOSIS OF ORAZIO PORTO   Fig. 330
Canvas, oval, 59 × 38 cm.; *c.* 1755–60.

Sketch for the preceding ceiling.
Ex coll. Kaulbach, Munich; Drey Coll., Munich-New York; Kress
Coll., New York, 1948; National Gallery of Art, Washington, 1951.
Gift of the S. H. Kress Foundation to the Seattle Museum, 1961.
A. Scharf, in *Cicerone*, 1929, with repr.; S. De Vito Battaglia, 1930,
with repr.; Cat. of Paintings and Sculpture from the Kress Coll.,
Washington, National Gallery, 1951, p. 152, fig. 153; Cat. of the
S. H. Kress Coll. in the Seattle Museum, Seattle, 1954, p. 76.

SEUSSLITZ, near Grossenhain, Saxony, formerly Harck Coll.

THE EDUCATION OF BACCHUS
Canvas, 100 × 197.5 cm.; grisaille on gold ground.

Belongs to the series of mythological subjects formerly in the Van
Dircksen Coll., Berlin (q.v.).
Present whereabouts unknown. Not seen by me.
Sack, p. 193.

SPRINGFIELD, Mass., Museum of Fine Arts

MADONNA AND CHILD   Fig. 82
Canvas, 130 × 84 cm.; 1759.

Commissioned from Tiepolo on February 6th, 1759, and presented on
August 3rd, 1759, to the Board of Works of the church of S. Maria
Materdomini, Venice. It served as model for a banner which is still
preserved in the church, and was consecrated on June 10th, 1762
(Gradenigo, 1942, p. 87).
Ex coll. Transche-Schwanenberg, Riga; Bayer, New York.
Molmenti, p. 142, p. 141; Sack, p. 218, fig. 205; L. Venturi, 1933, III,
pl. 588; Morassi, p. 31; Pallucchini, *Emporium*, 1944, pp. 3–18 with
repr.; Lorenzetti, p. 131, fig. 94.

HEAD OF AN OLD ORIENTAL
Canvas, *c.* 80 × 60 cm.

By Domenico.
Purchased 1948.
Ex coll. J. Russel, London; Sir Ernest George, sold at Christie's, 1919;
C. H. Morley Coll.; Sabin, London; Koetser, New York.
Engraved in 'Raccolta di Teste' (De Vesme, 142).
Molmenti, fig. p. 309, after the engraving, as Giambattista.
In the Museum attributed to Giambattista.

STAMFORD, Lincs., Burghley House, The Marquess of Exeter

CHRIST IN THE GARDEN OF OLIVES   Fig. 51
Canvas, sketch in brown monochrome, 46 × 28 cm.; *c.* 1750–60 (?)

The group of Christ and the Angel is inspired by the earlier composi-
tion by Giambattista in Hamburg, Kunsthalle.
Bought at Christie's, 13.7.1891, from the G. C. Bentinck Coll.
Catalogue of the Paintings at Burghley House, no. 164.

STARNBERG, formerly Würmgaumuseum

MADONNA AND CHILD WITH THE LITTLE S. JOHN
See Utrecht, Koenigs Coll.

STOCKHOLM, National Museum

THE DECOLLATION OF S. JOHN THE BAPTIST   [1955, fig. 16]
Canvas, 33 × 43 cm.; 1732–33.

Sketch for the fresco in the Colleoni Chapel, Bergamo.
Acquired in 1736 by Count G. de Tessin, Swedish Minister at Venice;
Luisa Ulrica Coll.; Gustavus III of Sweden Coll.
Sack, p. 206, records an old copy of this painting in the Wennerberg
Coll. in Stockholm, and another in the Gernert Coll., Munich.
Belongs to the same series as the *Preaching of the Baptist* in the Treccani
Coll., Milan.
Sirén, 1902, p. 103 ff.; Molmenti, p. 155, note 8; Sack, p. 205–206,
fig. 46; Sirén, Cat. of the Museum, 1928, p. 33; Morassi, p. 20;
Lorenzetti, p. 48, fig. 36.

THE CONTINENCE OF SCIPIO   [1955, pl. 29]
Canvas, 60 × 44 cm.; 1743.

Sketch for the fresco in the Villa Cordellina, Montecchio, executed in
1743. Pendant to the *Family of Darius* now in the Senator Crespi Coll.,
Milan.
Ex coll. Luisa Ulrica and Gustavus III of Sweden.
Sack, p. 206, fig. 76; Sirén, Cat. of the Museum, 1928, p. 34; Morassi,
p. 26, fig. 79; Lorenzetti, p. 72, fig. 55.
A masterpiece of very high quality. A poor copy, wrongly attributed to
Tiepolo was exhibited in Paris (*Chefs d'oeuvre des collections parisiennes*),
Musée Carnavalet, Cat. 1951, p. 42, fig. XVII; probably identical with
the one mentioned by Sack (p. 185) as in the Lippman Coll., Berlin.

Six monochrome frescoes transferred to canvas:

DONATO DA PORTO MADE A VENETIAN PATRICIAN (1579)
Canvas, 265 × 177 cm.

GEROLAMO DA PORTO APPOINTED PREFECT OF PIEDMONT
(1509)
Canvas, 265 × 162 cm.

FRANCESCO DA PORTO APPOINTED GENERAL OF THE VENETIAN
REPUBLIC (1554)
Canvas, 227 × 130 cm.

IPPOLITO DA PORTO DECORATED BY CHARLES V (1572)
Canvas, 265 × 110 cm.

GIOVANNI DA PORTO APPOINTED GENERALISSIMO (1660)
Canvas, 230 × 130 cm.

JACOPO DA PORTO APPOINTED GOVERNOR OF VICENZA
Canvas, 230 × 130 cm.

Executed c. 1755–60 for the Palazzo Porto in Vicenza, together with the
ceiling of the *Apotheosis of Orazio Porto*, now in Seattle Museum (q.v.).
The monochromes show clearly the collaboration of Domenico and
represent the illustrious deeds of the da Porto family from the 11th to
the 17th Centuries.
Removed from the Palazzo (probably about 1900) and transferred to
canvas.
Ex coll. Simon (until 1929), Berlin; Axel Wennergren Coll.,
Stockholm.
Descrizione di Vicenza, 1779, II, p. 86; Molmenti, p. 27, figs. pp.
269–270; Sack, pp. 91, 183; Sammlung Dr. Simon, Berlin, 1929,
pp. 42–52, figs. XV–XX. (See bibliog. s.v. Seattle, Art Museum.)

STOCKHOLM, University Museum

DANAE   [1955, col. p. IV]
Canvas, 41 × 53 cm.; c. 1736.

Painted just before 1736, the year in which it was bought in Venice by
Count G. de Tessin, the Swedish Minister there. Later in the Coll. of
the librarian Sergesteen; Pierre Swartz Coll., Stockholm.
An old copy was, a few years ago, in Verona.
Sirèn, 1902, p. 109; Sack, p. 205; Morassi, p. 23, fig. 88; Lorenzetti,
p. 62, fig. 45.

THE BANQUET OF ANTONY AND CLEOPATRA   [1955, fig. 32]
Canvas, 67 × 41 cm.; c. 1745–50.

Sirèn, 1902, p. 111, with repr.; Sack, p. 206; Morassi, p. 29; Lorenzetti,
pp. 87–88, fig. 64.
This sketch is closely related to the fresco in the Palazzo Labia, Venice.
A copy of it is in the Museum of Amiens. Another bad copy with some
variations is in Strasbourg. Another contemporary copy (canvas,
56.5 × 42 cm.), wrong attributed to Tiepolo, is in the Museo Villa
Cagnola, Gazzada (Varese). The same subject in London, Alexander
Coll., is related to the picture in Archangel.

STOCKHOLM, Bergsten Coll.

FOUR SAINTS (Philip Neri, Francis of Paola, Andrew and Nicholas of
Bari, with a choir boy)
Canvas, medium size.

By Francesco Fontebasso, wrongly attributed to Giambattista Tiepolo.

STRA, Villa Pisani

APOTHEOSIS OF THE PISANI FAMILY   [1955, fig. 78]
                                              Figs. 396, 397, 399, 400
Fresco on the ceiling of the main saloon, 23.5 × 13.5 m.; executed
between the autumn of 1761 and the early part of 1762, according to
some of Tiepolo's own letters. In one to Algarotti, of May 10th, 1760,
he says that he has to prepare the *modello* for this ceiling, and in others,
also to Algarotti, one of March, 1761, the second of April 4th, 1761, he
says that he is painting the ceiling at Strà. Another letter (to Algarotti
or Farsetti?), of December 22nd, 1761, written before his departure for
Spain, mentions the fresco in Ca' Pisani as almost finished. A letter,
dated Venice, December 5th, 1761, from the Duke of Montealegre,
Spanish ambassador in Venice, to the Marques de Esquillache, relating to
Tiepolo's engagement in Madrid, reports that the 'supremi Inquisitori'
of Venice had pressed Procurator Pisani to release Tiepolo, who had
been paid in advance for his work in Strà. It seems that Tiepolo was to
have been employed by Pisani for two years or more, and that he had

at last to leave the work in Strà unfinished when he was forced to
depart for Spain. Alessandro Longhi in his *Vite* (1762, but written
1761), says that Tiepolo was going to fresco the great saloon of the
magnificent Palazzo Pisani at Strà. It is the most grandiose of all his
ceilings in private palaces in Italy.
Around the large ceiling fresco, architecture painted in chiaroscuro,
with figures of SATYRS AND SATYRESSES represented sitting or lying
over the doors and the windows.
Between the doors and windows, over the balcony, there are eight
ALLEGORICAL SCENES with many figures representing: (1) MINERVA
WITH THE ARTS AND SCIENCES, (2) VIGILANCE, (3) COMMERCE, WITH
MERCURY, (4) AGRICULTURE, WITH CERES, (5) WAR, (6) PEACE,
(7) VICTORY, (8) SACRIFICE, all in grisaille on feigned gold ground,
indubitably by Domenico Tiepolo. Below the balcony, pairs of
MYTHOLOGICAL FIGURES as simulated statues, also in grisaille, by
a pupil of Tiepolo, perhaps Crosato.
Molmenti, p. 116, figs. pp. 114, 114a, 115; Sack, pp. 136, 177, fig. 129;
Morassi, p. 36, figs. 116–117; Gallo, 1945, pp. 72–73.
The *modello* for this ceiling is in the Museum of Angers (q.v.).

STRASBOURG, Musée des Beaux-Arts

S. ROCH   Fig. 155
Canvas, 44 × 31 cm.; c. 1730–35.

One of the many similar versions of this subject painted for the
members of the Confraternity of the Scuola di S. Rocco, Venice.
Acquired in Venice in 1890 by von Bode for the Museum.
Molmenti, p. 268; Sack, p. 194, fig. 188.

THE VIRGIN APPEARING TO SS. LAURENCE AND FRANCIS OF
PAOLA
Arched canvas, 220 × 119 cm.

By Domenico: wrongly attributed to Giambattista.
Molmenti was wrong in stating that this altarpiece came from the
church of S. Apollinare, Venice. It was originally in the church of
Cavenzano (Friuli), as a gift from Counts Antonini, and was bought in
1900 by von Bode from the antique dealer Volpi in Florence.
Molmenti, pp. 267–268, fig. p. 264; Sack, pp. 193–194, fig. 187, with
erroneous attributions to Giambattista; Goering, *ad vocem*, rightly gives
it to Domenico.

AESCULAPIUS AMONG CLOUDS
Octagonal canvas, 105 × 100 cm.

By a follower of Tiepolo, certainly F. Zugno.
Formerly it decorated the ceiling of a pharmacy in Venice, whence it
was acquired in 1893 by von Bode for the Museum.
Molmenti, p. 268, fig. p. 265; Sack, p. 46, fig. 28, wrongly as Giambattista.

THE MEETING OF ANTONY AND CLEOPATRA
THE BANQUET OF ANTONY AND CLEOPATRA

Two small sketches, sometimes held to be the *modelli* for the frescoes in
the Palazzo Labia, whereas they are only bad late copies.
Not in the Museum Catalogue.

STRASBOURG, Private Coll.

GROUP OF FIGURES
See: Berlin, formerly Voss Coll.

STUTTGART, Staatsgalerie

THE COMMUNION OF S. JEROME   [1955, fig. 17]
Canvas, 33.5 × 44.5 cm.; c. 1732–33.

Ex coll. Barbini-Breganze, Venice, acquired 1852.
Pendant to the *Death of S. Jerome* in the Museo Poldi-Pezzoli, Milan.
Zanotto, Cat. of Barbini-Breganze Coll., Venice, 1850, No. 215;
Molmenti, p. 266; De Luca, 1909, p. 319; Sack, p. 194; Lorenzetti,
p. 46, fig. 33; *Catalogue* of the Gallery, 1957, p. 290, fig. 53.

APOLLO CONDUCTING HIS BRIDE TO BARBAROSSA
Canvas, 65.3 × 106.5 cm.; 1751.   [1955, fig. 36]
Sketch for the Kaisersaal, Würzburg.
Ex coll. Barbini-Breganze, Venice (Cat. of the coll. by Zanotto, 1850, No. 216).
Acquired by the Museum in 1852.
Molmenti, p. 266, fig. p. 162; Sack, p. 194, fig. 86; Cat. of the Würzburg Exhibition, 1951, p. 16; Freeden, *Arte Veneta*, 1951, p. 214; see also Freeden, 1956, p. 50; *Catalogue* of the Gallery, 1957, p. 290.
In the Catalogue of the Würzburg Exhibition and in *Arte Veneta*, Dr. Freeden considers this painting to be a work by Domenico rather than Giambattista. In his opinion the original is a sketch exhibited at Würzburg in 1951, but, in my view, this is a weak copy of a much later date, whereas the Stuttgart sketch is the excellent original *modello* by Giambattista himself.

S. JOSEPH WITH THE CHRIST CHILD
Canvas, 44 × 36 cm.; *c.* 1760–70.
By Domenico.
Ex coll. Barbini-Breganze, Venice, Cat. by Zanotto, 1850, No. 217.
Molmenti, p. 267, fig. p. 134; Sack, p. 194, fig. 189, both attributing it wrongly to Giambattista.
No longer existing in the Gallery.

NEPTUNE ABDUCTING THEOPHANE
Canvas, 50.5 × 31.5 cm.
By a contemporary imitator of Tiepolo.
Ex coll. Barbini-Breganze, Venice, Cat. by Zanotto, 1850, No. 218.
Molmenti, p. 266, as a copy; Sack, p. 194, regards it as an original and dates it in the early period; *Catalogue* of the Gallery, 1957, p. 291, as 'workshop.'

MOSES SAVED FROM THE WATERS
Canvas, 71.6 × 148 cm.
Excellent old copy, probably by Domenico, of the picture in Edinburgh.
Molmenti, p. 267, rightly calls it a copy; Sack, p. 195, fig. 190, considers it a sketch for the painting now in Edinburgh; *Catalogue* of the Gallery, 1957, p. 291.

STUTTGART, formerly Beyerlen di Bossi Coll.

S. DOMINIC
S. ROSE OF LIMA
Two canvases, 42 × 35 cm. each.
By Domenico.
Sack, p. 195, figs. 191–192, attributing them to Giambattista.

TIME DISCOVERING TRUTH
Canvas, 98 × 25 cm.
Said by Sack, p. 196, to be similar to the subject in the Palazzo Barbarigo fresco in Venice or to that in the Villa Biron, near Vicenza. (The size is in any case very strange, and no reproduction exists to judge the authenticity of the work).
Missing.

A WORKSHOP OF A PAINTER
FAMILY SCENE
Both on one canvas, 44 × 59 cm.
These pictures are attributed to Giambattista by Sack, p. 196.
Present whereabouts unknown. No photo exists of the painting.

SYDNEY, National Gallery of New South Wales

S. ROCH   Fig. 162
Canvas, 53 × 41 cm.; *c.* 1730–35.
Presented to the Gallery in 1912 by J. S. Heron.
One of the many devotional paintings for the Scuola di San Rocco.
Hitherto unpublished.

TERRAGLIO (Treviso), Villa Vettor Dolfin

Da Canal, 1732, p. XXXII, notes that 'In the Palace of the N.H. Vettor Dolfino at Terraglio Tiepolo painted the whole of an apartment and several rooms in fresco with various stories.'
This cycle of works, which seems to have been rather important, is not otherwise mentioned in the old sources. 'Terraglio' means the road from Venice to Treviso. In this locality there were many Venetian Villas (see G. Mazzotti, *Le Ville Venete*, Treviso, 1953, II ed., where some ex-Dolfin Villas are mentioned, none of which corresponds to that indicated by Da Canal).
Molmenti, p. 89; Sack, p. 34, 177.

TESCHEN, Czechoslovakia, formerly F. Franze Coll.

S. ANTONY PREACHING TO THE FISHES
Canvas, 34.5 × 43.5 cm.
Listed by Sack, p. 307, under the works by Domenico (wrongly as in the Suida Coll., Vienna), but considered by him as a very early painting by Giambattista, *c.* 1720.
Present whereabouts unknown.
Not seen by me.

TOLEDO, Ohio, Museum of Art

HEAD OF AN OLD MAN
Canvas, 47 × 41 cm.
By Domenico.
Ex coll. Edward Drummond Libbey, until 1925.
Catton Rich, 1938, p. 24; Catalogue of European Paintings of the Toledo Museum of Art, 1939, p. 18, fig. p. 19, both as by Giambattista.

TOURS, Musée des Beaux Arts

THE HOLY TRINITY APPEARING TO DOMINICAN SAINTS
(S. John of Mata and S. Felix of Valois.)
Canvas, 78 × 39 cm.; grisaille.
Wrongly attributed by De Chennevières (p. 115) to Tiepolo, assigned by Sack (p. 222) to S. Ricci.
Certainly by an Austrian painter, such as Maulpertsch or more probably Franz Sigrist.

TREVISO, Museo Civico

FLORA
Fresco in ochre grisaille, 300 × 124 cm.; *c.* 1735–40.
Detached from the main room on the ground floor of the Villa Cornaro in Merlengo (q.v.) about 1901. On the pedestals, in capitals: FLORA.
Hitherto unpublished.

S. JOHN THE BAPTIST PREACHING
Canvas, 56 × 102 cm.
Wrongly attributed to Giambattista by Meissner, 1897, p. fig. 30 and Molmenti, p. 132, fig. p. 130. Undoubtedly a work by Domenico, rightly assigned by Sack, p. 314, and Lorenzetti, p. 166, fig. 117, to him.

TREVISO, S. Maria Maggiore

According to Federici (*Memorie Trevigiane*, 1803), there was in this church a 'very beautiful ceiling' by Tiepolo. No other mention of this work is known. Federici must have confused the decoration by the Bolognese Antonio Cerva with Tiepolo, as Coletti (Treviso, Catalogue, Rome, 1935, p. 323) supposed, and Sack (p. 178), who thought that Tiepolo painted a ceiling, later whitewashed, must also be wrong.
See also Molmenti, p. 87.

TREVISO, Palazzo Onigo a S. Andrea

AURORA
NIGHT
Two frescoes originally decorating the Palazzo Onigo, executed probably *c.* 1750–60. Detached at the beginning of the present century

and acquired by the art-dealer Grandi of Milan. One (*Aurora*) is now in the Museum of Sarasota (q.v.); the whereabouts of the other is unknown.

The frescoes are completely ignored by the old sources, since Federici (1803) and Crico (1833) do not mention them.

Bailo, *Gazzetta di Treviso*, 4-5-11-1905; Molmenti, p. 117, note 10, both as by an imitator.

TRIESTE, Museo Civico

THE TRIUMPH OF AMPHITRITE
Canvas, 52×68.5 cm.

Said to be the sketch for the picture in Dresden (formerly Villa Girola). It is wrongly attributed to Giambattista, whereas it is the work of a pupil.

A similar sketch is in Lisbon.

Ex Sartorio Coll., Trieste.

Molmenti, p. 269, fig. p. 277; Sack, p. 202; Catalogue of the Italian Exhibition, R.A., London, 1930, p. 176, as by Giambattista in each case.

TRIESTE, formerly Opuich-Fontana Coll.

HEAD OF AN OLD ORIENTAL
Canvas, 34×28 cm.

Attributed by Sack (p. 202, No. 403), to Giambattista, but judging from the reproduction, it is more probably a School work, perhaps by Domenico after the engraving reproduced in Molmenti, *Acqueforti*, 1896, p. 159, r. Similar, but without the hand, the two paintings, one in the Museum of Baltimore, the other in New York, formerly American Art Association. The original, by Giambattista, was formerly in the Orloff Coll., Paris (now in Prague).

TRIESTE, Rusconi Coll.

HEAD OF AN OLD ORIENTAL   Fig. 410
Canvas, 65×48 cm.; *c.* 1750-60.

One of the series of the *Heads*, later engraved by Domenico.

Ex coll. Opuich-Fontana, Trieste; lent to Ca' Rezzonico, Venice.

Molmenti, p. 246; Sack, p. 202, fig. 200; Lorenzetti, p. 99, fig. 71.

A contemporary copy (60×50 cm.) was on the art market in Vienna, *c.* 1959.

TROYES, Musée des Beaux-Arts

THE CHARIOT OF APOLLO
Canvas, 81×100 cm.

Considered by Benesch to be an early work by Tiepolo. Formerly attributed to F. A. Kraus and probably by this German painter. Catalogue of Exhib., R.A., London, 1954-55, No. 314.

S. THOMAS AQUINAS
Attributed by Galetti-Camesasca, *Enciclopedia*, Milan, 1950, *ad vocem*, to Tiepolo, is, judging only from the reproduction, a work from his school, probably by Zugno.

TUCSON, Arizona, University of Arizona

THE CIRCUMCISION OF THE CHILDREN OF ISRAEL
Canvas, 51×72 cm.

Wrongly attributed to Tiepolo. Pendant to the following painting. It is a contemporary copy of the picture in the Museum, Bassano.

Ex coll. Smith-Barry, Marbury Hall, England; Kress Coll., New York, 1950; National Gall., Washington, 1951. Given by the S. H. Kress Foundation to the University of Arizona in 1957.

Waagen, Treasures of Art in Gt. Britain, 1857; Cat. of Paintings and Sculpture from the Kress Coll., Washington, Nat. Gall., 1951, p. 154, repr. p. 155; The Samuel H. Kress Collection at the University of Arizona, 1957, no. 20, with repr., as by Tiepolo in each case.

THE SACRIFICE OF IPHIGENIA
Canvas, 50×69 cm.

Wrongly attributed to Tiepolo. Pendant to the preceding painting. Ex coll. Smith-Barry, Marbury Hall, England; Kress Coll., New York, 1950. National Gallery, Washington, 1951. Given by the S. H. Kress Foundation to the University of Arizona.

Old copy of the painting in the Patino Coll., Paris.

Waagen, *Treasures of Art in Gt. Britain*, 1857; Cat. of Paintings and Sculpture from the Kress Coll., Washington, National Gallery, 1951, p. 156, repr. p. 157, as by Giambattista in both cases.

TURIN, Pinacoteca

TRIUMPH OF AURELIAN   Fig. 314
Canvas, 263×402 cm.; *c.* 1728-32.

Perhaps part of the decoration originally in the Ca' Zenobio, Venice, since Zenobia is represented walking in chains before the chariot of the Emperor, and her name recalls that of the patrons.

The *Allegory* in S. Lazzaro, Venice (q.v.), is also from Ca' Zenobio.

Formerly in the coll. of Cardinal Fesch in Rome. Gift of F. Marsengo, 1869.

Da Canal, 1732, p. XXXIII, mentions a room painted with various stories by Tiepolo in his very early period in Ca' Zenobio; Moschini, 1815, II, p. 280; Molmenti, p. 245, fig. p. 246; Sack, p. 178; Morassi, p. 20.

With its light silvery colours also stylistically similar to the ceiling of S. Lazzaro degli Armeni, Venice (q.v.).

SS. FIDELIS OF SIGMARINGEN AND JOSEPH OF LEONESSA
Canvas, 42×35 cm.; *c.* 1752-57.   Fig. 117
Sketch for the altarpiece at Parma.
Molmenti, p. 245; Sack, p. 178.
A fresh and rapidly painted *modello* of high quality.

TURIN, Accademia Albertina

MADONNA AND CHILD
Unfinished canvas.

Ex coll. Princes Del Drago, Rome.

Very similar in type to the *Madonna* ex Lederer, Budapest (now Sarkany Coll., Budapest; see Munich, Böhler), and to that once in Karlsbad, Coll. Maier.

Attributed to Giambattista by De Vesme, in *Paralipomeni tiepoleschi*, 1912 and by others; but it is certainly an Italian (Neapolitan?) fabrication of the late 19th Century.

TURIN, S. Filippo Neri

Sack, p. 178, mentions in this church a *Supper at Emmaus* among the lost works by Tiepolo which Bartoli (1776) ought to have known. De Vesme, 1912, rightly shows that Sack misread Bartoli and identifies this picture with the *Supper at Emmaus* still in the sacristy, executed (as results from F. S. Quadrio, *Dissertazioni sulla Rezia*, 1755-56, vol. III, p. 496) by Ligari.

TURIN, formerly Colonna Coll.

GIFTS OFFERED TO CLEOPATRA
See: Pavia, Necchi Coll.

TURIN, Private Coll.

HALBERDIER
See: London, formerly Tree Coll.

UDINE, Museo Civico

S. FRANCIS OF SALES   Fig. 186
Arched canvas, 232×96 cm.; 1733.

Commissioned by the Patriarch Dionigi Dolfin for the church of S. Maria Maddalena dei Filippini. Tiepolo was paid L. 356, in 1733.

(Documents in the Archivio, Civico, Udine.) After the suppression of the convent of the Filippini the two pictures became the property of the State.

Maniago, *Guida*, 1839, p. 36; Molmenti, p. 82, repr. p. 82; Sack, p. 179; Goering, *ad vocem;* Someda de Marco, *Cat.* of the Museum, 1956, p. 180, 182.

GUARDIAN ANGEL   Fig. 220
Arched canvas, 232×98 cm.; 1737.

Commissioned by the Patriarch of Aquileja, Daniele Dolfin, for the church of S. Maria Maddalena dei Filippini, now demolished, in Udine. The altarpiece was paid for together with the one representing the *SS. Hermagoras and Fortunatus* (Udine, Cathedral) on 25.6. 1737. (See Biasutti, 1957, p. 19.)

Two canvases of not high imagination, superficially executed.

ALLEGORY OF FORTITUDE AND WISDOM (with *Fame* at the top and *Invidia* at the bottom)   Fig. 144
Canvas, shaped for a ceiling, 479×251 cm.; *c.* 1740–45.

Until 1924 in the Pal. Caiselli, Udine; then exhibited in the Accademia, Venice, until 1935. A sketch, perhaps for this ceiling (or for the Barbarigo one now in the Ca' Rezzonico) is in the Museo Poldi-Pezzoli, Milan.

Molmenti, p. 121, fig. p. 122; Sack, p. 179, fig. 77a.

Very similar in style and composition to the contemporary ceilings in the Villa Cordellina at Montecchio and the one for Pal. Barbarigo, now in Ca' Rezzonico, Venice.

MEETING OF THE GRAND COUNCIL OF THE KNIGHTS OF MALTA (CONSILIUM IN ARENA)   [1955, fig. 29]
Canvas, 125×194 cm.; 1749–50.

Painted with considerable assistance from Domenico; commissioned by Count Montegnacco of Udine to commemorate a meeting of the Council which admitted him and his friend Count Florio to the Order of Malta. In the possession of the town of Udine from 1789, bequeathed by Count Tommaso de Rubeis. The contemporary documents were published by Joppi, *op cit.*

Maniago, *Guida*, 1839, p. 25; Joppi, 1889, II, p. 137; Molmenti, p. 211, fig. p. 208b; Sack, p. 179, all attribute it only to Giambattista; Morassi, p. 29, figs. 80–81 first recognizing the collaboration of Domenico; Lorenzetti, p. 97, fig. 70; Pallucchini, 1946, p. 175, also by both Giambattista and Domenico; Pignatti-Mazzariol, 1951, p. 64, by Domenico alone; Someda de Marco, *Cat.* of the Museum, 1956, p. 180; Rizzi, *Fiore*, 1960, p. 338; Exhib. Cat., Petit Palais, Paris 1960–61, No. 397.

It is quite clear that the execution of this masterpiece is due to Domenico; but it is also indubitable that Giambattista was responsible for it and gave the directing idea to his son, or approved Domenico's ideas.

UDINE, Castello

PROCESSION OF WARRIORS, ETC.

Monochrome frescoes on the lower part of the walls of the principal saloon. In very bad condition and only surviving in parts. They must have been done before 1732, since they are mentioned by Da Canal. Da Canal (1732); Moschini, 1809; Maniago, *Guida*, pp. 16–17; Sack, p. 179; Kutschera-Woborsky, 1922, pp. 1–8 with repr.; Goering, *ad vocem.*

These frescoes were in a bad state by the end of the 18th century, since Maniago (*Guida, cit.*) says that they were restored—unsuccessfully—in 1794.

PUTTI HOLDING MEDALS WITH WAR SCENES   Figs. 381, 384
Four monochrome frescoes, in bad condition, over the four windows. These were certainly also painted before 1732, probably when Tiepolo worked in the Cathedral, 1726. In the same principal saloon.
Riccoboni, in *Arte Veneta*, 1956, p. 165 ff. with repr.

UDINE, Cathedral

CHOIR OF ANGELS AND CHERUBIM (in the vault)   Figs. 221, 223
SACRIFICE OF ISAAC and the DREAM OF JACOB (at the sides of the altar)   Fig. 6

Monochrome frescoes in the Chapel of the Sacrament.

On June 4th, 1726, the Board of Works of the Cathedral gave permission to the Confraternity of the Holy Sacrament to commission the frescoes from the 'celebrated' Tiepolo, and they were, in fact, certainly executed soon afterwards.

Da Canal, 1732; Maniago, *Guida*, 1839, p. 30; Molmenti, p. 82; Sack, p. 178; Morassi, *Burlington Magazine*, 1934, II–III, p. 127 ff., pl. II; Morassi p. 17, fig. 18; Riccoboni, in *Arte Veneta*, 1956, p. 165 ff. with repr.

THE RESURRECTION   Fig. 61
Arched canvas, 90×45 cm.; *c.* 1726–28.

Painting in the ciborium of the Chapel of the Sacrament.
Da Canal, 1732; Maniago, *Guida*, 1839, p. 30; Molmenti, p. 82; Sack, p. 178; Goering, *ad vocem.*
Stylistically related to the above-mentioned frescoes.

THE CRUCIFIXION   Fig. 423
Canvas, 195×103 cm.; *c.* 1730–35.
Recently discovered in the Sacristy of the Cathedral by Prof. C. Someda de Marco, between other neglected paintings.
Originally in the Chapel of S. Nicolò of the same Cathedral, later demolished.
This canvas is mentioned as by Tiepolo in a ms. in the Biblioteca Civica in Udine.
The Madonna and St. John the Evangelist stand below the Cross; in the foreground St. Mary Magdalen and St. Ermagoras, Patron of the Friuli.
Not one of his best works. Painted with the assistance of a pupil.

CHRIST CRUCIFIED, WITH GOD THE FATHER   Fig. 56
Arched canvas, 320×160 cm.; 1737–38.

Altarpiece on the first altar on the right. Commissioned by Cardinal Daniele Dolfin (together with the *SS. Hermagoras and Fortunatus* and the *Guardian Angel*) for the altar of the SS. Trinity. The painting was paid for on 5.7. 1738. (Biasutti, 1957, p. 19; Rizzi, in *Arte Veneta*, 1959–60, pp. 241–242.)
Maniago, *Guida*, 1839, p. 31; Molmenti, p. 82; Sack, p. 178; Goering, *ad vocem.*

SS. HERMAGORAS AND FORTUNATUS (patron Saints of Aquileja)
Arched canvas, 308×168 cm.; 1737.   Fig. 147

Altarpiece commissioned from Tiepolo by Cardinal Daniele Dolfin for the new altar of the patron Saints. The canvas was paid for on 26.5. 1737, together with the *Guardian Angel* now in the Museo Civico, Udine (q.v.). (Biasutti, 1957, p. 19; Rizzi, in *Arte Veneta*, 1959–60, pp. 241–242.) A rather conventional work.
Maniago, *Guida*, 1839, p. 31; Molmenti, p. 82; Sack, p. 178; Goering, *ad vocem.*

UDINE, Chiesa della Purità

THE ASSUMPTION (in the centre)   [1955, fig. 53]
ANGELS AND PUTTI (in the two compartments above and below)
The whole ceiling measures 19×10 m.   Figs. 200, 201

Painted between August 14th and September 16th, 1759; signed at the bottom: *Gio. Batta. Tiepolo. f.*
The composition resembles the *Madonna del Carmelo* in the Scuola dei Carmini, Venice, of 1741, but the elements are more dispersed and the atmosphere lighter. The colours have the incandescent vividness of some of the work in the Villa Valmarana, of 1757. This is one of the most charming ceilings of Tiepolo's late Italian period.
Maniago, *Guida*, 1839, p. 35; Molmenti, pp. 83–86, figs. pp. 90–90a; Sack, p. 179, fig. 72; Vale e Masotti, 1932 (with doc.); Morassi, pp. 35–38, fig. 112.

EIGHT SCENES FROM THE OLD AND NEW TESTAMENTS
Monochrome frescoes on the walls; by Domenico. The first on the right is signed and dated 1759.
Maniago, *Guida*, 1839, p. 35; Molmenti, p. 86; Sack, p. 179, fig. 49, wrongly attributing three of them to Giambattista. (*David with the head of Goliath, The Maccabees, The Entrance into Jerusalem;* this last wrongly said to be dated 1734); v. Kutschera-Woborsky, 1922, pp. 1–8, with rep.; Vale e Masotti, 1932 (with documents); Morassi, pp. 35–38.

THE IMMACULATE VIRGIN   Fig. 79
Arched canvas, 240×122 cm.; 1759.
Altarpiece of the high altar, imitating a marble statue. It has a gold ground and is in rather bad condition.
Maniago, *Guida*, 1839, p. 35; Molmenti, p. 86, fig. p. 89; Sack, p. 179; Vale e Masotti, 1932 (with documents).

UDINE, Palazzo Arcivescovile, formerly Palazzo Dolfin

Frescoes over the Grand Staircase;
In the centre:
THE FALL OF THE REBEL ANGELS, 1725, 400×194 cm.   Fig. 1
Surrounding it: monochrome fresco decoration with EIGHT STORIES
FROM GENESIS   Fig. 2

Frescoes in the Gallery;
On the main wall, from left to right:
THE ANGEL APPEARING TO SARAH   [1955, pls. 6, 8]
RACHEL HIDING THE IDOLS   [1955, pls. 3–5]
THE ANGELS APPEARING TO ABRAHAM   [1955, pls. 7, 9]

In the three medallions of the ceiling:
THE SACRIFICE OF ABRAHAM   [1955, pl. 2]
HAGAR IN THE DESERT   Fig. 11
JACOB'S DREAM   Fig. 12

In the medallions in violet and ochre grisaille on gold ground on the main wall of the Gallery beside the central scene of *Rachel hiding the idols:*
THE MEETING OF ESAU AND JACOB
JACOB WRESTLING WITH THE ANGEL   Fig. 8

Between the minor scenes, on the main wall:
TWO PROPHETESSES (Deborah and Maria), imitation statues in greenish monochrome.

On the wall facing the frescoes, between the windows:
FOUR PROPHETESSES (Anna, Elisabeth, Anna I Regina, Holda IV Regina).
Also imitation statues in greenish monochrome.
G. Mengozzi-Colonna was responsible for the illusionistic and perspective parts of this room (Gallery).

Frescoes in the 'Sala Rossa':
THE JUDGEMENT OF SOLOMON, 655×360 cm.; signed, lower right, *Gio. Batta. Tiepolo. f.*   [1955, pl. 10]
FOUR PROPHETS in the corner medallions, c. 200×250 cm. each.
                                                         Figs. 27–30
The Staircase was painted in 1725 or 1726; the Gallery about the same time; the Sala Rossa perhaps a little later, in 1727 or 1728.
Da Canal, 1732; Maniago, *Guida*, 1839, p. 38; Molmenti, p. 83, with repr.; Sack, p. 178, figs. 23–25; Goering, *ad vocem*; Morassi, *Le Arti*, 1942, pp. 93 ff. figs. 14–30; Morassi, pp. 17–18, figs. 19–29.
This whole fresco cycle, not precisely dated and rather neglected in the older literature, must be considered one of the most important of Tiepolo's early works, showing him surpassing all contemporary fresco painters.

In the large Throne Room ('Sala del Trono') there is a series of *Portraits of the Patriarchs of Aquileja* frescoed by some Tiepolesque painters. None can be assigned to Giambattista himself; but some could be by

Domenico. As the Patriarchate of Aquileja was suppressed in 1751 and the Tiepolos came back from Würzburg only in November, 1753, the portraits by Domenico may have been executed only after this date. There is nothing about them in the *Guida* by Maniago (1839) or in Molmenti; whereas Sack (p. 178) lists them among Tiepolo's works, but without any comment.
Recently Don Guglielmo Biasutti, Director of the Biblioteca Arcivescovile in Udine, has claimed (*Vita Cattolica*, Udine, 19.5.1956) that the inscriptions for the portraits of the Patriarchs were dictated by the Archiepiscopal Librarian Bernardino Serlio in 1729; a date which seems unlikely for these frescoed portraits but perhaps fits other ones. It may also be that the former portraits were later repainted by Tiepolesque artists.

UTRECHT, W. O. Koenigs Coll.

MADONNA AND CHILD WITH THE LITTLE S. JOHN
Canvas, 87×68 cm.
Formerly in the Würmgaumuseum in Starnberg; then J. Böhler Coll., Munich.
Goering, *ad vocem*, as by Giambattista.
Possibly by Domenico, to judge from the reproduction.

VADUZ, formerly Liechtenstein Gallery

THE ANGEL APPEARING TO ABRAHAM AND SARAH
Canvas, 61×46 cm.
By Domenico; wrongly attributed to Giambattista.
Formerly Roger Coll., Vienna. Exhibited at Lucerne (1948) as by Giambattista.
Goering, *ad vocem;* Catalogue of the Exhibition: 'Meisterwerke aus den Sammlungen des Fürsten von Liechtenstein,' Kunstmuseum, Lucerne, 1948, p. 10, as by Giambattista in each case. Another painting, almost identical, was formerly in the Schloss Coll., Paris.
Now in the M. Crespi Coll., Milan.

CHRIST IN THE GARDEN OF OLIVES
Canvas, 57×77 cm.
Attributed to Giambattista by Meissner, 1897, fig. 8 and by Molmenti, p. 55, fig. p. 49; Sack, p. 205 to F. Trevisani. Still in the Catalogue (Führer) of the Gallery, Vienna, 1931 (no. 270) wrongly as by Giambattista. It is clearly a work by S. Ricci.

VASCON, Parish Church

STORIES OF S. LUCY
Ceiling fresco painted by Tiepolo, according to Da Canal (1732, p. XXXII). No traces exist of these pictures, which are not mentioned in any other source. The present ceiling is a poor work by a Tiepolesque follower.

VAUX-LE-PENIL, near Melun, Château of the Princess Faucigny-Lucinge

TRIUMPH OF VENUS
Ceiling, 11×6 m.
By a late follower of Tiepolo.
According to Molmenti, brought to this Château in 1893 by M. Michel Ephrussi, owner of the castle at that time.
Molmenti, p. 261, wrongly as by Giambattista.

VENICE, Accademia

THE RAPE OF EUROPA	[1955, fig. 6]
DIANA AND ACTAEON	Fig. 248
DIANA AND CALLISTO	Fig. 250
APOLLO AND MARSYAS	Fig. 247

Four canvases, 99×134 cm. each; c. 1720–22.
In poor condition and rather restored.
The first pair was acquired in 1898 from Count Agosti at Belluno; the

second pair was acquired in 1907 from the Countess Capponi of Belluno, with an attribution to S. Ricci, under which name they appeared at the Mostra della Pittura del Seicento e Settecento, Florence, 1922.

Sack (p. 163) mentions, without titles, two canvases made known to him by Prof. J. v. Schlosser in the Coll. of Count Agosti in Belluno. These are certainly to be identified with two of the four Mythologies attributed till 1922 to Seb. Ricci, which Schlosser was then able to assign, rightly, to Tiepolo. Voss, 1922, p. 423 ff. with figs. (the first to attribute them to Giambattista); Fogolari, 1923, pp. 57–58 with repr.; Fiocco, 1929, p. 50; Morassi, p. 14, fig. 8; Marconi, Cat. 1949, pp. 92–93; Lorenzetti, pp. 17–20, figs. 9–12.

These four canvases are of great importance in the study of Tiepolo's first period, when he was developing a more luminous style from the strong chiaroscuro effects of the Piazzetta School. Before Voss correctly gave them back to Tiepolo, they had also been attributed, by Fiocco, to Fontebasso.

CHRIST HEALING THE PARALYTIC   Fig. 46
Canvas, 63×46 cm.; c. 1718–20.

Formerly attributed to S. Ricci or Piazzetta.
Ex coll. Candrian, Venice; acquired in 1902.
Voss, 1922, p. 423 ff. with fig. (the first to attribute it to Giambattista); Fogolari, 1923, p. 54 with repr.; Arslan, 1936, p. 249; Marconi, Cat. 1949, p. 93; Lorenzetti, p. 27, fig. 18.
Very Piazzettesque, in poor state. A contemporary copy was on the London market some years ago.

S. DOMINIC IN GLORY   Fig. 114
Canvas, 78×77 cm.; c. 1720.

Formerly attributed to J. Guarana.
Acquired from A. de Burlett, Berlin, 1922.
Voss, 1922, p. 423 ff., with fig. (the first to attribute it to Giambattista); Fogolari, 1923, p. 56, with repr.; Marconi, Cat. 1949, p. 93.
Fogolari (1923) believed that it might be the sketch for the ceiling of the Chapel of S. Dominic in SS. Giovanni e Paolo, which was later executed by Piazzetta, and differs in composition.

S. JOSEPH WITH THE CHRIST CHILD AND SS. ANTONY OF PADUA, FRANCIS OF PAOLA, ANNE AND PETER OF ALCANTARA
Canvas, 210×116 cm.; c. 1730–35.   Fig. 148
Altarpiece formerly in the church of S. Prosdocimo, Padua (Brandolese, 1795, p. 161).
Molmenti, p. 67, fig. p. 62; Sack, p. 161, fig. 149; Marconi, Cat. 1949, p. 93.
Very characteristic work of the period of transition from the Piazzetta influence to his own style; but not as early as Sack assumes. Sometimes wrongly doubted. A sketch for it was exhibited in Venice, 1896, and is mentioned by Sack (p. 161) as in the coll. of Francesco Vason, Venice. A copy of part of the altarpiece, *St. Joseph with the Christ Child* (wood, 56×40 cm.), wrongly attributed to Tiepolo, was on the Paris art market c. 1958.
(This painting was for long in the store of the Museum.)

THE HOLY FAMILY WITH S. GAETANO   Fig. 97
Canvas, 129×73 cm.; c. 1735–40.

Small altarpiece, formerly in the chapel of the Pal. Labia, Venice. Acquired in 1887.
Molmenti, p. 67, fig. p. 63; Sack, p. 160, fig. 148; Fogolari in *Il Settecento Italiano*, 1932, p. 8, states that in the Palazzo Labia it was called Domenico, but it is undoubtedly an original by Giambattista. Marconi, Cat. 1949, p. 93.
A very fine and delicate private devotional painting.

THE BRAZEN SERPENT   Fig. 15
Canvas, 1.64×13.56 m.; c. 1733–35.

Originally in the church of SS. Cosma e Damiano on the Giudecca. This painting is not cited in Boschini (Zanetti, 1733) but is mentioned in the *Cronaca Veneta*, November, 1735. It can be assumed therefore that the canvas was executed between 1733 and 1735. After the sup-

pression of this church by Napoleon it was taken to Castelfranco and left rolled up in a garret. It was restored at the end of the 19th Century and acquired by the Accademia. A small sketch was formerly in the Beyerlen Coll., Stuttgart, later in the Drey Coll., Munich (q.v.).
Cronaca Veneta, November, 1735; Zanetti, 1771, p. 468; Molmenti, p. 66, figs. pp. 59, 61; Sack, p. 161, fig. 57; Morassi, p. 21; Marconi, Cat. 1949, p. 92.
This is one of the most impressive examples of Tiepolo's early monumental style and a decorative interpretation of a Biblical theme. The colour scheme is based on pale blue and silver and has the finest nuances of Tiepolo's palette. Traces of the old damage still remain.

THE MIRACLE OF THE HOLY HOUSE OF LORETO   Fig. 87
Canvas, oval, 124×85 cm.; c. 1743.

Modelletto for the ceiling in the church of the Scalzi. Another such *modelletto* is in the Rosebery Coll., London. Formerly in a private chapel at Crespano, Treviso; acquired in 1931 from the Dal Zotto Coll., Venice.
Molmenti, p. 65, fig. p. 56; Sack, p. 162, fig. 63; Fogolari, 1931, p. 24 with repr.; Morassi, p. 26, fig. 50; Marconi, Cat. 1949, p. 94; Lorenzetti, p. 67, fig. 50; Exhib. Cat., Petit Palais, Paris 1960–61, no. 392, fig. 50.
Both this and the Rosebery version are excellent works.

PRAYING FIGURES ON A BALCONY   Figs. 387–388
Two large fresco fragments, c. 4×2 m. each; 1743–44.

Formerly in the corners of the ceiling of the Scalzi Church, destroyed October 24th, 1915.
For Lit. cf. Venice, Chiesa degli Scalzi; Marconi, Cat. 1949, p. 94.

THE DISCOVERY OF THE TRUE CROSS   Fig. 122
Circular canvas, 51 cm. diam.; c. 1740–45.

Sketch, or rather the first project, for the ceiling of the church of the Cappuccine at Castello (see below).
Acquired in 1913 from Gen. Añes of Toledo.
Cat. of the Gallery, 1933, p. 146; Marconi, Cat. 1949, p. 94.

THE DISCOVERY OF THE TRUE CROSS   Fig. 121
Circular canvas, 490 cm. diam.; c. 1740–45.

Ceiling painted for the church of the Cappuccine at Castello, which was later suppressed. The ceiling was originally framed by perspectives by Mengozzi Colonna.
Zanetti, 1771, p. 468; Molmenti, p. 67, fig. p. 43f; Sack, p. 160, fig. 147; Marconi, Cat., 1949, p. 92.
One of the most important ceilings by Tiepolo on canvas, this luminous picture is intended to be seen from a great distance as is shown by its rather dispersed composition and the shortening of the figures.

ANTIA AND ABROCOME AT THE FEAST OF DIANA   Fig. 426
Canvas, 53×71 cm.

Formerly in the possession of Count Algarotti; entered the Gallery 1911 from the art dealer Luigi Grassi, Florence.
Painted by Amigoni, as *modello* for the picture commissioned by Algarotti for Dresden 1743. There is no doubt, in my opinion, that this canvas was in large part repainted by G. B. Tiepolo, as the differences in style and taste are clearly identifiable. (There is a similar case of repainting in the 'Mystic Marriage of St. Catherine' of the Hausammann Coll., Zurich, q.v.).

VENICE, Museo Corrèr

SAINT MARTIN OF TOURS WITH A CHORISTER HOLDING THE PASTORAL   Fig. 176
SAINT BLAISE WITH THE PORTRAITS OF A YOUNG WOMAN AND OF A MAN   Fig. 177
Two oval canvases, the first 88×74 cm., the second 92×76 cm.; c. 1718–20.

The first with an inscription on the book: SAN⁵. MARTIN.⁵ EPISC.⁵ TURON.⁵ etc. identifying the bishop of Tours. The *S. Blaise* bears on the column the initials A.M. probably referring to the committent.

These two paintings were probably executed for a sacristy or for the family of the sacristan, as the three 'heads' (the chorister and the young woman with a man) are undoubtedly portraits. Given to Corrèr by Pianton 1883.

They are certainly identical with the pictures mentioned by Paoletti, 1840, in the Misericordia as works by Tiepolo. (Cf. Lorenzetti, 1956, pp. 399–400, on the history of the Misericordia.)

These paintings have always been kept in the store of the Museum and have been restored only recently. They are very interesting specimens of Tiepolo's early style, under the influence of Piazzetta. I was happy to recognize in the two canvases the 'hand' of the young Giambattista. Tiepolo's authorship is in fact beyond question although Prof. Fiocco attributes the works to G. Ceruti.

Pignatti, *Catalogue* of the Museum, 1960, pp. 332–334 with repr., as doubtfully by Giambattista; Levey, *Burlington Magazine*, Sept. 1956, p. 399, sharing Pignatti's doubts.

VENICE, Museo di Ca' Rezzonico

ALLEGORY OF FORTITUDE AND WISDOM   Fig. 345
Canvas, 280 × 420 cm.; 1744–45.

The date is proved by the receipt for the payment in the archives of the Pal. Barbarigo a S. Maria Zobenigo, where the picture originally was. Passed later to the Donà dalle Rose family; acquired by the City from them, 1934. The sketch is in the Museo Poldi-Pezzoli, Milan.

Molmenti, p. 65, fig. p. 64; Sack, p. 149; Lorenzetti-Planiscig, *La Collezione Donà dalle Rose*, Venice, 1934, p. 19, fig. 35; Lorenzetti, *Ca' Rezzonico*, 1936, p. 28, fig. 20; Lorenzetti, p. 81, fig. 60; Pignatti, *Catalogue*, 1960, p. 331 with repr.

Very closely related to the ceilings in the Museum (ex Pal. Caiselli), Udine, and the Museum, Vicenza (ex Villa Cordellina).

TRIUMPH OF ZEPHYR AND FLORA   Fig. 262
Canvas, oval, 395 × 225 cm.; *c.* 1746–50.

Originally in Ca' Pesaro; entered the Museum 1936.

Sack, p. 235, No. 621, as *Bacchus and Ariadne;* Fiocco in *Rivista della Città di Venezia*, 1925, p. 396; Lorenzetti, *Ca' Rezzonico*, 1936, p. 50, fig. 23; Lorenzetti, p. 51, fig. 38; Pignatti, *Catalogue*, 1960, p. 330 with repr.

ORIENTAL HEAD (Exhib. No. 71): See Trieste, Rusconi Coll.

MARTYRDOM OF S. THEODORA
Canvas, 55 × 34 cm.

By a contemporary imitator of Tiepolo.
Wrongly called *Martyrdom of S. Agatha.* Copy of the sketch in the Falck Coll., Milan (q.v.).

Gift of Luca Beltrami, 1903. Formerly in the Piccinelli Coll., Bergamo.
Molmenti, p. 77; Sack, p. 162; Beltrami, 1928; Lorenzetti, *Ca' Rezzonico*, 1936, p. 58, fig. 32, all wrongly as by Giambattista; Pignatti, *Catalogue*, 1960, p. 334 as a school work.

NABAL AND ABIGAIL
Canvas, 55 × 72 cm.

Attributed by Molmenti, p. 75 and Sack, p. 163, fig. 150, erroneously to Tiepolo. A school work, certainly by Battaglioli with figures by Zugno.
Lorenzetti, Catalogue of Ca' Rezzonico, Venice, 1936, p. 58, as Giambattista; Pignatti, *Catalogue*, 1960, p. 399 as by Zugno.

VENICE, Galleria Querini-Stampalia

PORTRAIT OF THE PROCURATOR GIOVANNI QUERINI
[1955, pls. 35–36]
Canvas, 235 × 158 cm.; *c.* 1749(?) or later.

The identity of the sitter is not certain. The date of the portrait is still discussed and has recently been put in the 1750s. Now by M. Levey (in *The Burlington Magazine*, April 1961, p. 139 ff.) attributed to Domenico, but unconvincingly.

Molmenti, p. 77; Sack, p. 162, fig. 83a; Morassi, p. 27, fig. 71; Muraro, 1949, p. 162; Pignatti, 1950, p. 218; Lorenzetti, p. 95, fig. 69; M. Dazzi, *Arte Veneta*, 1951, pp. 178–185, figs. 182–184, with complete literature; Exhib. Cat. Petit Palais, Paris 1960–61, no. 393, fig. 51.

Another portrait, among the few known by Tiepolo, was one of Count Algarotti. He was represented near a statue of Victory, according to a letter from Tiepolo to Algarotti of April 4th, 1761. No other mention or trace of this portrait is known. (See Chronological Table.)

VENICE, S. Alvise

THE ROAD TO CALVARY, 450 × 517 cm.   [1955, fig. 20]
THE FLAGELLATION, 450 × 194 cm.
THE CROWNING WITH THORNS, 450 × 135 cm.

Canvases painted *c.* 1738–40.

The canvases are firstly mentioned in the *Guide* by Albrizzi, of 1740. They were given to the church by Alvise Cornaro. The sketch for the *Calvary* is in the Berlin Museum; a sketch of the *Crowning*, believed to be by Tiepolo, was in a private coll. in Bergamo, but it is a contemporary copy of the S. Alvise picture.

The Calvary was engraved by Rebellato in Zanotto's *Pinacoteca Veneta*, Venice, 1867, fig. 34.

Albrizzi, 1740, p. 171; Zanetti, 1771 (ed. of 1792, p. 604); Molmenti, p. 66, figs. p. 58, 58a; Sack, p. 157, figs. 65–67; Morassi, p. 23, figs. 54–56; Lorenzetti, p. 64, figs. 47–49.

Two canvases (105 × 68 cm.), believed to be the sketches for the *Flagellation* and the *Crowning*, on the market in Paris in 1957, are copies by a follower after the original large pictures.

VENICE, formerly S. Anna (later secularised)

S. SCHOLASTICA
S. BENEDICT

Two canvases recorded in the accounts of the church of S. Anna in 1728 with the attribution to Tiepolo.

In 1809 Moschini wrote that the two pictures no longer existed and the church was secularised.

Zanetti, 1797, I, p. 127, believed the paintings to be 'works in the style of T.'

Molmenti, p. 52; Sack, p. 230. No further trace of the paintings.

VENICE, S. Antonino

Da Canal, 1732, p. XXXIII, mentions 'in the triangle of the vault *S. John* and *S. Luke*' which were probably painted in fresco. Lost perhaps in 1760 when the church, according to Gradenigo (p. 51) was whitewashed.

Moschini, 1815, p. 89, mentions the works without any attribution; Sack, pp. 32, 230.

VENICE, SS. Apostoli

THE COMMUNION OF S. LUCY   Fig. 118
Canvas, 122 × 101 cm.; *c.* 1740–45.

Small altarpiece, painted probably for a private chapel of the Cornaro family. It came into the Cornaro chapel of this church to replace a *S. Lucy* by Benedetto Diana. Albrizzi (ed. 1765) mentions the Diana, but in the ed. of 1772 he notes the Tiepolo there. The sketch in Milan, Museo Civico.

Albrizzi, ed. 1765, p. 197; Zanetti, 1771 (ed. of 1792, p. 604); Moschini, 1815, I, p. 665; Molmenti, p. 66, fig. p. 43e; Sack, p. 157, fig. 142; Orlandini, 1914, p. 43; Moschini, 1931, p. 44; Lorenzetti, p. 93, fig. 68.

An old copy of the central part was in the A. Chiesa Coll., Milan, sold in New York, American Art Assoc., 1927 (Cat. IV, No. 60).

VENICE, S. Benedetto

S. FRANCIS OF PAOLA   Fig. 183
Arched canvas, 221 × 107 cm.; *c.* 1735–40.

Altarpiece.

Mentioned by Tassis in his *Aggiunte* to Zanetti's *Guida* of 1733, f. 178. (Fiocco, 1927.)
Molmenti, p. 50 (calling it *S. Vincenzo di Paola*); Sack, p. 156, fig. 141. The figure in his effected gesture reflects the passionate stadium of Tiepolo's early maturity.

VENICE, Chiesetta delle Madri Cappuccine presso S. Gerolamo

From a note by Gradenigo on March 12th, 1756, we know that three altars were remade and 'the ceiling was painted by the famous Gio. Batta Tiepoletto.' Nothing else is known about this work.
Gradenigo (ed. 1942), p. 21; Moschini, 1815, II, p. 46, mentions the three altars, but not the ceiling.

VENICE, S. Cassiano

ABRAHAM AND THE ANGELS
Lunette (*c.* 5.5 m.), mentioned by Sack, p. 158, as possibly by Giambattista, but it is certainly by Domenico who also frescoed the other lunette with a scene from the life of Abraham.
Lorenzetti, *Guida*, 1926, p. 443; Muraro, *Guida*, 1953, pl. 263, as by Domenico.

VENICE, Chiesa della Fava

THE EDUCATION OF THE VIRGIN   [1955, p. 16]
Canvas, 362 × 200 cm.; 1732.

Altarpiece, first mentioned by Zanetti, 1733.
Zanetti, 1733, p. 190; Albrizzi, 1765, p. 95; Zucchini, 1784, II, p. 524; Moschini, 1815, I, p. 216; Molmenti, p. 51, fig. p. 43b; Sack, p. 157, fig. 33; Arslan, 1936, p. 248; Morassi, p. 19; Lorenzetti, p. 44, fig. 31.
A masterpiece of the critical moment in Tiepolo's evolution towards a more luminous style, though still bounded by the dramatic chiaroscuro of Piazzetta.

VENICE, S. Francesco della Vigna

THE FOUR EVANGELISTS   Figs. 193–194
TWO GROUPS OF THREE VIRTUES   Fig. 216

Monochrome frescoes in the Sagredo Chapel; 1743(?).

One Evangelist in each pendentive; the two groups of Virtues in medallions, also in grisaille fresco, surrounded by festoons of fruit.
An epitaph in the Sagredo Chapel attests that the decoration was finished in 1743, and probably this statement refers also to the frescoes.
Engraved by Domenico (De Vesme, 50–53, 79–80).
Frescoes of intense plastic effects. Some parts are faded.
Zucchini, 1784 (as by Gerolamo Pellegrini!); Moschini, 1815, I, p. 47; Molmenti, p. 54, fig. p. 48, repr. of the engravings; Sack, p. 156, fig. 140, repr. of one of the engravings; Goering, 1944, p. 101, with figures; Lorenzetti, *Guida*, 1926, p. 368.

VENICE, Chiesa dei Frari

HAGAR AND ISHMAEL WITH THE ANGEL
Canvas, *c.* 150 × 70 cm.

Mentioned by Sack (p. 158) as an early work by Tiepolo in the Sacristy of the church, it is a weak picture, probably by Zugno.

VENICE, Chiesa dei Gesuati (S. Maria del Rosario)

Frescoes on the ceiling, in three compartments:

S. DOMINIC INSTITUTING THE ROSARY, in the centre;
                    [1955, col. pl. III]
THE VIRGIN HEARING THE PRAYERS OF THE SAINT   Fig. 95
and
S. DOMINIC IN GLORY, in the other compartments; 1737–39.
                    Fig. 93
Around the frescoes fourteen grisailles in greenish-ochre, alternating in oval and shaped stucco frames with SCENES FROM THE NEW TESTAMENT (*Annunciation, Visitation, Adoration*, etc.), these last evidently executed by Tiepolo's assistants after his projects. Recently G. M. Pilo suggested that they are partly to be assigned to F. Zugno (*Paragone*, March, 1959, p.34, fig. 30).

On the ceiling of the apse behind the High Altar:
ANGEL APPEARING TO DAVID
Central circular fresco, surrounded by four oval grisailles with *Prophets*.

On the main wall of the apse, another circular grisaille representing the *Crucifixion* (not in a good state).

The frescoes were begun after May, 1737, and finished in October, 1739.
Modelletti for the *Institution of the Rosary* are in the Berlin Museum and in the Crespi Coll., Milan.
The sketches related to the two smaller compartments are in Philadelphia, Johnson Coll. and in a private coll. (lent to the Fogg Art Museum, Cambridge, Mass., in 1923).
Zanetti, 1771, p. 466; De Chennevières, 1892, pp. 21–2, figs. pp. 15, 17, 19; Meissner, 1897, p. 25 ff., figs. 17, 18; Molmenti, pp. 55–60, figs. pp. 50, 50a, 52; Sack, pp. 154–155, fig. 59; Morassi, pp. 23–24, fig. 57; A. Vardanega, in *Arte Cristiana*, 1958, no. 10–11, pp. 84, 88.

MADONNA WITH SS. ROSE, CATHERINE AND AGNES
Arched canvas, 340 × 168 cm.; shortly before 1740.   Fig. 102

Altarpiece on the first altar on the right. Tiepolo received 100 *zecchini* for it. Engraved by Domenico (De Vesme, 54).
Zanetti, 1771, p. 466; Moschini, 1815, II, p. 320; Molmenti, p. 65, fig. p. 43d; Sack, p. 155, fig. 74; Fogolari, 1932–33, p. 2 ff. with colour detail; Arslan, 1932, mentions the 1740 edition of the *Forestiere Illuminato* by Albrizzi where this altarpiece is already listed as in the church.
One of Tiepolo's best-known religious paintings in Venice. This altarpiece is as popular for its vivid colour as for the expressive, and rather languid, figures. These female Saints are the incarnation of Venetian Settecento ideals of beauty when sacred and profane were strangely combined.
A drawing by Fragonard after this painting was etched by the Abbé de Saint-Non (Wildenstein, *Fragonard acquafortiste*, Paris, 1956, p. 18).

VENICE, S. Lazzaro degli Armeni

JUSTICE AND PEACE   Fig. 215
Canvas ceiling, oval, 170 × 192 cm.; *c.* 1728–32.

Probably originally at Ca' Zenobio, where it formed part of the decorative cycle, recorded by Da Canal (1732), to which the *Triumph of Aurelian*, now in Turin, may also have belonged. Taken to the Island of S. Lazzaro by the Armenian Order of Mechitarists from Pal. Zenobio dei Carmini.
Moschini, 1815, II, p. 280; Fontana, 1865, p. 367; Molmenti, p. 51; Sack, p. 154, fig. 139; Lorenzetti, p. 57, fig. 41.

VENICE, S. Marco, Sacristy of the Canons

THE ADORATION OF THE INFANT JESUS   Fig. 38
Canvas, 220 × 155 cm.; 1732–33.

Altarpiece originally in the church of S. Giuliano.
The date may be deduced from the 'Descrizione' of Zanetti (1733).
Zanetti, 1733, p. 486; Zucchini, 1784, II, p. 376; Molmenti, p. 50, fig. p. 43a; Sack, p. 158, fig. 27; Arslan, 1936, p. 248; Morassi, p. 19; Lorenzetti, p. 39, fig. 28.

VENICE, S. Martino

S. CECILIA

This canvas, mentioned by Da Canal (1732, p. XXXIII) as *S. Cecilia with her husband and rejoicing Angels*, by Tiepolo, is a work by Segala.
Sack, p. 32; Lorenzetti, 1926, p. 303.

VENICE, S. Maria Materdomini

BANNER WITH THE MADONNA AND CHILD
Embroidery after the picture now in Springfield (q.v.).

VENICE, Chiesa dell' Ospedaletto

THE SACRIFICE OF ABRAHAM [1955, fig. 3 with erroneous caption]
Canvas, shaped to fit over an arch, 305 × 390 cm.; *c.* 1715–16.

Listed by Zanetti in his 'Descrizione,' 1733. The date 1716 appears on a book held by one of the prophets in this series, but the attribution to Tiepolo of some other prophets is very doubtful.

Da Canal, 1732, p. XXXII; Zanetti, 1733, p. 255; Moschini, 1815, I, p. 184; Molmenti, pp. 46–50, fig. p. 45; Sack, p. 156; De Vito Battaglia, 1931, p. 477, with repr.; Modigliani, 1933, p. 147; Goering, *ad vocem;* Morassi, pp. 12–13, fig. 2; Lorenzetti, p. 5, fig. 1.

This picture forms the basis of our knowledge of Tiepolo's beginnings. On the question, much discussed at one time, of the attribution of other pictures in this church to Tiepolo, see especially De Vito Battaglia, Modigliani, Morassi and Lorenzetti, cited above. The first writer attributes many of the paintings to Tiepolo, Modigliani only two, and myself only this one, with which Lorenzetti concurs.

It is quite certain that, of this series, the *Sacrifice of Abraham* is the only work by Tiepolo. The different attributions have arisen from a *lapsus memoriae* of Da Canal (1732) who noted as *Apostles* the two figures of the *Sacrifice;* and even more from a probable confusion in the text of Zanetti (1733), which mentions *Two Prophets* over the pulpit, and, later, a *Sacrifice* as existing over a *Pool of Bethesda* by Lazzarini. Since there are neither *Apostles* nor *Prophets* over the pulpit, but the *Sacrifice* by Tiepolo (which was never hung above the canvas by Lazzarini), the mistake is evident.

VENICE, Chiesa della Pietà

TRIUMPH OF FAITH, large fresco in the central compartment of the ceiling; [1955, fig. 43]
FAITH, HOPE AND CHARITY, oval fresco in the vault of the choir; Fig. 214
DAVID AND THE ANGEL, round grisaille (in bad state), also in the choir, under the *Faith, Hope and Charity* fresco.

Begun on June 13th, 1754, according to Gradenigo's Diary; unveiled August 2nd, 1755. The oval with the *Three Virtues* was engraved by Domenico (De Vesme, 78). In creating this ceiling Tiepolo was no doubt influenced by the musical atmosphere of the neighbouring Conservatoire of the Esposti: A *modello* for the central large fresco is in the Rosebery Coll.

Gradenigo, *Notatori* (ed. Livan), 1942, pp. 12, 17; Zanetti, 1771, p. 466; Molmenti, p. 76, fig. p. 43g; Sack, p. 155, figs. 104, 105; Morassi, p. 33, figs. 94–95.

One year after his return from Würzburg Tiepolo here created another imaginative masterpiece of delicate colour and harmonious style. Because of its very high position, the view up into this 'Heaven' is in very steep perspective, so that the figures are extremely foreshortened.

VENICE, S. Polo

THE VIRGIN APPEARING TO S. JOHN NEPOMUK Fig. 104
Arched canvas, 346×145 cm.; *c.* 1754.

Altarpiece, unveiled on May 8th, 1754, according to Gradenigo's Diary (ed. 1942, p. 11); evidently painted immediately after Tiepolo's return from Würzburg (8.11.1753).
Restored in 1938.

Zanetti, 1771, p. 467; Molmenti, p. 50; Sack, p. 158; Moschini, *Le Arti*, I, 1938, p. 312 with repr.

Zanetti also records an *Apostle before a Tyrant* in the same church, said to have been painted in Tiepolo's youth. This altarpiece is not mentioned again after the rebuilding of the church in the early 19th Century, nor is it recorded by Moschini (1815).

VENICE, S. Provolo

MADONNA WITH S. JOHN NEPOMUK, S. FRANCIS OF PAOLA AND S. ANTHONY OF PADUA
Altarpiece mentioned by F. M. Tassis (f. 221) in his 'Aggiunte' to Zanetti's *Guida* of 1733 (Fiocco, 1927). The church was secularised in 1808 and Moschini (1815) does not mention it. Perhaps the altarpiece now in Moscow, Pushkin Museum (q.v.).

VENICE, S. Salvatore

S. AUGUSTINE AND OTHER SAINTS
Altarpiece; 1737–38.

In the archives of the church there are documents referring to the painting commissioned from Tiepolo by the Cornaro Family. On January 29th, 1737, Tiepolo was paid for the canvas on which he had to depict 'S. Augustine and other Saints'. On July 15th, 1738, Tiepolo was paid L. 800 (See Chronological Table). The painting was later (in the eighteenth century) destroyed by fire. In the *Guide* by Albrizzi of 1765 the altarpiece appears still as existing, but in the 1772 edition of the same *Guide* it is no longer mentioned.

A drawing for an engraving of the altarpiece is preserved in the Graphische Sammlung in Munich. This drawing, attributed by Maria-cher to Tiepolo himself, is more probably by a pupil. In any case it corresponds to the sketch in York (q.v.). As to the engraving there is no trace of it. A first idea for the altarpiece is perhaps to be identified with the sketch in the National Gallery, London (q.v.). A probable 'record' of the painting in the Lycett Green Coll., York Art Gallery (q.v.).

Molmenti, p. 52; Sack, p. 157, fig. 143 of the drawing; Fiocco in *Rivista di Venezia*, 1927, IV, p. 141; Levey in *The Burlington Magazine*, IV 1955, pp. 116–120; Mariacher, in *Arte Veneta*, 1959-60 pp. 237-238.

VENICE, Chiesa degli Scalzi

THE MIRACLE OF THE HOLY HOUSE OF LORETO [1955, fig. 23]
Ceiling fresco, destroyed by a bomb on October 28th, 1915:

Executed in 1743–44, with the assistance of Mengozzi-Colonna for the ornamental parts. A *modelletto* is in the Accademia, Venice, and another in the Rosebery Coll., London. Two fragments of the fresco, with praying figures, are in the Accademia, Venice.

Zanetti, 1771, p. 466; Molmenti, pp. 65, 79 n. 19, fig. p. 56b; Sack, p. 154, fig. 64; Lorenzetti, *Guida*, 1926, p. 430; Fogolari, 1931, pp. 24 ff. with repr.; Morassi, p. 25, fig. 64.

This ceiling was the most important of Tiepolo's church decorations, and was universally praised as one of his most impressive creations. The history of the commission and the payments are given in Fogolari's article.

APOTHEOSIS OF S. THERESA [1955, fig. 5]
Fresco in the vault of the Chapel of S. Theresa (second on the right) and *imitation statues; c.* 1720–25.

Mentioned by Da Canal, 1732, who asserts that it is one of Tiepolo's first works, and by Zanetti in his *Descrizione*, 1733. The illusionistic part is due to G. Mengozzi-Colonna.

Da Canal, 1732, p. XXXIII; Zanetti, 1733, p. 421; Zanetti, 1771, p. 466; Molmenti, p. 54, fig. p. 43c; Sack, p. 154, fig. 32; Fogolari, 1931, pp. 24 ff.; Morassi, p. 14, fig. 7. Some critics—Sack, Fogolari, Arslan (in *Critica d'Arte*, 1936) and others—believe that it was painted about 1715, but the style is more advanced and near to the Pal. Sandi ceiling (just before 1725). Here Tiepolo is seen surpassing Piazzetta in monumental decoration. On the relationship between Tiepolo and Piazzetta (whose ceiling in SS. Giovanni e Paolo is certainly later than this one), see Morassi in *Arte Veneta*, 1949, p. 72.

CHRIST IN THE GARDEN OF OLIVES Fig. 50
Fresco in the Chapel of the Redeemer (the first on the left).

In grisaille, simulating a bas-relief; *c.* 1732–33.

Zanetti, 1733, p. 420; Zanetti, 1771, p. 466; Molmenti, pp. 54–55, fig. p. 49; Sack, p. 154; Fogolari, 1931, pp. 24 ff.

According to Fogolari this was certainly painted after 1732, since in that year the Carmelites were given a reliquary and undertook to decorate this chapel. Da Canal (1732) does not mention it, but it is recorded by Zanetti in 1733 and must therefore have been painted between 1732 and 1733; with the assistance, according to Zanetti, of Mengozzi-Colonna.

VENICE, S. Sofia

Madonna with Saints Nicholas, Cajetan and Lawrence

Altarpiece mentioned by F. M. Tassis (f. 391) in his 'Aggiunte' to Zanetti's *Guida* of 1733 (Fiocco, 1927, pp. 141–176, saying the altarpiece is lost) as existing in the Sacristy.
Zanetti, *Della Pittura Veneziana*, 1797, II, p. 84, mentions the work as by Segala. No trace of the painting.

VENICE, S. Stae

The Martyrdom of S. Bartholomew
[1955, fig. 1, with erroneous caption]
Canvas, 167 × 139 cm.; *c.* 1721.

Commissioned with eleven other pictures by various other painters for the decoration of the church.
Da Canal, 1732, p. 34; Zanetti, 1733, p. 440; Molmenti, p. 50; Sack, p. 158; Arslan, 1936, pp. 184, 254; Morassi, p. 15, fig. 6; Lorenzetti, p. 10, fig. 4; Exhib. Cat., Petit Palais, Paris 1960–61, No. 386.

Trajan Commanding S. Eustace to Fight
Moschini, 1815, mentions the canvas as a work by Tiepolo; Molmenti, p. 50, note 6, believes it to be a very early work by Tiepolo and adds that it is in bad condition. Sack, p. 230, does not consider it by the master and lists the painting recorded by Moschini among the 'Lost Works'; Lorenzetti, 1926, p. 448 doubted it and Muraro, 1953, p. 267, notes the picture as by Domenico.
In reality the painting is a weak and badly repainted work perhaps by Menescardi.

VENICE, S. Teresa (Ospizio degli Orfani)

Sack, p. 158, mentions in the meeting room, S. Gerolamo Emiliani Embracing an Orphan Boy, a small canvas listed also by Moschini and by Guides of the 19th century. The church, now belonging to the 'Ente Comunale d'Assistenza' of Venice, no longer possesses this picture which was already omitted from an 'Inventory' by Prof. Barbantini and Prof. Lorenzetti, *c.* 1930. (This is known to me from a kind communication by Dr. Elena Bassi.)
Moschini writes that the painting was executed 'with care and love.'
Moschini, 1819, p. 308; *Il Forestiere istruito, ecc.*, Venice, 1819, p. 433.
Certainly to be identified with the *S. Girolamo Miani* (51 × 62 cm.) by Domenico, now in the Ca' Rezzonico, Venice (see repr. in Pignatti, *Catalogue*, 1960, p.338).

VENICE, S. Trinità (S. Ternita)

S. Francis and a Companion
Altarpiece listed by Zanetti, 1733, p. 230, as 'a worthy work,' and is certainly the one mentioned by Da Canal, 1732, p. XXXIII, as 'S. Francis receiving the Stigmata' and recorded as still existing by Moschini, 1809. The painting was probably lost during the secularisation of the church which took place in 1832.
Molmenti, p. 52; Sack, p. 230.
It should be recorded that a *S. Francis*, also missing, was in the coll. of the engraver Pietro Monaco, etched by him, and perhaps was iconographically related to this altarpiece.

VENICE, Scuola dei Carmini

Decorations on the ceiling of the principal saloon.
In the centre:

The Madonna del Carmelo with S. Simeon Stock
[1955, fig. 22]
Canvas, 533 × 342 cm.; dated on the tombstone, 1740.
Placed in position soon after June 2nd, 1743.

Four lateral compartments with the Virtues:

Faith, Hope and Charity	Fig. 204
Prudence, Grace and Innocence	Fig. 205
Strength and Justice	Fig. 206
Meekness and Humility	Fig. 207

Shaped canvases, 235 × 240 cm.; the last is dated at the bottom, 1744.
Four other lateral compartments:

Angels Raising Souls from Purgatory	Fig. 218
An Angel Saving a Boy Falling from a Building	Fig. 219
Angels Bearing the Indulgences of the Carmelites	Fig. 208
An Angel with Scapular, and Another with Lilies	Fig. 209

Shaped canvases, 180 × 240 cm.

On December 21st, 1739, the Scuola decided to entrust the work to Tiepolo, who accepted in a letter of January, 1740. All the subjects were accurately described by the committents. The ceiling was unveiled on June 2nd, 1743. The *Madonna del Carmelo* was engraved by Domenico (De Vesme, 57) and also the *Angels* (De Vesme, 75–77).
Zanetti, 1771, p. 468; Molmenti, pp. 60–65, figs. pp. 52a–52b, 53–55; Sack, p. 155, figs. 68–71; Morassi, p. 25, figs. 62–63; Exhib. Cat., Petit Palais, Paris 1960–61, No. 394, 395.
Sack (p. 156) mentions some canvases in the Albergo of the Scuola dei Carmini: (1) *Martyrdom of Christians*, (2) *Two Carmelites before the Virgin*, (3) *Sibyls;* and in the neighbouring room *Four Evangelists* and *Four Prophets*, wrongly as by Giambattista Tiepolo. They are by Giustino Menescardi who also painted the sketch relating to *Two Prophets*, in the Chiaramonte-Bordonaro Coll. in Palermo, also wrongly attributed by Sack to Tiepolo (q.v.).

VENICE, Scuola di S. Rocco

Abraham and The Angels	Fig. 5
Hagar and Ishmael	[1955, pls. 14–15]

Two canvases, 140 × 120 cm. each; *c.* 1732.

They did not originally belong to the Scuola but were acquired in 1789.
Molmenti, p. 326, fig. p. 331; Sack, p. 158, figs. 144–145; Morassi, p. 19; Pallucchini, 1945, p. 127; Lorenzetti, p. 41, figs. 29–30; *Exhib. Cat.*, Petit Palais, Paris 1960–61, No. 389.

VENICE, Scuola di S. Teodoro

S. Peter
S. Paul

Two canvases quoted by Da Canal, 1732, p. XXXIII, and by Zanetti, 1771, p. 476 ('in the part of the window over the pew') in the Albergo of the Scuola. In 1809 Moschini wrote that the two pictures no longer existed.
Molmenti, p. 52; Sack, pp. 32, 230. No further trace of the canvases.

VENICE, Doge's Palace

Neptune Offering to Venice the Riches of the Sea
Canvas, 112 × 175 cm.; *c.* 1745–50.   [1955, pls. 42–44]
Overdoor in the 'Sala delle quattro Porte.'
Engraved by Domenico (De Vesme, 97).
Zanetti, 1771, p. 468; Zanotto, 1858, II, Tav. LXI, p. 6; Molmenti p. 51; Sack, p. 151; Lorenzetti, p. 63, fig. 46.

VENICE, Palazzo Baglioni

Apollo and the Muses

Ceiling fresco attributed by Sack (p. 149), Molmenti (p. 54) and others to Tiepolo, but rightly given to Zugno by Fiocco in 'Rivista della Città di Venezia,' 1927 (Aggiunte al Tassis), where it is reproduced together with a sketch in Milan, Museo Civico.
Da Canal, 1732, p. XXXII, records a room frescoed by Tiepolo in this Palace, now lost and in any case not identical with this ceiling.

VENICE, Palazzo Barbarigo (Fondamenta Barbarigo e Duodo)

Fresco decoration in a room of the *piano nobile*.

Time Discovering Truth
Fig. 322
Ceiling, oval, *c.* 350 × 250 cm.; *c.* 1740–45.

The female figure much restored.

This 'Allegory' is surrounded by a rich and very fine painted decoration with illusionistic feigned elements.

A sketch closely related to the ceiling (in reverse) in the von Hirsch Coll., Basle (q.v.). In the same room:

TWO ALLEGORICAL FEMALE FIGURES
Grisailles in pale violet monochrome fresco as overdoors, canvas 100 × 130 cm. each.

In another larger room also on the *piano nobile*, on the ceiling surrounding a large rectangular stucco frame in which was the canvas of the ALLEGORY OF FORTITUDE AND WISDOM (now in the Museum of Ca' Rezzonico, q.v.) eight medallions, part round and part oval-shaped stucco-cornices with:

ALLEGORIES OF THE ARTS AND SCIENCES Figs. 382–383, 385–386
Grisailles, some in a mauvish and some in yellowish colours.

In the same room also:

THREE ALLEGORICAL FEMALE FIGURES as overdoors in grisaille.
Fig. 374

(All eleven grisailles were detached from the walls some years ago and are now preserved in the Palazzo Luccheschi on the Canal Grande.) G. Mengozzi Colonna collaborated with Tiepolo in the works of the Palace (see Chronological Table).

In the same Palazzo Barbarigo there was also the canvas with the ARMS OF THE BARBARIGO-DUODO FAMILY (see Venice, Donà dalle Rose Coll.).

Sack, p. 149; Morassi, p. 26; Muraro, in *Gazette des Beaux-Arts*, January, 1960, pp. 19–34 with repr.

VENICE, Palazzo Barbaro

Until 1874, when they were sold, this Palace contained the following paintings: a ceiling with THE APOTHEOSIS OF FRANCESCO BARBARO (see New York, Metropolitan Museum) and four overdoors: (1) THE BETROTHAL (see Copenhagen, Museum); (2) TARQUIN AND LUCRETIA (see Augsburg, Museum); (3) GIFTS OFFERED TO CLEOPATRA (see Pavia, Necchi Coll.); (4) TIMOCLEA AND THE THRACIAN COMMANDER (see Washington, National Gallery).

VENICE, Ca' Cornaro at S. Polo

According to Da Canal, 1732, p. XXXII, Tiepolo painted some overdoors with portraits and pictures 'of a good taste.' Since Cornaro was elected Doge in 1709 and died in 1722, it is probable that Tiepolo painted before 1722 in the Palace; that is, in his very early period. Molmenti, pp. 49–50; Sack, p. 151. Nothing more is known about the paintings.

VENICE, Palazzo Corner Mocenigo a S. Polo

MARRIAGE ALLEGORY OF THE CASA CORNARO
Ceiling originally executed by Tiepolo for the Palace. Now in the Contini-Bonacossi Coll., Florence (q.v.).

VENICE, Palazzo Giovanelli

MINERVA AS PROTECTRESS OF ARTS AND SCIENCES
Elliptical fresco, with four small chiaroscuro medallions in the corners.

Mentioned by Sack, p. 152, as an early work still showing evidence of inexperience. No trace of these frescoes can now be found, nor is there any painting in the Palace which can be assigned to the 18th Century. It may be that the frescoes noted by Sack were covered by a modern work, following the Giovanelli Sale about 30 years ago. There is no other reference to the fresco in the whole of the Venetian literature.

VENICE, Palazzo Grassi a S. Samuele

ALLEGORY OF THE GRASSI FAMILY
Ceiling fresco in the staircase, attributed by Sack, p. 149, to Tiepolo, and

by Molmenti, pp. 317–18, fig. p. 322, doubtfully to Fabio Canal, but it is more probably by Guarana.

VENICE, Palazzo Grimani ai Servi

Ceiling fresco, originally executed by Tiepolo for a saloon of the Palace. Two fragments of it are existing, one with the *Angel of Fame* (formerly Ventura Coll., Florence, q.v.), the other with *Two Putti* (see Florence, Uffizi).

VENICE, Palazzo Labia

Frescoes in the principal saloon. (Height 11 m.; Breadth, 11.75 m.; Length, 12.15 m.).

On the ceiling:

GENIUS ON PEGASUS PUTTING TIME TO FLIGHT Fig. 326

On the walls, framed in imitation architecture painted by Mengozzi-Colonna:

MEETING OF ANTONY AND CLEOPATRA [1955, pls. 46, 48]
BANQUET OF ANTONY AND CLEOPATRA [1955, pls. 47, 49]

Other figures and allegories in the spaces between the columns and in the volutes of the ceiling.

Painted *c.* 1745–50. Some small damages suffered during the war (1945) have been repaired. Sketch for the *Meeting* in Edinburgh, for the *Banquet* in Stockholm. Other sketches related to these subjects in Paris, London, etc.

Molmenti, pp. 73–74, figs. pp. 67–68, 68a, 68c, 69, 72a, 72b; Sack, p. 152, figs. 114, 115, 117, 119, 121; Morassi, p. 28, figs. 74–77.

The most famous of Tiepolo's fresco cycles in a private palace in Italy and a creation of perfect illusionism. At this period Tiepolo's art was dominated by a classical feeling, here of crystalline purity. Sack and others date this cycle after the Würzburg period; but there can be no doubt, since the style recalls that of the Villa Cordellina (1743), that the Labia saloon was executed before Tiepolo went to Germany.

According to Watson (*Connoisseur*, November, 1955, p. 214) the cycle can be dated more closely, since Cochin in his *Voyage d'Italie* does not mention the frescoes, although he describes the Labia Palace (he visited it probably in the early summer 1750); but Reynolds made a sketch of the *Meeting* (now in the British Museum) in the summer of 1752 when he was in Venice. As Tiepolo left in November, 1750, it is presumable that he painted the frescoes in the summer and early autumn of 1750 (or earlier if the neglected mention of Cochin is really a positive proof that the frescoes did not exist).

Tiepolo's self-portrait is visible in the *Banquet*, at the left behind the Moor.

A drawing by Fragonard of the *Banquet* was etched by the Abbé de Saint-Non (Wildenstein, *Fragonard aquafortiste*, Paris, 1956, p. 21).

In another room:

ZEPHYR AND FLORA Fig. 257
Elliptical ceiling fresco in a painted decoration (220 × 400 cm.).

On the walls:

IMITATION ALLEGORICAL STATUES IN IMITATION NICHES
In monochrome.

On the walls were formerly six circular canvases, with monochrome allegorical figures on gold grounds (71 cm. diam.) four of which were formerly in New York, Silbermann Coll., and are now in Milan, Bolchini-Bonomi Coll., and in New Haven, Yale University. They were formerly in the Oreffice Coll., Venice, all reproduced in Molmenti, p. 69a and 69b.

Present whereabouts of the other two unknown.

A sketch related to *Zephyr and Flora* in Paris, with Birtschansky.

Sack, p. 152, fig. 123.

In a further room:

BACCHUS AND ARIADNE Fig. 265
Shaped ceiling fresco (250 × 420 cm.).

Sack, p. 152, fig. 124.

VENICE, Palazzo Morosini a Santo Stefano

APOTHEOSIS OF FRANCESCO MOROSINI PELOPONNESIACO
Ceiling canvas, originally painted by Tiepolo for the palace. Now in Milan, Palazzo Isimbardi (q.v.).

VENICE, Palazzo Nani

Da Canal, 1732, p. XXXIII, notes that Tiepolo executed 'a great lateral picture for the N.H. Zani at S. Trovaso.' It is certainly to be identified with Palazzo Nani, where there is no work by Tiepolo. In any case this picture is not mentioned in any other source.
Molmenti, p. 52; Sack, p. 152.

VENICE, Palazzo Papadopoli, now Arrivabene

In a large room called 'of the Allegories':
ALLEGORY OF FORTITUDE AND WISDOM (AND VICE?) WITH FLYING PUTTI

Fresco on an oval ceiling.
There is a painted date, possibly 1741.
The fresco is in bad condition, recently restored.

In another room called 'of the alcove,' on the ceiling:
THREE FLYING PUTTI WITH PIGEONS
The whole room is decorated with fine stuccoes. In oval medallions, in grisaille on golden background:
ALLEGORICAL FIGURES OF THE FOUR SEASONS   Fig. 373
Hitherto unpublished.
(I owe the knowledge of these frescoes to the kindness of Dr. Muraro, Venice.)

VENICE, Palazzo ex Pisani-Moretta a S. Polo
(now Giusti del Giardino)

ALLEGORY WITH MARS AND VENUS   Fig. 259
Frescoed ceiling; c. 1740–45.

Probably executed c. 1742, when important decorative works were undertaken in the Palace.
Badly restored, especially in the breast of Venus and in the centre.
Wide frieze in grisaille.
Fontana, 1865; Morassi, p. 26.
This fresco is not recorded by Molmenti or Sack. The latter, however, gives the fresco in the next room (see below) to Tiepolo. Unfortunately, the Allegory has recently been damaged and badly restored; otherwise, it is an excellent work showing many links with the fresco in Pal. Clerici, Milan, of 1740. The modello for this ceiling is in a private coll. in Paris, formerly Flameng Coll. (q.v.).
The fresco in the next room, Apollo in the Chariot of the Sun, attributed (by Sack, p. 152; by Goering, ad vocem) to Tiepolo, is, in fact, by Guarana.

VENICE, Palazzo Polignac (Canal Grande)
now belonging to the Duc Decazes

A SACRIFICE
A ROMAN TRIUMPH

Frescoes, transferred to canvas; c. 90 × 300 cm.

By Domenico.
Both friezes once formed part of a decorative cycle in the Palazzo Corrèr at Santa Fosca, Venice, together with two other Roman Scenes and a frieze with Satyrs and Satyresses, this last probably by Giambattista Tiepolo or, at least, after his sketches. All the friezes were detached from the walls (c. 1900), transferred to canvas and bought by the art-dealer Barozzi of Venice. Apart from the two scenes now in the Palazzo Polignac, they are lost.
In the Palazzo Corrèr there was also a ceiling painted by Giambattista Tiepolo (or Domenico?) in the salon called 'Sala d'oro,' which was later taken to Cologne, Palais Guillaume (q.v.), and is now destroyed.
Melani, 1903, pp. 89–90 with repr. of the whole cycle; Molmenti, p. 273, with a repr. of one Satyr at p. 284.

VENICE, Palazzo Rezzonico

Ceiling fresco in the 'Sala della Cappella':
ALLEGORY OF MARRIAGE   [1955, fig. 54]
Around the ceiling a large frieze with Satyrs and Satyresses, certainly by Domenico.

Ceiling fresco in the 'Throne Room':
MERIT BETWEEN NOBILITY AND VIRTUE   [1955, fig. 52]
(Also called Apotheosis of the Poet Quintiliano Rezzonico)
Around the fresco a large frieze with Eight female Allegorical Figures.
Certainly painted about 1758, with the assistance of Domenico. The sketch for the Allegory of Marriage is in Verona; what is probably a first idea for the Merit is in a private coll. in Madrid.
Molmenti, pp. 67–69, figs. pp. 62a, 62b, 64; Sack, p. 153, figs. 79–80; Lorenzetti, Ca' Rezzonico, 1936, pp. 21–22, 25–27, figs. 17–19; Morassi, p. 35, figs. 109–111; Lorenzetti, pp. 121–123, figs. 85–87.
Tiepolo was certainly in touch with the Rezzonico family when he was working at the Villa Valmarana, Vicenza, and soon afterwards he painted the altarpiece in Noventa Vicentina for Carlo Rezzonico (1758–60). The two frescoes in Pal. Rezzonico must have been painted about 1758, when Ludovico Rezzonico married Faustina Savorgnan (January 18th) and Carlo Rezzonico was elected Pope Clement XIII (July 13th).
The quadriga in the first ceiling, with its rearing white horses, recalls the theme developed at Würzburg in the Marriage of Barbarossa.

The paintings on canvas by Tiepolo in this palace are listed under Museo di Ca' Rezzonico.

VENICE, Palazzo Sagredo

There was originally in the Palace a decorative cycle, executed by Tiepolo, representing:
Juno and the peacock, ceiling fresco now in the Crespi Coll., Milano (q.v.), with grisailles frescoes of Finding of Moses and Apollo and Midas, now in Bergamo, Private Coll. (q.v.).
Homage to Venice, ceiling fresco, 4 × 2.90 m., which was, according to Sack, p. 153, later completely repainted.
Nobility and Fortitude, ceiling on canvas, mentioned by Sack, p. 64, as having been taken from Venice to Paris, Stettiner Coll. and present whereabouts unknown.
Sack, p. 64, 153; Molmenti, 1911, p. 198.

VENICE, Palazzo Sandi

Fresco on the ceiling of the principal saloon; c. 1724–25.

ALLEGORY OF THE POWER OF ELOQUENCE   [1955, fig. 10]
6.50 × 10.70 m.; illustrated by the following episodes:
Orpheus reclaiming Eurydice from Hades.
Amphion building the Walls of Thebes by his Music.
Bellerophon killing Chimera.
Hercules and the Chained Cercopes.
In the far distance in the centre are Minerva and Mercury.
The modello for this ceiling is in Zurich, private coll. (q.v.).
The canvases which formerly decorated the walls are now in Castelgomberto (q.v.).

Da Canal, 1732; Moschini, 1815, I, p. 603; Selvatico, 1847, p. 434; Molmenti, pp. 54, 78; Sack, p. 153; Morassi, Le Arti, 1942, pp. 91–92, figs. 8–13; Morassi, pp. 15–16, figs. 12–15.
According to Moschini (1815), the Palace was built for the nobleman Tomaso Sandi in 1721 by the architect Domenico Rossi. The old guides do not record when the Palace was finished, and it is not until Sack (1910) that the date 1725 is given as that of the completed work. In any case this date must be approximately correct, since the frescoes are stylistically earlier than those at Udine. This was the first large fresco painted in a private palace by Tiepolo. Before this date, according to Da Canal (1732), he had painted in the Palace of the Doge Cornaro (d. 1722) some overdoors, portraits and canvases—i.e., no frescoes.

The first illustration of this ceiling, previously almost unknown in the literature, in Morassi, *Le Arti*, 1942.

The scene of Hercules and the Cercopes was restored—i.e. repainted—by Tiepolo himself, much later, presumably on account of damage. (Morassi, *Burlington Magazine*, I, 1955, pp. 6–7.)

VENICE, Palazzo Servi-Manin

TRIUMPH OF VIRTUE AND FORTITUDE

Ceiling (now in the Contini-Bonacossi Coll., Florence, q.v.) originally executed by Tiepolo for Palazzo Servi-Manin. Iconographically and stylistically related to the *Allegory of Fortitude and Wisdom* at Ca' Rezzonico, Venice which is of 1744–45.

Sack, p. 153, mentions in the Palace another ceiling with the *Glory crowning the Virtue*, present whereabouts unknown. This last was etched by Domenico (De Vesme, 103; Molmenti, 1896, fig. p. 113) with the inscription: JO:ᵉ DOMINICUS TIEPOLO PINXIT ET FECIT, which proves that Domenico himself painted the ceiling.

VENICE, Palazzo Zen

Sack, p. 153, mentions a fresco on the ceiling of a room on the first floor in the middle of the three palaces (Fondamenta Zen), representing *Nobility and Virtue*, as an early work by Tiepolo and badly repainted. The fresco must be identified with the one executed by Jacopo Guarana, signed on a label held by a maid, below, leaning on the parapet. The decorations with feigned architecture and statues and medallions on the walls, in an almost neo-classic taste, are also certainly by Guarana. In a small room nearby is another small fresco, oval (*c.* 180×120 cm.) with an *Allegory*, is also by Guarana.

VENICE, Ca' Zenobio

Da Canal, 1732, p. XXXIII, writes that Tiepolo painted 'a room in Ca' Zenobio, divided into various stories, one of his first works.' Of all these works only the ceiling with *Justice and Peace* is now in S. Lazzaro degli Armeni (q.v.). Perhaps also the *Triumph of Aurelian* now in Turin (q.v.) belonged to Pal. Zenobio.

Moschini, 1815, II, p. 280, wrote that Tiepolo here painted 'in his early period a room with various stories.'

Molmenti, p. 51; Sack, p. 154.

VENICE, Congregazione di Carità

MADONNA AND CHILD WITH S. ANTHONY
Canvas, 70×35 cm.; *c.* 1730–35.

Originally in the Casa di Ricovero (the Asylum).

Another very similar small painting is in the Cini Coll., Venice; and another in Rome, private coll.

Pallucchini, *Emporium*, 1944, p. 14, fig. 10.

Rather poor in preservation.

VENICE, formerly Count Algarotti Coll.

PORTRAIT OF FRANCESCO ALGAROTTI STANDING NEAR A VICTORY

Tiepolo states in a letter of April 4th, 1761, to Algarotti, that he was painting the portrait of the Count. It is not known if he finished this canvas, no further information about it being available. Probably the picture was left unfinished in Venice, because of Tiepolo's departure for Spain in March, 1762, and was certainly lost after his death. Algarotti himself died in 1764.

From the description in Tiepolo's letter, we know that Count Algarotti was represented standing near a statue of Victory.

Precerutti-Garberi, in *Commentari*, April-June, 1958, pp. 120–123.

From the *Catalogue* of the collection of Count Algarotti, among other works all identified, we learn of a 'Diana bathing,' described as: 'She is standing surrounded by her nymphs, and Actaeon is visible in the distance, transformed and running away. On canvas, 1 foot 8 inches high, 1 foot, 3 inches wide.' (C. 57.5×42 cm.)

This picture is lost.

Another canvas with the same subject also from the Algarotti Coll. was in a private coll., New York (q.v.), now in Zürich, Bührle Coll.

Molmenti, p. 236; Sack, p. 231.

VENICE, formerly Andrighetti Coll.

S. FRANCIS OF PAOLA WITH OTHER SAINTS

Canvas mentioned in a manuscript by Cicogna, 1811, in the Museo Corrèr, Venice, as belonging to the Andrighetti Coll. in Venice (Sack, p. 231).

The MS. mentioned by Sack is not now traceable in the Museo Corrèr.

VENICE, formerly Pinacoteca Valentino Benfatto

The three canvases mentioned in the Catalogue by Zanotto (1856) can be identified with the MARTYRDOM OF S. THEODORA, now probably in the Falk Coll., Milan (q.v.); the BETHESDA (canvas, 110×162 cm.) by Domenico, now in Paris, private coll., and published by Molmenti, *Dedalo*, 1927, pp. 43–50 as by Giambattista; CHRIST AND THE ADULTERESS (canvas, 111×178 cm.) by Domenico, pendant to the former (ibidem, also as by Giambattista). Till 1927 or later in Paris, present whereabouts unknown.

Sack, pp. 131, 232.

VENICE, Brass Coll.

MADONNA WITH THE SLEEPING CHILD   Fig. 75
Canvas, oval, 52×41 cm.; *c.* 1720–22.

Morassi, *Le Arti*, 1942, p. 90, fig. 5.

This oval, still Piazzettesque, has much in common with the *Madonna* in Biella (q.v.).

VENICE, formerly Brass Coll.

THE CRUCIFIXION   Fig. 55
Canvas, 71×54 cm.; *c.* 1720–22.

Exhibited at the Galleria Antiquaria, Rome, in 1941, with an attribution to Fontebasso.

Morandotti, Cat. 1941, p. 68; Morassi, *L'Arte*, 1944, VI, p. 3 ff., figs. 1–2; Pallucchini, *Emporium*, 1944, p. 14, fig. 9.

A youthful work, rather close in style to the four *Mythologies* in the Accademia (also attributed at one time to Fontebasso) but more forced and showy.

THE ADORATION OF THE SHEPHERDS
Canvas, 37×38 cm.

Attributed by Goering to Tiepolo (*ad vocem*), but by F. Zugno.

Morandotti, *Catalogue*, 1941, p. 44, fig. 39 (as a late work by Giambattista).

VENICE, formerly Pinacoteca Barbini-Breganze

OLD PHILOSOPHER
Canvas, 47×36 cm.

Listed in the *Catalogue* of the Pinacoteca (Zanotto, 1847), together with other pictures by Giambattista (mostly now in Stuttgart). No further trace of the canvas.

The painting is described as rapidly sketched and with much chiaroscuro.

Sack, p. 233.

VENICE, formerly Bruini Coll.

PHAETHON ENTREATING APOLLO TO ALLOW HIM TO DRIVE THE CHARIOT OF THE SUN   Fig. 238
Canvas, 21×44 cm.; *c.* 1720.

Sketch for an unknown or never executed ceiling.

Hitherto unpublished. Now in the Sonino Coll., Venice.

VENICE, Count Cini Coll.

THE EDUCATION OF THE VIRGIN   Fig. 73
Canvas, 50×28 cm.; *c.* 1730–35.

Iconographically rather like the pictures in Dijon and Genoa, but of later date.
Pallucchini, *Emporium*, 1947, p. 238, fig. 7; Lorenzetti, p. 14, fig. 7.

MADONNA AND CHILD WITH S. ANTHONY OF PADUA Fig. 103
Canvas, 46×35.5 cm.; *c.* 1730–35.

Sketch very similar to the picture belonging to the Congregazione di Carità. Hitherto unpublished.

ALLEGORICAL FIGURE   Fig. 349
Fresco transferred to canvas, shaped at the corners, representing a winged female figure with a torch in her right hand, flying over a wheel and with a star over her head (Fortune or Truth?); 221×221 cm.; *c.* 1755–60.
Hitherto unpublished. It formed part of a ceiling executed for the Palazzo Vecchia in Vicenza, representing the *Triumph of Virtue* (q.v.). This small ceiling must date from about the same period as the Villa Valmarana, Vicenza, on account of stylistic similarities to some ceilings in the Palazzina.
Molmenti, 1885, p. 186; Molmenti, 1928, p. XVI.

VENICE, formerly Dal Zotto Coll.

THE DEPOSITION FROM THE CROSS
Judging from the photograph (Naya-Böhm, 1477) stylistically very close to the works of Tiepolo about 1730 and inspired by the *Deposition* by Luca Giordano now in the Academy in Venice.
Present whereabouts unknown.

THE FEAST IN THE HOUSE OF LEVI (MARRIAGE FEAST AT CANA?)
                                                                 Fig. 48
Attributed by Molmenti, p. 77, fig. p. 76 to Tiepolo, but, judging from the reproduction, the picture seems unconvincing except that it may be a work of his earliest period. It is reproduced also in Fogolari's *Tiepolo* (s.d. [1913]), p. 36, fig. 64.

HEAD OF AN OLD ORIENTAL (with dark beard, a turban and a golden collar with medal).
By Domenico.
Wrongly attributed to Giambattista (Brogi photograph, 19088, also as Giambattista). Reverse of the engraving in the 'Raccolta di Teste.' Very similar to that of a Private Coll., Milan, published in Morandotti, *Catalogue*, 1941, p. 41, fig. 36.

S. ANNE WITH S. ANTHONY ABBOT AND A BISHOP SAINT
Wrongly attributed to Tiepolo (Naya-Böhm photograph, 1894).
A work by F. Zugno.
Present whereabouts unknown.

VENICE, formerly Donà dalle Rose Coll.

THE ARMS OF THE BARBARIGO-SAGREDO FAMILY   Fig. 422
Canvas, 156×182 cm.; *c.* 1743.

Ex Pal. Barbarigo, Donà dalle Rose Coll., Venice; M. Crespi Coll., Milan.
Sack, p. 149; Lorenzetti-Planiscig, *Catalogo della Collezione Donà dalle Rose*, Venice, 1934, p. 19, with fig.; Morassi, p. 26.
Present whereabouts unknown.

VENICE, formerly Carlo Du-Bois Coll.

THE PRODIGAL SON
Canvas, 44×58 cm.

Sketch mentioned in 1849 at the Sale of the Du-Bois Coll. as by Giambattista, Sack, p. 233. Certainly to be identified with the painting in Milan, Private coll. (see Addenda).

VENICE, Gatti-Casazza Coll.

MADONNA AND CHILD HOLDING THE ROSARY
Wood, oval; *c.* 12×9 cm.; *c.* 1720–25.
A little devotional painting, rather rare in Tiepolo's oeuvre.

VENICE, formerly Gatti-Casazza Coll.

S. ROCH   Fig. 154
Canvas, *c.* 45×33 cm.; *c.* 1730–35.

One of the devotional paintings for the Scuola di S. Rocco.
In the Coll. wrongly attributed to Domenico (perhaps because of its many repaints), whereas it belongs undoubtedly to Giambattista.
Now in the possession of Count Arrivabene in Venice.

VENICE, formerly Giovanelli Coll.

At the Tiepolo Exhibition in Venice, 1896 (*Catalogue*, No. 34) there was a sketch for a ceiling representing a MYTHOLOGICAL SUBJECT (canvas, 65×50 cm.) as by Giambattista, which cannot at present be identified. Molmenti, p. 77; Sack, p. 162.

VENICE, Giustiniani-Recanati Coll.

THE SACRIFICE OF IPHIGENIA   Fig. 232
Canvas, 65×112 cm.; *c.* 1725–30.

Molmenti, p. 77, fig. p. 75; Sack, p. 162, fig. 26; Morassi, 1934, p. 92; Morassi, p. 17, fig. 17; Lorenzetti, p. 32, fig. 22.
The Homeric theme, developed later at Merlengo and the Villa Valmarana, is here still simple and far from the grandiose later treatment.

VENICE, formerly Maffeo Pinelli Coll.

In the *Catalogue* of the Pinelli Coll., in Venice, 1785, the following paintings are listed as by Giambattista:

THE HOLY FAMILY, canvas, grisaille, 82×24.5 cm.

VENUS AND A SATYR, canvas, 29.2×22.5 cm. (described in the *Catalogue*: Venus only half dressed, sitting near a globe and touching a satyr with the sceptre).
Sack, p. 233. Both paintings are missing.

VENICE, Private Coll.

S. LOUIS GONZAGA
Canvas, oval, 12.5×10.4 cm.

By Domenico.
Goering, 1944, p. 97 with fig., wrongly attributes it to Giambattista.

VENICE, Private Coll.

S. CATHERINE AND ANGELS   Fig. 203
Fresco transferred to canvas, circular, *c.* 2 m. diam.; *c.* 1732–35.

The Saint is seated on clouds, surrounded by child angels, and holding a palm, emblem of her martyrdom, in her right hand. The fresco, of excellent quality, has the light colours and the style of the Villa Loschi figures (Vicenza, 1734).
Pallucchini, *Emporium*, 1944, I, p. 15, fig. 12.

VENICE, formerly Private Coll.
S. ROCH   Fig. 161
Canvas, *c.* 45×33 cm.; *c.* 1730–35.

Belonging to the many devotional paintings for the Scuola di San Rocco.
Present whereabouts unknown.
Not seen by me.

VENICE, formerly Private Coll.

BUST OF AN OLD WARRIOR
Canvas, 96×74 cm.

Attributed to Tiepolo, but is a work by a contemporary imitator copying one of the 'Heads' engraved by Domenico in his 'Raccolta di Teste' (See Molmenti, *Acqueforti del Tiepolo*, 1896, p. 154).
Another *Head of an old man*, half-length with a white beard, in oriental costume and with a large collar, by the same hand as the one in Venice, is in a private coll. in Milan.

VENICE

THE CROSSING OF THE RED SEA

Quoted by Da Canal, 1732, p. XXXII, as one of the first works of Giambattista, exhibited on the day of St. Roch in Venice and 'applauded.' This is the only mention of the picture of which there is no further trace.

Molmenti, p. 46; Sack, p. 230.

VENICE

CHRIST ADMINISTERING THE SACRAMENT TO THE APOSTLES

Mentioned by Da Canal, 1732, p. III: 'In ten hours only on commission he painted, life-size, the twelve Apostles receiving the sacrament from Christ, a work admired for its incomparable speed.'

This painting of his youth is not recorded by any other source. The only painting similar in subject and in size, which could be related to this, is the large canvas once in the Suermondt Coll. in Aachen (q.v.).

VENICE

PORTRAIT OF A LADY WITH A FUR

Canvas, 72 × 53.5 cm. (?); c. 1750–60.

Half-length, three quarters to the right, she is nude except for a fur-lined cape over her right shoulder.

The original, from which the pastel in Washington (q.v.) was copied. Nothing is known about this painting, which appeared on the art market about thirty years ago. Certainly a 'pendant' to the Lady with a parrot now in Oxford, Ashmolean Museum (q.v.).

VENICE

Gradenigo records on July 5th, 1757, that Tiepolo 'was executing an altarpiece with S. George on horseback of much beauty, and commissioned by the Ambassador of the King of Spain at the London Court, where the picture of the value of 200 zecchini was sent.' Of this painting, certainly executed as a gift from the King of Spain to George II of England, there is no other mention. The King of England seems to have appreciated the gift, for three years later—according to Gradenigo, on September 1st, 1760—he commissioned from T. a painting of Frederick, King of Prussia on horseback commanding a victorious army of which there is no other mention and we do not know if it was exer executed. The Surveyor of the Queen's Pictures, Sir Anthony Blunt, kindly informs me that in the inventories of the Royal Collections in the 18th century there is no trace of anything by Tiepolo and there is certainly nothing in the collection today which could be even remotely associated with this painter.

The story is indeed mysterious.

See also: M. Precerutti-Garberi, in Commentari, April-June, 1958, pp. 116–120.

VENICE

CHRIST BEFORE PILATE

It is probable that Tiepolo painted, possibly on a large canvas, this subject in his early period, as a contemporary copy exists (73 × 98.5 cm.) in the Cini Coll., Venice, after this lost original.

VEROLANUOVA, near Brescia, Parish Church

| THE GATHERING OF THE MANNA | [1955, pls. 21–23] |
| THE SACRIFICE OF MELCHISEDEK | [1955, fig. 21] |

Two canvases, 10 × 5.25 m.; c. 1735–40.

Probably commissioned by Count G. F. Gambara, appointed Podestá of Verolanova in 1735.

The two sketches, formerly belonging to the painter Maccari in Venice, now in Buenos Aires (q.v.), are certainly the modelli. These are the largest canvases Tiepolo ever painted.

Molmenti, p. 150; Sack, p. 179; Molmenti, 1920, p. 145 ff. with figs.; Marini, Verolanuova, Brescia, 1907, p. 145 ff.; Molmenti, p. 150; Sack, p. 179; Molmenti, 1920, p. 145 ff. with figs.; Morassi, p. 22, figs. 48–49; Cristini, Brescia, XI–XII, 1952, pp. 8–11 with repr.

There is a tradition that the contract for these two pictures was pre-served in the archives of the Counts Gambara, and that Tiepolo was paid 10,000 lire. It seems, therefore, reasonable that Count G. F. Gambara ordered the two paintings from Tiepolo. The spectacular composition may have been inspired by Celesti's picture in the same church, nearly as big, but painted many years earlier. Recently the two canvases have been restored.

VERONA, Museo di Castelvecchio

HELIODORUS PILLAGING THE TEMPLE Fig. 26

Canvas, 195 × 231 cm.; c. 1725–30.

Originally in the church of S. Sebastiano, Verona, forming part of a series of other pictures by Balestra, Brentana, Bellòtti, Salis, Torelli, Perini, Prunati and Dorigny; in 1897 to the Museum.

Dalla Rosa, 1803, p. 101; Da Persico, Descrizione di Verona, 1820, I, p. 207; Molmenti, p. 113; Morassi, 1937, p. 53; Morassi, p. 17; Pallucchini, 1944, p. 14; Lorenzetti, p. 26, fig. 17.

The rather crowded composition was certainly designed to be placed high up. The style is very similar to that of the canvases formerly in Ca' Dolfin, Venice.

ALLEGORY OF THE REZZONICO-SAVORGNAN MARRIAGE

Canvas, 41 × 68 cm.; c. 1758 (?). Fig. 352

Related to the fresco in the Ca' Rezzonico, Venice. From the Gallery of Antonio Pompei; bequeathed to the Museum.

Trecca, Cat. of the Pinacoteca Communale di Verona, Bergamo, 1912, p. 138; Lorenzetti, 1935, p. 392 with repr.; A. Avena, Il Museo di Castelvecchio, 1937, p. 11; Lorenzetti, 1938, p. 21; Lorenzetti, p. 121, fig. 86, always as original by G.B.

A rapid sketch, very close to Domenico.

There are some differences between the sketch and the executed ceiling; but Molmenti (p. 113) and Sack (p. 180) are wrong in regarding this as the modello for the ceiling of Pal. Canossa. Perhaps after an original sketch by Giambattista, now lost or present whereabouts unknown.

VERONA, Palazzo Betti, later Faccioli at S. Tommaso

A ceiling mentioned by Dalla Rosa, 1803, p. 238, as by Tiepolo, was destroyed in 1852 by the priest Turri in renewing the Palace.

Battistella, 1903; Molmenti, 1911, p. 99, Note 2.

VERONA, Palazzo Canossa

Fresco in the ceiling of the principal saloon:

TRIUMPH OF HERCULES [1955, pl. 77]

Oval, c. 14 × 8 m.; 1761.

The grisailles representing the Quarters of the Earth and the five over-doors representing Allegories of Virtues were painted by Domenico. The architect Pietro Visconti also collaborated with the painter, as is recorded by Zaccaria Betti Veronese in his eulogy of Tiepolo's work, 1761. From some letters of Duke of Montealegre, Spanish ambassador in Venice, to Marques de Esquillache, regarding Tiepolo's planned voyage to the Royal Court of Madrid, and from a letter of Tiepolo himself to Montealegre (see Chronological Table), we learn that in September of 1761 the painter was in Verona, certainly working in the Palazzo Canossa. The frescoes were finished at about the middle of October, 1761.

L. di Canossa, Studi e ricerche intorno al Pal. Canossa, Verona, 1898; Molmenti, pp. 112–113, fig. p. 112a; Sack, p. 180, fig. 128; Morassi, p. 36, figs. 114–115.

This ceiling fresco and the overdoors were badly damaged during the last war, in 1945, when the old Castelvecchio bridge was destroyed. It was an open composition with large areas of transparent blue sky; to some extent it was a development of the ceiling at Würzburg.

A sketch is in Manchester, Currier Gallery (q.v.).

VERONA, Palazzo Orti

A painting by Tiepolo, without indication of the subject, is mentioned by Dalla Rosa, 1803, p. 238, in the Coll. Orti at Verona.

Molmenti, 1911, p. 99, Note 2. The work cannot be traced.

VICENZA, Museo Civico, Pinacoteca

THE IMMACULATE CONCEPTION   Fig. 66
Arched canvas, 380×190 cm.; c. 1734–36.

Formerly in the church of the Aracoeli in Vicenza, and later given to
the gallery by Clemente Barbieri.
Descrizione delle architetture, pitture e scolture di Vicenza, Vicenza, 1779,
I, p. 2; Molmenti, p. 94, fig. p. 94; Sack, p. 180; Arslan, 1934, *ad loc.*;
Morassi, p. 21; Pallucchini, 1946, pp. 164–165.
A splendid and popular work, silver-blue in tonality, and stylistically
close to the Villa al Biron frescoes (1734). There is a sketch related to
this altarpiece, but with some variations, in the Museum at Amiens
(q.v.); another sketch was recorded by Sack (p. 188) in the Weber Coll.,
Hamburg, as by Tiepolo, although Molmenti (p. 311, fig. p. 316) says
it is by an imitator. It is now in the Art Institute, Detroit (q.v.).

ALLEGORY OF FORTITUDE AND WISDOM   Fig. 347
Fresco transferred to canvas, c. 9×5 m.; 1743.

Until 1917 on the ceiling of the principal saloon of the Villa Cordellina
at Montecchio Maggiore.
The *modelletto* for this ceiling is in the Dulwich College Gallery, London.
Molmenti, p. 96, fig. p. 96; Sack, p. 174; Molmenti, 1927, pp. 42–43
with figs.; Morassi, p. 26.
The fresco was removed from the Villa on account of the dilapidated
state of the building, which was, until recently, completely desolate.
The fresco suffered in many places and was also badly restored (compare
the photographs reproduced by Molmenti in 1909 (p. 96) and in 1929
(*Dedalo*, p. 43).
Now replaced in the Villa Cordellina (1956).

TIME DISCOVERING TRUTH   Fig. 327
Shaped oval canvas, 3.40×2.54 m.; c. 1743.

Formerly a ceiling in the Villa Cordellina at Montecchio Maggiore, and
later brought to Palazzo Cordellina, Vicenza; from there to the Museum
in 1935.
Goering, *ad vocem*; G. Fasolo, *Guida del Museo di Vicenza*, Vicenza,
1940, p. 112.
An excellent version of a theme often painted by Tiepolo, similar in
composition to the ceiling of Pal. Pisani-Moretta, Venice. The same
model evidently posed for *Truth* as for the *Amphitrite* in Dresden,
painted at about the same time.

DECOLLATION OF S. JOHN THE BAPTIST
Canvas, 186×107 cm.

By Domenico.
Originally in the Palazzo Alvise Monza, where it was recorded in the
Descrizione, 1779, II, pp. 65, 122, as *opera bella del Tiepoletto, singolarmente
per la corporatura del carnefice*. Caversazzi, *Emporium*, 1899, p. 213 and
Molmenti, p. 95 also give it to Giambattista; Sack, p. 181, mentions it
only in reference to Arnaldi. The Museum Guide (1912, p. 54 with
repr.) attributes it to Domenico; as does Goering, *ad vocem*.
Certainly painted under Giambattista's direction, and very close to him.

VICENZA, Church of Corpus Domini

Arnaldi, 1779 and Vendramini-Mosca, *Descrizione . . . di Vicenza*,
Vicenza 1779, p. 17, write that in this church there was 'around the walls
beginning from the right, a painting with a *Bishop vesting a nun* a work
among the first by Tiepolo.'
Molmenti, p. 95; Sack, p. 181. No further trace of the picture.

VICENZA, S. Stefano

Shutters of the ciborium of the High Altar; c. 1750–60.

In the centre:
THE RESURRECTION, 164×44 cm.   Fig. 62

At the sides:
S. PETER and S. JOHN THE BAPTIST, 100×44 cm.

Three canvases, painted in monochrome on a gold ground.
In rather poor condition.
Descrizione, 1779, I, p. 122; Molmenti, pp. 94–95; Sack, p. 180;
Molmenti, 1927, p. 40; I. Battistin, *Numero Unico della Chiesa di S.
Stefano*, Vicenza, 1933, pp. 18–19, with repr.; Goering, *ad vocem*.

VICENZA, Palazzo Porto (now Biego)

APOTHEOSIS OF ORAZIO PORTO
Remains of the ceiling fresco, detached about 1900 and now in Seattle
(q.v.). The detachment (*strappo*) of the fresco was limited to the top
layer, which allowed the original colour to penetrate the wall and to
form a second layer with large traces of the composition. These traces
were skilfully completed and repainted, so that the whole ceiling now
gives the impression of being the original one.
In a neighbouring room decorated with stuccoes of the 16th century,
there are three ceiling frescoes: one, in the middle, octagonal, the two
others square (c. 1.5 m. each) with *Sky and clouds with pigeons, a wheel,
a quiver*.
There is no bibliography for these small frescoes except some local
Guides (e.g., Veneto, Touring Club Italiano, Milan, 1954, p. 210).
The grisailles with the *Ancestors of the da Porto Family* are now in
Stockholm (q.v.).

VICENZA, Palazzo Valmarana-Trento

Frescoes in the principal saloon; c. 1757.
TRIUMPH OF TRUTH OVER ERROR, CALUMNY AND FALSEHOOD
                                                     [1955, fig. 51]
Shaped oval ceiling, c. 5×7 m.

In the corners of the ceilings were four medallions with *Allegories of Art,
Music, Science* and *History*. On the walls were four imitation *Statues*,
painted certainly with the assistance of Domenico, to whom also was
due, perhaps, part of the ceiling. The illusionistic parts were by
Mengozzi-Colonna.
Descrizione, 1779, II, p. 101; Molmenti, p. 95, fig. p. 95; Sack, p. 180,
fig. 78; G. Franceschini in *Emporium*, Sept., 1926; Molmenti, 1927,
p. 36 ff., with figs.; Morassi, p. 35.
This ceiling was very unusual, both in theme and in composition. It
seems stylistically very probable that these frescoes were painted at
about the same date as those in the Villa Valmarana (1757). Two
splendid drawings—first ideas—are in the Museo Civico, Trieste.
All the frescoes were destroyed by air raids in 1945. Only two feigned
statues, one of a *Girl with a lamb* and one of a *Young man bearing a
necklace* with a pendant shaped as a heart, and traces of some decorative
motives, skilfully restored, now survive from the principal salon.

One ceiling, formerly unknown, has survived:
ALLEGORY   Fig. 407
Circular fresco, now transferred to canvas, 302 cm. diam.; c. 1757.

Certainly painted with the assistance of Domenico.
Lorenzetti, p. 113, fig. 81.
Now in a private coll., Milan.

VICENZA, Villa Valmarana

Frescoes in the 'Palazzina':
1. SALA D'IFIGENIA (of Iphigenia)

On the ceiling: DIANA AND ÆOLUS. On the main wall: SACRIFICE
OF IPHIGENIA; on the wall facing the *Sacrifice:* THE GREEK FLEET
IN AULIS.   [1955, fig. 49]

2. STANZA DELL'ILIADE (of the Iliad)

On the ceiling: MINERVA WITH PUTTI ON CLOUDS.
On the walls: (1) MINERVA PREVENTS ACHILLES FROM KILLING
AGAMEMNON; (2) EURYBATES AND TALTHYBIUS CONDUCTING
BRISEIS TO AGAMEMNON; (3) THETIS CONSOLING ACHILLES;
(4) AMOR IN THE SKY, ABOVE A LANDSCAPE.   Figs. 230, 231

3. STANZA DELL'ORLANDO FURIOSO

On the ceiling: AMOR BLINDFOLDED, ON A CAR DRAWN BY PUTTI. On the other walls: (1) ANGELICA AND MEDORO; (2) ANGELICA ENGRAVING THE NAME OF MEDORO; (3) ANGELICA AND MEDORO LEAVING THE PEASANTS; (4) ROGER LIBERATING ANDROMEDA. Fig. 268

4. STANZA DELL'ENEIDE (of the Aeneid)

On the ceiling: TRIUMPH OF VENUS, WITH PUTTI ON CLOUDS. On the walls: (1) VENUS ABANDONING AENEAS; (2) AENEAS PRESENTING AMOR WITH THE FEATURES OF ASCANIUS TO DIDO; (3) THE DREAM OF AENEAS; (4) VENUS ASKING VULCAN FOR THE ARMS FOR AENEAS. [1955, fig. 48]

5. STANZA DELLA GERUSALEMME LIBERATA

On the ceiling: VICTORY OF LIGHT OVER DARKNESS. On the walls: (1) ARMIDA SEDUCING RINALDO; (2) RINALDO AND ARMIDA SURPRISED; (3) RINALDO IS ASHAMED OF HIS PAST; (4) RINALDO ABANDONING ARMIDA. Figs. 269–270

Frescoes in the 'Foresteria':

1. SALA DELL'OLIMPO (of Olympus)

On the walls: (1) MARS, VENUS AND AMOR; (2) MERCURY; (3) CHRONOS; (4) APOLLO AND DIANA; (5) JUPITER.
[1955, figs. 47, 50]

All the other rooms in the 'Foresteria' are the work of Domenico and assistants, and not by Giambattista, as was believed until 1941. Mengozzi-Colonna helped with the decorative parts.
Executed in 1757, as may be seen from the date (hitherto wrongly read as 1737) in the *Stanza delle Scene Carnevalesche* (of the Carnival scenes) painted by Domenico in the 'Foresteria.'
G. Gozzi, in 'Gazzetta Veneta', XXII, April 19th, 1760; *Descrizione*, 1779, II, p. 113; G. A. Brocchi, *San Sebastiano . . .* (poems), Vicenza, 1785; Goethe, *Tagebuch der ital. Reise*, 1786 (ed. of 1908, Berlin, p. 106); Molmenti, 1880, *passim*; Molmenti, pp. 100–106, figs. pp. 100a, 101–106; Sack, p. 181; Morassi, *Le Arti*, 1941, pp. 251–262, figs. 8, 16–28 (first dating the whole cycle 1757 instead of 1737, and first attributing the painting in the Foresteria to Domenico); Morassi, 1945; Pallucchini, 1945; Morassi, p. 34, figs. 96–99.
During the war, in March, 1944, the ceiling of the Sala d'Ifigenia was destroyed and some others in the same building badly damaged. A great part of the frescoes in the Palazzina and the Foresteria were therefore detached from the walls and taken to safety. They have now been replaced. After the detaching of the frescoes, there still remained traces of colours on the walls and these (which are, of course, pale and fragmentary) were later transferred to canvas. They are now also in the Villa Valmarana. The Valmarana frescoes belong to a critical moment in Tiepolo's stylistic development, when some influence from the Rococo of France and South Germany is discernible, certainly derived from his stay in Würzburg as well as from the diffusion of a new taste in Venice at that time. The more nervous line and the iridescent colours are among the new elements. This critical moment had, in fact, no further consequences and some of the Valmarana frescoes remain isolated phenomena in Tiepolo's evolution. It is also interesting to observe that, while Giambattista was painting his mythological, historical and epic scenes, Domenico was creating in the 'Foresteria,' an entirely new type which anticipated the bourgeois and illustrative art of the late 18th century.

VICENZA, near, Villa Loschi al Biron

Frescoes on the Grand Staircase:
STATUES OF MERIT AND NOBILITY in two imitation niches Grisailles. Figs. 370, 371

On the ceiling of the staircase:
TIME UNVEILING TRUTH Fig. 325
Higher still, on the same staircase, two allegories:
INNOCENCE DRIVING AWAY VICE Fig. 360
INDUSTRY TRIUMPHING OVER IDLENESS Fig. 359

In the saloon:
ALLEGORY OF JUSTICE, FORTITUDE, TEMPERANCE AND TRUTH
Fresco in the central part of the ceiling. Fig. 365

In the lateral compartments of the ceiling, two further frescoes:
MARS, and GENIUS Figs. 366–367

On the walls, four allegorical frescoes:
FIDELITY WITH LOVE Fig. 361
CHARITY DISPENSING ALMS Fig. 363
COURAGE CROWNED BY GLORY Fig. 362
MODESTY PUTTING PRIDE TO FLIGHT Fig. 364

Executed by Tiepolo in 1734, for Count Nicolò Loschi, according to an inscription in the vestibule.
Lafond, 1902; Molmenti, pp. 99–100, figs. pp. 99–100; Sack, p. 181; Morassi, p. 21, figs. 46–47.
This cycle was executed rather hastily, and certainly with the help of assistants, as Lafond rightly suggested. Not all the scenes are of the same high quality, which may be due to the short time at his disposal as may be gauged from a letter, dated Venice, November 17th, 1734, to Lodovico Feronati of Bergamo, saying that he had been working in Vicenza 'day and night without stopping for breath.' In this cycle however, there are already some traces of the beginning of his new classical style.
A series of drawings related to the frescoes is in the Museo Civico, Trieste, and the Victoria and Albert Museum, London. The first drawing for the project for the *Justice, Temperance and Truth* ceiling is in the Rasini Coll., Milan.

VICENZA, Palazzo dei Conti Vecchia, later Malaspina-Thiene, now Baron Romanelli

Ceiling painted in oil with a *Triumph of Virtue* in the main saloon (noted in the *Descrizione . . .* 1779, II, p. 114) but already sold by the time of Molmenti and Sack (1909 and 1910) and present whereabouts unknown. A ceiling fresco, transferred to canvas, coming from this Palazzo is now in the Cini Coll., Venice (q.v.).
Molmenti, 1885, p. 186; Molmenti, p. 95; Sack, p. 180; Molmenti, 1928, p. XVI.

VICENZA, Palazzo Marchesini, later Rossetti, a San Michele

Frescoes by Giambattista Tiepolo assisted by Mengozzi-Colonna in a gallery were mentioned in the *Descrizione . . . di Vicenza*, 1779, II, p. 72. They were later stripped from the walls, sold, and their present whereabouts are unknown.
The *Descrizione* says (p. 86): 'Molto commendabile si è la Galleria, non tanto per la sua forma, quanto per esser stata dipinta a fresco da Girolamo Colonna, per quello spetta all' Architettura, e da Gio. Battista Tiepoletto per le figure, ambidue celebri Pittori de' nostri tempi. Si vede inoltre dipinta la Sala con gruppi a finto bronzo e con quattro sopraporte; quandi un soffitto, con varie altre cose, del predetto Colonna.'
Molmenti, p. 95; Sack, p. 181.

VICENZA, da Schio Coll.
S. ROCH Fig. 171
Canvas, 43 × 33 cm.; *c.* 1730–35.

One of the numerous devotional pictures executed for members of the Scuola di S. Rocco.
Morassi, 1942, IV–V, p. 267, fig. 26.

VICENZA, Roi Coll.
HEAD OF AN ORIENTAL
Canvas, 58 × 48 cm.; *c.* 1750–60.
Lorenzetti, p. 99, fig. 73.

VICENZA, Villa Muttoni called 'La Caimpenta'

Frescoes in the main saloon, representing:

THE JUDGEMENT OF SOLOMON and
ALLEGORY OF THE OLD AND THE NEW YEAR
with other mythological figures in grisaille, wrongly attributed to
Tiepolo and Mengozzi-Colonna in the Guide *Veneto* (Touring Club
Italiano, 1932, p. 172). The frescoes, badly repainted, are by a poor
imitator of Tiepolo.

VIENNA, Kunsthistorisches Museum

ETEOCLES AND POLYNICES   [1955, fig. 12]
HANNIBAL CONTEMPLATING THE SEVERED HEAD OF
HASDRUBAL

Two canvases, 383 × 182 cm. each; *c.* 1725-30.

They bear the old inscriptions in Latin on the top, as well as the canvases
originally did (cf. Leningrad, Hermitage).
Originally in Ca' Dolfin, Venice, until 1870; ex coll. Miller von
Aicholz, Vienna; Castiglioni Coll., Vienna, until 1930 (Sale at Graupe,
Vienna, 27.11.1930).
They formed part of the group of ten canvases now dispersed between
the Hermitage in Leningrad (5) and New York, Castiglioni Coll. (3)
Da Canal, 1732; Bergeret et Fragonard, 1773-74, p. 386; Moschini,
1806, III, p. 75; Molmenti, p. 276, figs. pp. 275, 276; Sack, p. 151,
figs. 21-22; Derschau, in *Cicerone*, 1915, p. 13; *Pantheon*, January, 1931,
with the notice of the Museum acquisition; Fiocco, in *The Burlington
Magazine*, 1931; Morassi, 1942, IV, V, p. 259 ff., with figs.; Morassi, p.
16, figs. 34-35; Lorenzetti, p. 24, fig. 16; *Cat.* of the Museum, 1960, p. 120.

S. CATHERINE OF SIENA   Fig. 202
Canvas, oval, 70 × 52 cm.; *c.* 1740-45.

Originally in the convent of S. Giustina, Padua; then in the Imperial
Art Collection in Graz until 1765; then in Prague, and since 1822 in
Vienna. Engraved by Marco Pitteri and by Wagner.
Molmenti, p. 274, fig. p. 332a; Sack, p. 202, fig. 73; Lorenzetti, p. 81,
fig. 67; *Cat.* of the Museum, 1960, pp. 120-121.
The type of the Saint and the feeling of languid spirituality are very
close to the altarpiece in the Gesuati, Venice, of about the same period.
An old copy (canvas 89 × 52 cm.) is in the Museum at Düsseldorf.

VIENNA, Akademie

PHAETHON AND APOLLO   [1955, pl. 13]
Canvas, 67.8 × 52.5 cm.; 1731.

Modelletto for the Pal. Archinto, Milan. Another *modelletto* is at Barnard
Castle.
Molmenti, p. 274, fig. p. 273; Sack, p. 203, fig. 40; Morassi, 1942,
IV-V, p. 265, fig. 16; Morassi, p. 17; Lorenzetti, p. 35, fig. 24; Münz,
Catalogue, 1953, p. 42.
A masterpiece of high quality.

PHAETHON AND APOLLO
Canvas, 68 × 50 cm.

By a follower of Tiepolo.
Sold Frankfurt, Bangel, September 16th-17th, 1920, No. 53, repr. VIII.
Believed to be the original sketch for Palazzo Archinto (see above). In
very bad condition. Münz, Catalogue, 1953, p. 37.
Probably identical with the sketch in Hamburg, Sack Coll. (Sack,
p. 189).

S. BRUNO
Canvas, 97 × 61.7 cm.

Once wrongly attributed to Tiepolo (Molmenti, p. 299, fig. p. 300) and
to Ricci (Sack, p. 203), but by a Spanish master recently identified as
Matteo Cerezo. (See Münz, Catalogue, Vienna, 1953, p. 34, fig. 8.)

VIENNA, Liechtenstein Gall.
See Vaduz.

VIENNA, formerly Hoyos-Amerling Coll.

PRIAM IMPLORING ACHILLES TO SURRENDER THE BODY OF
HECTOR
Canvas, 42 × 75 cm.; said to be an early work.

Present whereabouts unknown.
Modern, 1902, p. 52; Molmenti, p. 281; Sack, p. 205.

VIENNA, formerly Private Coll.

HEAD OF AN OLD MAN
Canvas, 60 × 52 cm.

By Domenico.
From the Matthiesen Gall. in London (a few years before 1938).
Corresponding to one of the *Heads* etched by Domenico (reproduced
in Molmenti, *Acqueforti*, 1896, p. 165 left).
Froelich-Bume, *The Burlington Magazine*, 1938, February, p. 87, Plate
IIA (as Giambattista).

VIENNA, Private Coll.

THE THREE AGES OF MAN
Canvas, 56 × 73 cm.

Mentioned in the Catalogue 'Ausstellung Italienische Barockmalerei',
Vienna, Sanct Lucas Gall., 1937, p. 43, No. 129 as by G. B. Tiepolo.
Not seen by me. Present whereabouts unknown. No reproduction
exists.

VIENNA, Private Coll.

S. MARY MAGDALEN IN THE DESERT WITH ANGELS
Canvas, 67 × 51.5 cm.

Clearly by F. Fontebasso inspired by Tiepolo and attributed to Tiepolo
himself.

VIENNA, formerly Baron Nathaniel de Rothschild Coll.

REBECCA AND ELIEZER
175 × 120 cm.

Listed by Sack, p. 203, and by Modern, as an autograph work by
Tiepolo, cannot be identified as no reproduction exists.

VIENNA, formerly Silbermann Coll.

HEAD OF AN OLD MAN (in oriental costume with a book and com-
passes in the left hand)
Canvas, 56 × 62 cm.

The painting, believed to be by Tiepolo, belongs to the school of the
master, probably Gaetano Zompini.

VIERHOUTEN, Holland, van Beuningen Coll.

THE CRUCIFIXION   Fig. 57
Canvas, 75 × 80 cm.; *c.* 1745-50.

It formed part of a series similar to the paintings in Hamburg, in the
St. Louis Museum, and elsewhere.
Ex coll. von Nemes, Munich.
A. Venturi, *Studi dal vero*, Milan, 1927, p. 405, fig. 280; D. Hannema,
Coll. van Beuningen, 1949, No. 122, pls. 156 and 157.

VITTORIO VENETO, Cathedral

In the Sacristy:

THE CRUCIFIXION
Gouache, 50 × 35 cm.

By F. Fontebasso.

THE SACRED HEART
Canvas, 55 × 35 cm.

By F. Fontebasso.

Both the paintings are wrongly attributed to Tiepolo in some local
Guides (e.g. *Veneto*, Touring Club Italiano, Milan, 1954, p. 406).

WARSAW, National Museum

THE LAST SUPPER
Canvas, 77 × 88 cm.

Judging from the photograph, a work of the Tiepolo school, after the original in the Louvre. Fiocco (*Arte Veneta*, 1947, p. 283) wrongly considers this painting as the original, the Louvre picture as a poor replica. *Catalogue* of the Exhibition of Italian Painting in Polish Collections, Warsaw, 1956, No. 94, p. 105, Fig. 108 (as original).

WARWICK CASTLE, Earl of Warwick

S. JOHN THE BAPTIST WITH THE LAMB   Fig. 185
Canvas, 43 × 35.5 cm.; *c.* 1730–35.

In the style of the many S. Roch paintings.
In some way related to the altarpiece of the same Saint in the church of S. Massimo in Padua.
Not seen by me, but, judging from the photograph, certainly autograph.
Photo in the Witt Library.

WASHINGTON, National Gallery of Art, S. H. Kress Collection

SCENE FROM ROMAN HISTORY   [1955, fig. 19]
Canvas, 257 × 361 cm.; *c.* 1730–35.

Formerly in the Villa Grimani-Valmarana at Noventa Padovana; then, 1909, in the Ladyard-Blair Coll., New Jersey. S. H. Kress Foundation, New York, 1949. At Philadelphia, Museum of Art, exhibited temporarily on loan from the Kress Foundation. Given to the National Gallery of Art 1961.
On either side were formerly the *Hunter* and the *Horseman* now in the Crespi Coll., Milan (q.v.). The 'Founding of Rome' has been suggested as the subject.
Lorenzetti, 1937, *passim*, with repr.; Morassi, p. 20, fig. 45.

TIMOCLEA AND THE THRACIAN COMMANDER   Fig. 287
Canvas, oval, 140 × 110 cm.; *c.* 1745–50.

Painted for the Pal. Barbaro, Venice. One of a group of four overdoors of which the others are now in Copenhagen Museum, Augsburg, Museum, and Necchi Coll., Pavia.
Formerly Kranz Coll., Vienna; previously in the Springer Coll., Vienna, 1874–1893; Camondo Coll., Paris; Kress Foundation, New York, 1937 until 1939. Then given to the National Gallery of Art.
Molmenti, pp. 275–276, fig. p. 274; Sack, p. 150, fig. 137; Cat. of the Nat. Gall. of Art, Washington, 1941, p. 193; Morassi, p. 26, fig. 67.

APOLLO PURSUING DAPHNE   [1955, col. pl. IX]
Canvas, 69 × 87 cm.; *c.* 1755–60. Signed at lower left: *Gio B. Tiepolo*.

Ex coll. Ed. Kann, Paris; Mme. Delaney, Paris; Sale at Charpentier, Paris, 23.5.1950; S. H. Kress Coll. (1950). Gift of the S. H. Kress Foundation.
Certainly identical with the canvas mentioned by Sack (p. 233) as an overdoor in the Gsell Coll., Vienna, together with its pendant *Venus and Vulcan* now in the Johnson Coll., Philadelphia (q.v.).
Cat. of Paintings and Sculpture from the Kress Coll., Washington, National Gallery, 1951, p. 158, with repr.; Morassi, *Arte Veneta*, 1952, p. 92, figs. 88, 89.
This excellent work is of about the same period as the frescoes in the Villa Valmarana, Vicenza.

APOTHEOSIS OF SPAIN   [1955, pl. 79]
Canvas, 182 × 105 cm.; 1762.

Came from the Pagliano family of Venice, who had inherited, through family connections with Tiepolo, paintings and drawing by Giambattista and Domenico.
Afterwards in the Capel-Cure Coll., Badger Hall, England; Kress Coll., New York (1935). Gift of the S. H. Kress Foundation.
Sack, pp. 139, 223; Freeden und Lamb, 1956, p. 57, fig. 27.

Modelletto for the ceiling fresco in the throne room of the Royal Palace in Madrid. Very important, with few differences from the finished work. It was certainly painted in Italy before the departure for Spain, and it is to it that Tiepolo refers in a letter of March 13th, 1762, as the *Modello della gran opera*.

APOTHEOSIS OF A POET   Fig. 335
Canvas, 27 × 49 cm.; *c.* 1762–70.

Sketch for an unknown ceiling.
Ex coll. Capel-Cure, Badger Hall, England; Kress Coll., New York, 1932 until 1939. Gift of the S. H. Kress Foundation.
Cat. of the National Gallery of Art, Washington, 1941, p. 192.

MADONNA WITH THE GOLDFINCH
Canvas, 63 × 50 cm.

By Domenico.
Ex coll. Maier, Karlsbad; Steinmeyer and Bourgeois, Paris; Kleinberger, Paris. S. H. Kress Collection 1940. Gift of the S. H. Kress Foundation.
A. Venturi in *L'Arte*, 1904, I, as by Giambattista; Molmenti, p. 315, with repr., as by an imitator; Sack, p. 216, fig. 227b, as by Giambattista.

A YOUNG VENETIAN LADY IN DOMINO AND TRICORNE
Canvas, 62 × 49 cm.

By Domenico.
Ex coll. Pisa, Florence, where it was attributed to Longhi, in the Sale Catalogue, 1937, pl. CXXIV; Brass Coll., Venice; Kress Collection, New York 1948. Gift of the S. H. Kress Foundation.
Goering, *Pantheon*, 1937, with repr.; Morandotti, 1941, p. 43, fig. 38; Morassi, p. 28, fig. 73; Cat. of Paintings and Sculpture from the Kress Coll., Washington, National Gallery of Art, 1951, p. 160 with repr. (always attributed to Giambattista); Morassi, in *Art Quarterly*, Summer 1958, p. 185, fig. 7, as Domenico.

WASHINGTON, Smithsonian Institution.
National Collection of Fine Arts

CHRIST AND THE ADULTERESS
Canvas

Attributed to Tiepolo, it seems to belong to a pupil of his.
From the Ralph Johnson Coll. to the Mrs. Marshall Langhorne Coll., then to the Museum.
Exhibited 1929 and 1932 at the Smithsonian Institution.

THE BAPTISM OF CHRIST
Canvas

Wrongly attributed to Tiepolo, certainly by a good pupil of his. Same provenance and exhibitions as the above.

WEIMAR, Schlossmuseum

THE SACRIFICE OF IPHIGENIA
Canvas, 53 × 41 cm.

By Domenico.
Sack, p. 196, fix. 194; Goering, 1944, p. 101 with fig. Both wrongly attribute it to Giambattista.

WIESBADEN, formerly Dr. Hohmann Coll.

MADONNA AND SAINTS
Canvas, shaped at the bottom, 87 × 58 cm.; *c.* 1745–50.

A small devotional painting, probably for a private chapel.
To judge from the reproduction, certainly by Tiepolo.
From Wiesbaden the picture passed to the Mauthner Coll., Vienna, and was exhibited in Dusseldorf (15.7.1929, *Cat.* No. 36). Present whereabouts unknown.
Sack, p. 237, fig. 229a; Goering, *ad vocem* (Dusseldorf).

WIESBADEN, formerly Private Coll.

GLORY OF SAINTS
See Bremen, Kunsthalle.

WILLIAMSTOWN, Mass., Sterling and Francine Clark
Art Institute

THE CHARIOT OF AURORA   Fig. 256
Canvas, 48.5×48 cm.; c. 1730–35.

Formerly at Knoedler, New York.
A splendid sketch for a circular ceiling, close in style to the cycle in
Pal. Archinto, Milan.
Morassi, in *The Burlington Magazine*, I, 1955, p. 7, fig. 7.

WÜRZBURG, Residenz

Frescoes in the Kaisersaal:

On the ceiling:

APOLLO CONDUCTING TO BARBAROSSA HIS BRIDE, BEATRICE
OF BURGUNDY   [1955, pl. 56]

On the walls:

THE MARRIAGE OF BARBAROSSA   [1955, col. pl. VII]
THE INVESTITURE OF BISHOP HAROLD, signed and dated: GIO.
BTTA. TIEPOLO. 1752.   [1955, pl. 67]

Over the ten windows, in grisaille:
ALLEGORICAL FIGURES

Below the windows:
SOLDIERS, TRUMPETERS, HALBERDIERS, etc.

The sketch for the ceiling is in Stuttgart. The *modelletti* for the *Marriage*
are in Boston and the National Gallery, London; for the *Investiture* in
the Metropolitan Museum, New York.

Frescoes on the Grand Staircase, on the ceiling:
OLYMPUS WITH THE QUARTERS OF THE EARTH, AND
ALLEGORIES   [1955, pls. 57–63, 65, 68]
The *modello* for this ceiling was recently discovered in London, Hendon
Hall Hotel, now in New York, Wrightsman (q.v.).
Signed and dated: G. BTTA. TIEPOLO. 1753.
Leitschuh, 1896; Frizzoni in *Emporium*, 1902 (October); Molmenti,
pp. 161, 177, with repr.; Sack, pp. 100–103, 197, figs. 84–85; Sedlmaier
u. Pfister, *Die fürstbischöfliche Residenz zu Würzburg*, Munich, 1923;
Hetzer, 1943; Morassi, pp. 29–31, figs. 82–87; Gerstenberg, 1952, pp.
142–162; Freeden and Lamb, 1956 (on all Würzburg frescoes).
The Würzburg period marks one of the highest creative moments in
Tiepolo's career. He was then at the peak of his powers and was greatly
helped by his son Domenico, an infant prodigy. Domenico could work
so completely in his father's manner and could follow his direction so
closely that, in the frescoes, it is almost impossible to distinguish the one
from the other. Nevertheless in some parts his 'hand' is quite evident.
In the smaller easel-pictures it is not so difficult to discriminate between
them, although many confusions have been made in the works of the
Würzburg period. The key to Domenico's style is the set of overdoors
in the Kaisersaal, where he was quite independent of his father. Tiepolo
was also assisted by Franz Ignaz Roth, who worked at the gilding of
the saloon.

In the Chapel of the Residenz:

THE ASSUMPTION OF THE VIRGIN   Fig. 107
THE FALL OF THE REBEL ANGELS, signed and dated on the lower
stone: GIO. BTTA. TIEPOLO, F.A. 1752.   Fig. 224
Two altarpieces, on canvas, c. 7×2.50 m.
Molmenti, p. 177, figs. pp. 167–168; Sack, p. 197, figs. 89–90; Morassi,
p. 31; Freeden, Catalogue, 1951; Freeden and Lamb, 1956.

Sack (pp. 197, 219) records two sketches, said to be *modelli* for the above
altarpieces; one, the *Assumption*, in Würzburg, the other the *Fall*, in
Paris, Sedelmeyer Coll. The former is now in the Mainfränkisches
Museum, Würzburg (63×42.5 cm.), but is certainly by Domenico,
after the altarpiece, as it is signed with the initials D.T. *fecit*. The second
picture has now disappeared. (The *Assumption* was exhibited at Würzburg, see Freeden, Catalogue, 1951, p. 16, where there is also a list of
documents regarding Tiepolo's stay and works in Würzburg.) In the
Würzburg Exhib. there were also two copies of the altarpieces in the
Residenz, by a weak imitator of Tiepolo.

WÜRZBURG, Mainfränkisches Museum

APOLLO CONDUCTING HIS BRIDE TO BARBAROSSA
Canvas, 68×119 cm.

Attributed to Giambattista Tiepolo and considered the original *modello*
for Würzburg, it is certainly of a later period.
Exhib. Cat. Tiepolo in Würzburg, Würzburg, 1951, p. 15, No. 9 as
by G.B.

PORTRAIT OF THE SCULPTOR AUWERA
PORTRAIT OF CHRISTINE, WIFE OF THE SCULPTOR AUWERA
Two canvases, the first 62×53.5 cm.; the second, 61×53 cm.

Attributed by Molmenti, p. 181, fig. p. 170, to Giambattista, but they
are certainly by Lorenzo Tiepolo.
Freeden, *Catalogue*, 1951, p. 16, as by Lorenzo.

WÜRZBURG, University Museum

THE FAMILY OF DARIUS BEFORE ALEXANDER   Fig. 283
MUCIUS SCAEVOLA BEFORE PORSENNA   Fig. 285
Two canvases, 103×120 cm. each; 1751–53.

Painted with the assistance of Domenico.
Said to have come from the collection of Balthasar Neumann, architect
of the Würzburg Residenz; passed to his son-in-law Hartmann, until
1799. From him to his nephew; sold at auction, 1834; Siegel Coll.;
entered the Museum in 1870.
The subject of the first painting is said to be by Scerbaciova (1941,
note 24) representing 'Coriolanus at the walls of Rome'.
Molmenti, p. 181, fig. p. 171; Sack, p. 198, figs. 195–196; Morassi,
p. 32; Freeden, Catalogue, 1951, p. 14.

HEAD OF AN ORIENTAL
Canvas, 46×37 cm.

By Domenico.
Related to the series of engravings of 'Heads.'
Ex coll. Bonitas Bauer, Würzburg, until 1893.
Molmenti, p. 181, fig. p. 173; Sack, p. 199, both as Giambattista;
Freeden, Catalogue, 1951, p. 16, as by Domenico.

HEAD OF AN OLD ORIENTAL
Canvas, 65×50 cm.

By Domenico.
Related to the series of engravings of 'Heads.'
Molmenti, p. 181, fig. p. 172; Sack, p. 199, fig. 197; Freeden, Catalogue,
1951, p. 14 (as Giambattista in each case).

WÜRZBURG, formerly University Museum

THE AGONY IN THE GARDEN
Canvas, 50×62 cm.

By Domenico.
Molmenti, p. 181, fig. 174, as doubtful; Sack, p. 197, as by Giambattista
(he also records a pendant, of the *Last Supper*, from the Bonitas Bauer
Coll., Würzburg).
Present whereabouts unknown.

S. FRANCIS WITH THE CRUCIFIX
Canvas, 64 × 46.5 cm.

Attributed by Sack, p. 200, fig. 198, to Giambattista, *c.* 1750–70, and listed under 'Altertumsverein'; Molmenti attributes it doubtfully to Giambattista, p. 181, fig. p. 173. Perhaps by Domenico or by a painter close to him.
Unger Sale, Lepke, Berlin, 1.6.1926, p. 96, pl. 9; F. Mont, New York, 1946.

WÜRZBURG, Tiepolo Exhibition, 1951

CHRIST AND THE WOMAN OF SAMARIA
Canvas, 84 × 106 cm.

By Domenico.
Freeden, *Catalogue*, 1951, p. 15, attributed to Giambattista; M. Precerutti-Garberi, in *Commentari*, 3–4, 1960, p. 272, Tav. LXXXVIII, fig. 6 as Domenico.

WÜRZBURG, formerly Gutenberg Coll.

REBECCA AT THE WELL
CHRIST AND THE ADULTERESS
Two canvases, 83 × 105 cm. each; dated 1751.

By Domenico.
The *Rebecca* was sold at Christie's, Morton Sale, 8.6.1928, and is now in a private collection in Paris. The *Christ and the Adulteress* is now in the Harrison Williams Coll., New York.
Wrongly attributed to Giambattista by Molmenti, p. 181, fig. p. 176, 178; Sack, p. 305, fig. 318–319; M. Precerutti-Garberi, in *Commentari*, 3–4, p. 272, figs. 4–5, both rightly to Domenico.

YORK, City Art Gallery, Lycett Green Coll.

S. AUGUSTINE AND OTHER SAINTS
Canvas, 57.8 × 36.8 cm.

This painting seems a record (painted probably in the studio of Tiepolo) rather than a preliminary sketch for the altarpiece once in S. Salvatore, Venice (cf. the drawing of the altarpiece in Sack, p. 157) which was destroyed in a fire in the eighteenth century.
The York canvas may possibly be identified with the one once in the possession of Count Algarotti (cf. the description in the Catalogue of his Collection, Molmenti, p. 236). Sack, p. 231.
Cavendish-Bentinck Sale, 11.7.1891; Joseph Ruston Sale, 21.5.1898; Mr. Lycett Green.
Levey, *Burlington Magazine*, IV, 1955, pp. 116–120, fig. 24.
Not seen by me.

ZANESVILLE, Ohio, Art Institute

TARQUIN AND LUCRETIA
Canvas, oval, 130 × 103 cm.

Workshop replica of the autograph painting formerly in Munich, Haberstock Coll., now in Augsburg (q.v.).
Shown by the Dayton Institute, Dayton (Ohio), Exhib., March 5th, 1948–April 19th, 1948.
Other old copies were on the art market in New York years ago.
Perhaps the present is the same as the one in the Dieterich Sale, Anderson Gall., New York, 8–9.4.1920, No. 109, sold together with a companion piece of *Offerings to Cleopatra*, No. 108.
It may be recorded that one oval with *Tarquin and Lucretia* was in the Bevilacqua Sale, Sangiorgi, Venice, 15–22.10.1910, No. 490, pl. 55 (135 × 115 cm.).

ZÜRICH, Bührle Coll.

DIANA AND ACTAEON
See: New York, formerly M. de Rothschild Coll.

ESTHER AND AHASUERUS
See: Munich, formerly Gulbransson Coll.

ZÜRICH, Hausammann Coll.

THE MYSTIC MARRIAGE OF S. CATHERINE, S. JOHN AND THE INFANT BAPTIST   Fig. 108
Canvas, 80 × 116 cm.; *c.* 1745–50 (?).

This is a sixteenth-century picture, probably by Bonifazio Veronese, repainted by Tiepolo.
Ex coll. Lippmann, Berlin; Bromberg, Hamburg.
Sack, p. 185, fig. 228.
A very interesting example of a restoration by Tiepolo. He intended it as a *rinfrescatura* (i.e. 'freshening-up') of an old picture. The new parts, 'restored' by him, can be clearly distinguished from the older ones.
We know also from a letter by Algarotti (4.3.1760) to Tiepolo and from other letters of the Count, some to Tiepolo and some to Algarotti's brother, that the Count commissioned Tiepolo to repaint an old copy after the *Last Supper* in the Chiesa dei Servi in Venice by Veronese (now in the Louvre), in order to make this copy look like a *modello* by Veronese himself; but this work was never executed, as is known from a letter by Tiepolo of January 9th, 1762.

OLYMPUS   Fig. 319
Canvas, 99 × 63 cm.; *c.* 1740.

Sketch for a ceiling.
Ex coll. Groult, sale Charpentier, 20.3.1952.
Molmenti, p. 258, records it as in the Groult Coll., and adds, wrongly, that it is the sketch for the ante-room of the Royal Palace in Madrid.
An excellent, fresh sketch, related in some ways to the ceiling of the Pal. Clerici, Milan, and notwithstanding the iconographical differences, close in style and in general idea to the executed fresco.
Exhib. Cat., Munich 1958, p. 102, No. 201.

THE DEPOSITION   Fig. 60
Canvas, 59 × 47 cm.; *c.* 1762–70.

Ex coll. Lenbach, Munich; Emden, Brissago, Switzerland.
Morassi, p. 39; Lorenzetti, p. 134, fig. 95.
An impressive example of Tiepolo's last style, with a deep sense of pathos.

ZÜRICH, Private Coll.

VULCAN AND VENUS   Fig. 244
Canvas, 51.5 × 34.5 cm.; *c.* 1725–30.

Sketch for an unknown ceiling.
Morassi, 1941, p. 96, fig. 27.

ZÜRICH, Private Coll.

ALLEGORY OF THE POWER OF ELOQUENCE   [1955, fig. 9]
Canvas, 50 × 70 cm.; *c.* 1724–25.

Modello for the ceiling of Pal. Sandi, Venice, but with many differences from the executed fresco.
Important early work.
From a private coll. in Madrid.
Morassi, *Burlington Magazine*, I, 1955, pp. 4–7, figs. 2–6.

ZÜRICH, Private Coll.

PORTRAIT OF A GIRL WITH A BASKET OF FRUITS AND FLOWERS
Canvas, 80 × 68 cm.; *c.* 1720–25.   Fig. 427

Similar in style to the four mythological scenes in Venice and to the paintings of the 'Udinese period.'
The type of this *modello* appears in many other works by Tiepolo of this period.
Hitherto unpublished.

ZÜRICH, Private Coll.

HEAD OF AN OLD ORIENTAL   Fig. 428
Canvas, 45 × 40 cm.; *c.* 1750.

Formerly Count Kufner Coll., Prague; Benedict Coll., Paris.
Very similar to the engraving by Domenico (Molmenti, 1896, p. 154

left). Iconographically similar to the 'Head' in Trieste, Rusconi Coll. Certainly of the same period of the *Banquet* now in Melbourne.

ZÜRICH, Private Coll.

S. JOHN THE BAPTIST
Canvas, oval, 45 × 37 cm.; *c.* 1718–20   Fig. 192

Head in natural size. Hitherto unknown. The 'pendant' to *S. Peter* in Jacksonville (q.v.).
In a very Piazzettesque style, but with a more developed coloristic sense. Formed part perhaps of a series of Apostles.

ZÜRICH, Private Coll.

ALLEGORICAL FEMALE FIGURE   [1955, fig. 55]
Canvas, oval, 82 × 65 cm.; *c.* 1740–50.

Grisaille on gold background. Stylistically excellent, it belongs to the series mentioned by Waagen (*Art Treasures*, 1857, IV, p. 173) in the Cheney Coll., of which other examples are in the de Becker-Rothschild Coll., New York, and in the Rijksmuseum, Amsterdam.

ZÜRICH, Private Coll.

MADONNA WITH SS. ANTHONY OF PADUA, FRANCIS OF ASSISI AND LOUIS OF TOULOUSE   Fig. 84
Canvas, 73 × 50.5 cm.; *c.* 1730–35.

Ex coll. Schwabach, Berlin.
Similar to the sketch in Bergamo, formerly Piccinelli Coll. (q.v.),
which is the *modello* for the altarpiece now in Moscow, Pushkin Museum (q.v.).
Sack, p. 180, fig. 174.
A version (51 × 31.5 cm.) of this picture, almost identical but rather weak, was sold at the Brunner Gall., Paris, in 1920; Ehrich Gall., New York, 1921; Douwes, Amsterdam, 1938.

ZÜRICH, formerly Private Coll.

MUCIUS SCAEVOLA BEFORE PORSENNA
Canvas, old copy after the painting by Tiepolo in Leningrad.

Formerly in the Matthiesen Gallery, Berlin.
Listed by Goering, *ad vocem*, as by Tiepolo.

ZÜRICH, Ruzicka Coll.

SS. MAXIMUS AND OSWALD   Fig. 140
Canvas, 50.6 × 27.8 cm.; *c.* 1742–45.

Ex coll. Grandi-Baslini, Milan; Langton Douglas, London; Elkins, Philadelphia.
Sack, p. 79, fig. 62a; Lorenzetti, p. 78, fig. 58.
Excellent sketch, grey in tone, for the altarpiece in Padua, S. Massimo. The other rather similar sketches (Carrara Gall., Bergamo; National Gallery, London; Drey, New York) wrongly supposed to be related to this altarpiece, represent *S. Proculus, Bishop of Verona, visiting SS. Fermus and Rusticus* (see Bergamo and London).

ADDENDA

DIJON, Musée des Beaux-Arts

PORTRAIT OF A YOUNG MAN WITH A TURBAN
Canvas, 50 × 40 cm.; *c.* 1718–20.

From the Joliet collection. In the Museum attributed to Cappella. A very early work by Tiepolo, close to Piazzetta.

DIJON, Musée Magnin

MUCIUS SCAEVOLA BEFORE PORSENNA
Canvas, 47 × 26 cm.; *c.* 1725–30.

Original sketch, almost a 'prima idea' for the painting in Leningrad (q.v.).
J. Magnin, *Un Cabinet d'Amateur Parisien en 1922*, p. 145, fig. 87.

MILAN, Count Gerli coll.

THE BANQUET OF ANTONY AND CLEOPATRA
Canvas, 260 × 360 cm.

This large picture was found in a Venetian villa during the last war and
appeared in Venice about 1946 in the Spanio collection, where I saw it. It is clearly a work of the Tiepolo studio and Domenico Tiepolo had a large share in the execution. It is certainly later than the *Banquet* in Melbourne and can be dated about 1747–50.
R. Pallucchini in *Acropoli*, 1962, pp. 97 ff.

MILAN, Private coll.

THE PRODIGAL SON
Canvas, 44 × 58 cm.; *c.* 1720–22.

Formerly in the Du-Bois coll., Venice.
An early work, stylistically related to the two canvases in the Moizzi coll., Milan (q.v.).
Described in the *Catalogue d'une collection de 354 tableaux . . . représentée par Charles Du-Bois*, Venice 1850, nr. 381; Sack, p. 233.

MISSING WORKS KNOWN FROM ENGRAVINGS

ALLEGORY OF VENUS ENTRUSTING CUPID TO TIME

Oval ceiling painted by Giambattista and engraved by Domenico.
In composition and style related to the painting of 'Time abducting Beauty' in the Cotnareanu Coll., Paris, and to the ceiling of Palazzo Pisani-Moretta, Venice.
Probably painted about 1750–60. A similar subject in Lisbon (q.v.).
De Vesme, 100; Sack, p. 229, fig. 222.
Probably identical with the ceiling quoted by Molmenti, 1911, p. 201, in the Bischoffsheim Coll., London.

S. FRANCIS RECEIVING THE STIGMATA

Canvas once in the coll. of the engraver Pietro Monaco in Venice and etched by him with the inscription: *Pittura di Gio. Batta Tiepolo posseduta da me Pietro Monaco*. The Saint was represented seen from behind with outstretched arms, while a light is shining on him. The engraving was published in *Raccolta di 112 stampe di pitture di storia sacra incise per la prima volta in rame fedelmente, copiate dagli originali di celebri autori antichi e moderni esistenti in Venezia, da Pietro Monaco*, Venice, 1743.
Le Blanc, 1876, p. 212; Sack, pp. 229, 281.

S. JOHN PREACHING

Painting by Giambattista, engraved by Domenico, very similar to the fresco in the Colleoni Chapel in Bergamo and identical with the sketch in the Treccani Coll., Milan (maybe engraved from it).
Molmenti, 1896, fig. 104; De Vesme, 31; Sack, p. 231, fig. 224a.

BAPTISM OF CHRIST

Painting by Giambattista; engraved by Domenico. The connection with the Colleoni Chapel fresco in Bergamo is only in the subject. It was probably the pendant to the painting mentioned above.
Molmenti, 1896, fig. 108; De Vesme, 32.

MADONNA OF THE ROSARY WITH THE CHRIST CHILD

Oval, with the inscription *Regina Sacratissimi Rosarij*, engraved by A. Maratti after an unknown early painting by Giambattista. (Similar to the painting in Florence, Private Coll.)
Sack, p. 281, fig. 304.

THE AGONY IN THE GARDEN

Engraved by A. Maulbertsch after an unknown painting (or drawing?) by Giambattista signed *Tiepolo*. Christ is represented with two soldiers, one kneeling, the other holding a banner.
The engraving is in the Bibliothèque Nationale in Paris.
Sack, p. 281.

A SAINT IN A MONK'S COWL WITH A BOOK, A LILY AND A GLORY AT THE TOP LEFT

Engraved by Rossari after a drawing by A. Gandini (copying a painting by Giambattista) for the Count Giuseppe Sormani.
The engraving is in the Hofbibliothek in Vienna.
Sack, p. 282.

BIBLIOGRAPHY

IN CHRONOLOGICAL ORDER

Il gran teatro di Venezia ovvero raccolta delle principali vedute e Pitture che in essa si contengono. Venice, 1720.

da Canal, V.: *Vita di Gregorio Lazzarini.* Written in 1732, published by G. A. Moschini in Venice, 1809.

Zanetti, A. M.: *Descrizione di tutte le pubbliche pitture della città di Venezia.* Venice, 1733 (there are some contemporary 'Aggiunte' to this *Guide*, by F. M. Tassis, published by Fiocco in 1927).

Pacifico, P. A.: *Cronaca veneta sacra e profana.* Venice, 1736.

Lattuada, S.: *Descrizione di Milano.* Milan, 1737 (the 4th vol., with the description of S. Ambrogio, is of 1738).

de Brosses, C.: *Lettres familières écrites d'Italie en 1739 et 1740.* Paris, 1858.

Albrizzi, G. B.: *Il forestiere illuminato intorno le cose più rare e curiose . . . della città di Venezia e dell'isole circonvicine.* Venice, 1740 (2nd ed., 1765; 3rd ed., 1772).

Poesie dedicate al merito singolarissimo del Sig. Gio. Battista Tiepolo celebre pittore veneto imitatore di Paolo Veronese, in occasione che si trova in Milano a dipingere nella casa di S.E. il sig. marchese D. Giorgio Clerici nell'anno 1740. Milan, 1740.

Algarotti, F.: *Notes de dépences faites pour S.M. le Roi de Poulogne.* Ms. 1252 in the Biblioteca civica of Treviso (from 13.6.1743 to 1.5.1746).

Coronelli, V.: *Guida dei forestieri per la città di Venezia.* Venice, 1744.

Maccarinelli, F.: *Le glorie di Brescia* (1747-1751); ms. in the Biblioteca Queriniana in Brescia, published by C. Boselli in 'Supplemento ai Commentari dell' Ateneo di Brescia per il 1959. Brescia, 1959.

Gradenigo, P.: *Notatori ed Annali del N.H. Pietro Gradenigo* (1748–1774); ms. in the Biblioteca Marciana in Venice and in the Museo Correr, published by Livan, 1942.

Biancolini, G. B.: *Notizie storiche delle chiese di Venezia.* Venice, 1749.

Orlandi, P. A.: *Abecedario pittorico.* Venice, 1753.

Cochin, N.: *Voyage d'Italie.* Paris, 1758.

Rodella: *Pitture e sculture di Brescia.* Brescia, 1760.

Betti, Z.; Lorenzi, B.; Lorenzi, F.: *Componimenti poetici all'esimio pittore signor Giambattista Tiepolo.* Verona, 1761.

Bertotti-Scamozzi, O.: *Il Forestiere istruito delle cose più rare di Vicenza.* Vicenza, 1761.

Longhi, A.: *Compendio delle vite de' pittori veneziani, ecc.* Venice, 1762.

Monaco, P.: *Raccolta di 112 Stampe della Storia Sacra ecc. . . . incise da Pietro Monaco.* Venice, 1763.

Algarotti, F.: *Opere,* Pisa, 1764.

Dall'Abaco, G.: *Chronik des uralten U.L. Frauen-Stifts und Kloster der regulierten Chorherren unter der Regel des H. Augustinus zu Diessen.* 1718–93 (Ms. in the Staatsbibliothek at Munich, Cod. Germ. 1769-70).

Volkmann, J. J.: *Historisch-Kritische Nachrichten von Italien.* Leipzig. 1770.

Zanetti, A. M.: *Della pittura veneziana,* Venice, 1771.

Gori-Gandellini, G.: *Notizie istoriche degli intagliatori.* Siena, 1771.

Bergeret & Fragonard: *Journal inédit d'un voyage en Italie.* Written in 1773–74, published in 1895, Paris.

Pasta, A.: *Le pitture notabili di Bergamo.* Bergamo, 1775.

Ponz, A.: *Viaje de España.* 1st and 6th vol., 1776 (other editions 1769, 1772).

(Algarotti, F.): *Catalogo dei Quadri dei Disegni e dei libri che trattano dell'arte del disegno della Galleria del fu Sig. Conte Algarotti in Venezia.* Venice, 1779.

Meusel, J. G.: *Miscellaneen artistischen Inhalts.* Erfurt, 1779, I, p. 46.

Arnaldi, E.: *Descrizione delle architetture, pitture e sculture di Vicenza.* Vicenza, 1779.

Vendramini-Mosca, F.: *Descrizione dell'architettura, pittura e scultura di Vicenza.* Vicenza, 1779.

Rossetti, G. B.: *Descrizione delle Pitture . . . di Padova.* Padua, 1780.

Zucchini, T. A.: *Nuova Cronaca Veneta ecc.* Venice, 1784.

Brocchi, G. A.: *La magnifica e deliziosa villa di S. Sebastiano.* Vicenza, 1785.

Catalogo dei Quadri raccolti del fu Sig. M. Pinelli etc. in Venezia. Venice, 1785.

Bianconi, G.: *Nuova Guida di Milano.* Milan, 1787.

Raccolta di opere scelte rappresentanti la storia del vecchio e nuovo Testamento dipinte dai più celebri maestri, incise da Pietro Monaco. Venice, 1789, 2nd vol.

Vianelli, G.: *Catalogo dei Quadri esistenti in casa del Signor Dr. Giov. Vianelli, Canonico della Cattedrale di Chioggia.* Venice, 1790.

Algarotti, F.: *Opere: Lettere sulla pittura.* (Vol. VIII), Venice (Palese) 1792.

Hofstaeter, F. F.: *Nachrichten von Kunstsachen in Italien.* Vienna, 1792.

Bartoli, F.: *La Pittura, Scultura e Architettura della città di Rovigo.* Venice, 1793.

Conca, A.: *Descrizione odeporica della Spagna.* Vol. I, Parma, 1793.

Brandolese, P.: *Pitture, Sculture ecc. di Padova.* Padua, 1795.

Lanzi, L.: *Storia pittorica d'Italia.* Bassano, 1795–96 (2nd ed. Milan, 1824; 3rd ed. Venice, 1837).

de Renaldis, G.: *Della pittura friulana.* Udine, 1796.

Milizia, F.: *Dizionario delle arti del disegno.* Bassano, 1797.

Tassi, F. M.: *Le vite dei pittori ecc. bergamaschi.* Bergamo, 1797.

Céan Bermudez, J. A.: *Diccionario historico de los más illustres professores de las bellas artes en España.* Madrid, 1800, vol. V.

Bettinelli, S. Abate: *Opere edite e inedite ecc.* Vol. XVII, p. 226, Venice, 1800.

Fiorillo, F. D.: *Geschichte der Malerei.* Göttingen, 1801.

Federici, D. M.: *Memorie trevigiane sulle opere di disegno ecc.* Venice, 1803.

Dalla Rosa, S.: *Catastico della pittura e scultura in Verona ecc.* Ms. 1008 in the Library, Verona, 1803.

Alvares de Quindos y Baena, Don J. A.: *Descripcion Historica.* Madrid, 1804, p. 259.

Moschini, G. A.: *Della letteratura veneziana del sec. XVIII.* Venice, 1806.

da Canal, V.: *Vita di Gregorio Lazzarini.* Written in 1732, published by G. A. Moschini, Venice, 1809.

da Canal, V.: *Maniera del dipingere moderno,* in 'Mercurio filosofico,' Venice, 1810.

Bartsch, A.: *Le peintre-graveur.* Vienna, 1811, vol. XII, p. 161.

Moschini, G. A.: *Guida per la città di Venezia.* Venice, 1815 (French ed., 1819).

Fusslin, J. R.: *Allgemeines Künstlerlexikon.* Zurich, 1816.

Il forestiere istruito nelle cose più pregevoli e curiose antiche e moderne della città di Venezia e delle isole circonvicine. Venice, 1819.

Descrizione e Guida della città di Bergamo. Bergamo, 1819.

Quadri, A.: *Otto giorni in Venezia.* Venice, 1821.

Gamba, B.: *Galleria di letterati ed artisti delle provincie Austro-Venete nel sec. XVIII.* Venice, 1822.

Bottari, C.–Ticozzi, S.: *Raccolta di lettere sulla pittura.* Vol. VII, Rome, 1822.

Maniago, F.: *Storia delle belle arti friulane.* Udine, 1823.

Quilliet, F.: *Le arti italiane in Ispagna.* Rome, 1825.

Fabre, J. F.: *Descripcion de las Allegorias pintadas en las Bovedas de Palagio Real de Madrid.* Madrid, 1829.

Winckelmann, J. J.: *Opere.* 1st Italian ed., vol. VII, p. 556, Prato, 1831.

Crico, L.: *Lettere sulle belle arti trevigiane.* Treviso, 1833.

Nagler, G. K.: *Neues Allgemeines Künstler-Lexikon.* Munich, 1835–52 (2nd ed., 1870).

Ticozzi, S.: *Lettera intorno a due quadri di vaste dimensioni di Antonio Canal ecc.* Milan, 1836.

Zanotto, F.: *Storia della pittura veneziana,* Venice 1837, pp. 375–376.

Paoletti, E.: *Il fiore di Venezia.* Venice, 1837-40.

Maniago, F.: *Guida d'Udine*. S. Vito, 1839.

De Boni, F.: *Biografia degli artisti*. Emporreo biografico. Venice, 1840.

Driuzzo, F.: *Cenni . . . sopra un raro dipinto di Giambattista Tiepolo*. Venice, 1845.

Zanotto, F.: *Pinacothèque Barbini-Breganze*. Venice, 1847.

Zanotto, F.: *Pinacothèque Barbini-Breganze, décrite par François Zanotto*. Venice, 1850.

Becker, C.: *Nachrichten über ältere Künstler in Würzburg*, in Eggers 'Deutsches Kunstblatt,' 1851.

Selvatico, P.: *Storia estetico-critica delle arti del disegno*. Venice, 1851–56.

Selvatico, P.: *Catalogo delle opere d'arte della sala delle sedute della I. R. Accademia di Venezia*. Venice, n.d.

Selvatico, P.–Lazari, V.: *Guida di Venezia*. Venice, n.d.

Gonzati, B.: *La Basilica di S. Antonio da Padova descritta ed illustrata*. Padua, 1852.

Waagen, G. F.: *Treasures of art in Great Britain*. 3 vols., London, 1854–57 with supplement.

Berti, A.: *Elogio di G. B. Tiepolo*, in 'Atti dell'I.R. Accademia di Belle arti in Venezia.' Venice, 1856.

Zanotto, F.: *Nuovissima Guida di Venezia e delle isole della sua laguna*. Venice, 1856.

Zanotto, F.: *Pinacoteca di Valentino Benfatto veneziano*. Venice, 1856.

Zanotto, F.: *Pinacoteca veneta*. Venice, 1856.

Pirovano, F.: *Nuova Guida di Milano*. Milan, 1857.

Zanotto, F.: *Il Palazzo Ducale di Venezia*. Venice, 1858, vol. II.

de Brosses, C.: *Lettres familières écrites d'Italie en 1739 et 1740*. Paris, 1858.

Mariette, P. J.: *Abecedario*. Paris, 1858–59.

Mothes, O.: *Geschichte der Baukunst u. Bildhauerei Venedigs*. Leipzig, 1859.

Fontana, G. G.: *Cento Palazzi fra i più celebri di Venezia*. Venice, 1865.

Zanetti, V.: *Guida di Murano*. Venice, 1866.

Fechner, G. Th.: *Notizen*, in 'Arch. f. d. zeichnenden Künste,' XII, Leipzig, 1866.

Locatelli, P.: *Illustri bergamaschi*. Bergamo, 1867.

Blanc, Ch.: *Histoire des Peintres de toutes les Ecoles. Ecole Vénitienne*, Paris, 1868 (new ed., 1877).

Nagler, G.K.: *Neues Allgemeines Künstler-Lexikon*. Leipzig, 1870 (2nd ed.).

Bullo: *Sugli oggetti d'arte esistenti in Chioggia*. Rovigo, 1872.

Bonamico, E.: *Mirano, monografia*. Padua, 1874.

Cuccianiga: *Ricordo della Provincia di Treviso*. 2nd ed., Treviso, 1874.

Cenni storici intorno l'antica chiesa e convento di S. Bonaventura in Venezia. Venice, 1874.

Leroi, P.: *L'Italia farà da sè*, in 'L'Art,' IV, Paris, 1876.

Cavalcaselle, G. B.: *Vite e opere dei pittori friulani*. Ms. in the Library at Udine, 1876.

Meyer, R.: *Die beiden Canaletto*. Dresden, 1877.

Frizzoni, G.: *L'arte in Bergamo e l'Accademia Carrara*. Bergamo, 1877.

Wessely, J. E.: *Giov. Batt. Tiepolo*, in Dohme's 'Kunst und Künstler,' Leipzig, 1878.

Urbani de Gheltof, G. M.: *Tiepolo e la sua famiglia*. (Documents partially confused; cf. W. Arslan, 1932 and G. B. Cervellini, 1939), Venice, 1879.

Tassini, G.: *Alcuni Palazzi . . . di Venezia*. Venice, 1879.

Krsnjavi, I.: *Gio. Battista Tiepolo*, in 'Zeitschrift f. bild. Kunst,' XIV, 1879.

Hübner, J.: *Vorwort zum Verzeichnis der kgl. Gemäldegalerie zu Dresden*. Dresden, 1880.

Molmenti, P.: *Les fresques de Tiepolo dans la Villa Valmarana*. Venice, 1880 (the Italian ed. is of 1928).

Duplessis: *Histoire de la Gravure*. Paris, 1880, pp. 72–73.

Urbani de Gheltof, G. M.: *Tiepolo in Ispagna*, in 'Bollettino di Arti, industrie e curiosità veneziane,' III (almost totally confused, cf. Fogolari, 1932, and G. B. Cervellini, 1939) Venice, 1880–82.

Catalogue of works of art from The Collection of Edward Cheney, Esq., which will be sold by auction, by Messrs. Christie, Manson & Woods . . . on April 29, 1885.

Molmenti, P.: *Il Carpaccio e il Tiepolo*. Turin, 1885.

Feuerbach, A.: *Ein Vermächtniss*. Vienna, 1885, p. 158.

Molinier, E.: *Venise, ses arts décoratifs etc*. Paris, 1889.

della Rovere, A.: *I Prototipi di Gio. Batt. Tiepolo*, in "Il Tempo", Venice, 1889.

Guida artistica della chiesa di S. Michele in Isola. Venice, 1889.

Joppi, V.: *Di un quadro del Tiepolo nel Museo di Udine*, in 'Pagine Friulane,' No. 9, Udine, 1889.

Nicoletti, G.: *Lista di nomi di artisti tolta dai libri di tanse o luminarie della fraglia dei pittori*, in 'Ateneo Veneto', 1890.

Piot, M. F.: *Catalogue des Objets d'art etc*. Paris, 1890.

Stamminger, J. B.: *Würzburg Kunstleben im 18. Jhrdt*. Würzburg, 1893.

Berenson, B.: *The Venetian Painters of the Renaissance*. New York–London, 1894.

Joppi, V.: *Contributo IV alla storia dell'arte nel Friuli*. Venice, 1894.

v. Reber, F.: *Geschichte der Malerei vom Anfang des 14. bis Ende des 18. Jhdts*. Munich, 1894.

Valentinis, G.: *Opere d'arte in Friuli*. Udine, 1894.

Buisson, J.: *Jean Baptiste et Dominique Tiepolo*, in 'Gazette des Beaux Arts,' September–October, 1895.

Urbani de Gheltof, G. M.: *Guida storico artistica della Scuola di S. Giovanni Evangelista in Venezia*. Venice, 1895.

Bergeret & Fragonard: *Journal inédit d'un voyage en Italie*, written in 1733–34, published in Paris, 1895.

Molmenti, P.: *Tiepolo*, in 'Natura ed Arte.' 1895–96, pp. 619–626.

Melani, A.: *Per l'autenticità di una pala del Tiepolo*, in 'Arte e Storia,' IV, June, 1896.

Beltrami, L.: *G. B. Tiepolo*, in 'Emporium,' XII, 1896.

Molmenti, P.: *Acqueforti del Tiepolo*. Venice, 1896.

Catalogo della Mostra Tiepolesca. Venice, 1896.

Levi, P. ('L'Italico'): *Per G. B. Tiepolo e pel carattere italiano*. No. 4, p. 6, Rome, 1896.

Göbl, S.: *Würzburg, ein kulturhistorisches Stadtbild*, Würzburg, 1896.

Ricci, C.: *Rapporti di G. B. Tiepolo con Parma. Lettere inedite di lui. Notizie di un suo quadro*. Parma, 1896.

De Chennevières, H.: *Les Tiepolos de l'Hotel Edouard André*, in 'Gazette des Beaux Arts,' 1896, I, p. 121.

Ricci, C.: *Il Tiepolo*, in 'Nuova Antologia,' Rome, 1896, pp. 401–403.

Pietrogrande, G.: *Descrizione del celebre quadro di S. Tecla . . . esistente nel Duomo d'Este*. Este, 1896.

Leitschuh, F.: *G. B. Tiepolo, eine Studie zur Kunstgeschichte des XVIII Jahrhunderts*. Würzburg, 1896.

v. Schlosser, J.: *Venedig im XVIII Jhdt*. Beilage zur 'Allgm. Ztg.' No. 103. Munich, 1897 (also published in 'Präludien,' Berlin, 1927, p. 112 ff.).

Berenson, B.: *The Venetian Painters of the Renaissance*, New York–London 1897, 3rd ed.

Meissner, F. H.: *Tiepolo*, in 'Knackfuss Künstlermonographien,' Leipzig, 1897.

Molfese-Centelli, A.: *Gli affreschi di G. B. Tiepolo*. Turin, 1898.

De Chennevières, H.: *Les Tiepolo*. Paris, 1898.

Gronau, G.: *G. B. Tiepolo*, in 'Museum,' Berlin, 1898.

Gurlitt, C.: *Vom Würzburger Schloss*, in 'Velhagen & Klasings Monatshefte,' XII, 1898.

Barrès, M.: *Un homme libre*. Paris, 1899.

Schaeffer, E.: *Die Frau in der Venezianischen Malerei*. Munich, 1899, p. 156.

Caversazzi, C.: *Di alcuni dipinti di G. B. Tiepolo*, in 'Emporium,' 1899.

Tessier, A.: *Illustrazione alle due tele di G. B. Tiepolo esistenti nel Palazzo Bernardi a S. Apollinare in Venezia*. Venice, 1899.

Bode, W.: *Die Sammlung Kann*. Vienna, 1900.

Venturi, A.: *La Galleria Crespi a Milano*. Milan, 1900.

Gonse, L.: *Chef-d'oeuvres des Musées de France*. Paris, 1900.

Ferrari, L.: *Gli acquisti dell' Algarotti per il Regio Museo di Dresda*, in 'L'Arte,' III, 1900, pp. 150–154.

Boucher, H.: *Les fresques de Tiepolo à la Villa Soderini*, in 'Revue de l'art ancien et moderne,' Paris, 1901, p. 367.

Frizzoni, G.: *Illustrazione di alcune opere di G. B. Tiepolo*, in 'Emporium,' 1902, pp. 271–278.

Lafond, P.: *Les fresques de Tiepolo à la villa Biron à Vicence*, in 'Les Arts,' Paris, 1902.

Modern, H.: *G. B. Tiepolo, eine Studie*. Vienna, 1902.

Modern, H.: *Les peintures de Tiepolo à la villa Girola*, in 'Gazette des Beaux-Arts,' II, 1902, pp. 239-241.

Oreffice, P.: *La villa di Strà*, in 'Arte Italiana decorativa e industriale,' Milan-Bergamo, 1902.

Sirén, O.: *Dessins et Tableaux de la Renaissance italienne dans les collections de Suède*. Stockholm, 1902 (on the project to call T. to Sweden, pp. 103-144).

Battistella, O.: *La villa Soderini e gli affreschi di G. B. Tiepolo a Nervesa.* Treviso, 1903.

Paoletti, P.: *Catalogo delle R.R. Gallerie di Venezia*. Venice, 1903.

Melani, A.: *Un fregio quasi sconosciuto di G. B. Tiepolo*, in 'Arte italiana decorativa e industriale,' Milan-Bergamo, 1903, pp. 88-90.

Molmenti, P.: *La pittura veneziana*. Florence, 1903.

Bailo, L.: *Monumenti e cose monumentali a Treviso—Gli affreschi del Pal. Onigo venduti e asportati*, in 'Gazzetta di Treviso,' November 4th-5th, 1905.

De Vesme, A.: *Le peintre-graveur italien*. Milan, 1906.

Marini, G. F.: *Verolanuova. Appunti di Storia d'Arte*. Brescia, 1907.

Monnier, Ph.: *Venise au XVIII e siècle*. Paris, 1907.

Sentenach, N.: *La pintura en Madrid*. Madrid, 1907.

de Wyzewa, T.: *Les maîtres italiens d'autrefois*. Paris, 1907.

Simonson, G.: *Guardi and Tiepolo*, in 'The Burlington Magazine,' July, 1907.

Nebbia, U.: *Il Palazzo Clerici a Milano*, in 'Rassegna d'Arte,' 1907.

Fogolari, G.: *Ritrovamento d'un dipinto del Tiepolo*, in 'Bollettino d'Arte,' 1908, p. 115.

de Cuenca, C.: *G. B. Tiepolo*, in 'Blanco y Negro,' Madrid, 1908.

Malaguzzi-Valeri, F.: *Quattro nuovi dipinti di Tiepolo*, in 'Rassegna d'Arte,' October, 1908, p. 179.

Molmenti, P.: *La storia di Venezia nella vita privata: parte terza: il decadimento*. Bergamo, 1908.

Monnier, Ph.: *La Peinture Vénitienne au XVIII e siècle*, in 'L'Art,' March, 1908, No. 36, p. 561 ff.

Molmenti, P.: *G. B. Tiepolo*. Milan, 1909 (French ed., 1911).

De Luca, E.: *Recensione al Tiepolo del Molmenti*, in 'Emporium,' October, 1909.

Jakobsen, E.: *La Galerie Querini-Stampalia à Venise*, in 'Gazette des Beaux-Arts,' 1909.

Patzak, B.: *Ein neuer Tiepolo*, in 'Cicerone,' vol. I, 1909, p. 357 ff.

Simonson, G.: *A connecting-link between Tiepolo and the Guardi Family*, in 'The Burlington Magazine,' 1909.

Molmenti, P.: *Il Palazzo Grassi a Venezia e un affresco attribuito al Tiepolo*, in 'Emporium,' March, 1909.

Muther, R.: *Geschichte der Malerei*. Leipzig, 1909, vol. III, pp. 76-86.

Swarzenski, G.: *G. B. Tiepolo 'Heilige aus dem Hause Crotta' im Stædelschen Kunstinstitut zu Frankfurt*, in 'Münchener Jahrbuch d. bild. Kunst,' 1909.

Lafenestre, G.: *G. B. Tiepolo. A propos d'un livre récent*, in 'La Revue de l'Art ancien et moderne,' 1910, p. 447.

Exhibition: *Alte Gemaelde aus Wiesbad. Privatbesitz*, Wiesbaden, 1910.

Weiner, P.-Benois, A.: *Les anciennes écoles de Peinture dans les palais et collections privées russes*, Bruxelles, 1910.

Serra, L.: *G. B. Tiepolo ecc.*, in 'Arte Italiana decorativa e industriale,' January–February, 1910.

Sack, E.: *G. B. und D. Tiepolo*. Hamburg, 1910.

Fogolari, G.: *La 'Dafne' di G. B. Tiepolo*, in 'Emporium,' 1911, p. 77.

Molmenti, P.: *G. B. Tiepolo*. Milan, 1911, French ed. (the Italian ed. is of 1909).

Heil, W.: *Exhibition of Venetian Paintings*, London, 1911.

Fogolari, G.: *Dipinti veneziani settecenteschi della Galleria del Conte F. Algarotti*, in 'Bolletino d'Arte,' 1911.

De Vesme, A.: *Paralipomeni tiepoleschi*, in 'Scritti vari di erudizione e di critica in onore di R. Renier,' Turin, 1912.

Focillon, H.: *Les eaux-fortes de Tiepolo*, in 'Revue de l'Art ancien et moderne,' 1912.

Mireur, H.: *Dictionnaire des Ventes d'art*. Vol. VII, Paris, 1912.

Ojetti, U.: *Quattro tele del Tiepolo trafugate*, in 'Emporium,' July, 1912, pp. 64-69.

Hermanin, F.: *Nuovi acquisti alla Galleria Corsini in Roma*, in 'Bollettino d'arte,' 1912.

Kristeller, P.: *Ein Skizzenbuch Tiepolos*, in 'Kunst und Künstler,' June, 1912, p. 485.

Fogolari, G.: *G. B. Tiepolo nel Veneto*. Milan, 1913.

Fogolari, G.: *Il Piazzetta e il Tiepolo e il Pittoni al Museo di Vicenza*, in 'Emporium,' 1913.

Burroughs, B.: *Allegorical sketch for a ceiling by Tiepolo*, in 'Metropolitan Museum Bulletin,' 1913. New York.

Fogolari, G.: *L'Accademia Veneziana di pittura*, in 'L'Arte,' 1913.

Willis Fred, C.: *Ein unbekanntes Porträt Tiepolos*, in 'Der Cicerone,' V, February, 1913.

Brunetti, M.: *Per la storia del viaggio in Spagna di G. B. Tiepolo*, in 'Ateneo Veneto,' 1914.

Rumor, S.: *La sala dei Settecenteschi nel Museo di Vicenza*, in 'Arte Cristiana,' pp. 132-140, May, 1914, Milan.

Malaguzzi-Valeri, F.: *Ignoti dipinti veneti del '700 a Milano*, in 'Rassegna d'Arte,' 1914.

Molmenti, P.: *Due tele tiepolesche nella Pinacoteca di Atene*, in 'Emporium,' April, 1914, p. 315.

Molmenti, P.: *I quadri di soggetto sacro di G. B. Tiepolo*, in 'Emporium,' May, 1914.

Orlandini, G.: *La Cappella Corner nella Chiesa dei SS. Apostoli*. Venice, 1914.

v. Derschau, J.: *Tiepolos Schlachtbilder im Wiener Privatbesitz*, in 'Cicerone', 1915.

Fogolari, G.: *La distruzione del Tiepolo degli Scalzi a Venezia*, in 'La Lettura,' 1915.

Feulner, A.: *Beiträge zu Tiepolos Tätigkeit in Würzburg*, in 'Monatshefte für Kunstwissenschaft,' p. 128, 1915.

Morassi, A.: *Die Malereien im Palazzo Steffaneo zu Crauglio*, in 'Jahrbuch der Zentralkommission für Denkmalpflege,' Vienna, 1915.

Kutschera-Woborsky, O.: *Tiepolos Decke des Merito im Palazzo Rezzonico zu Venedig*, in 'Monatschrift für Kunstwissenschaft,' 1916.

Cantalamessa, G.: *Un quadretto tiepolesco*, in 'Bollettino d'Arte,' X, Rome, 1916.

Dogson, C.: *The three versions of Tiepolos Phaeton*, in 'The Burlington Magazine,' 1917.

Kutschera-Woborsky, O.: *Udine im 18. Jahrhundert*, in 'Zeitschrift für bild. Kunst,' 1918.

Ricci, C.: *Rembrandt in Italia*. Milan, 1918.

Morazzoni, G.: *La Sede della Scuola Sup. Femm. A. Manzoni, 'Strenna benefica' ecc*. Milan, 1918.

Kutschera-Woborsky, O.: *Tiepolo und Rom*, in 'Kunstchronik,' N. F. 30 (1918-19), pp. 934-40.

Modigliani, E.: *Venise au XVIIIe–XIXe siècles*. Paris, 1919 (Exhibition Catalogue).

Molmenti, P.: *Due tele di G. B. Tiepolo in Verolanuova*, in 'Dedalo,' I, 1920.

Zelbi, G.: *Quattro affreschi tiepoleschi nel Palazzo della Congregazione di Carità di Milano*, in 'Città di Milano,' September, 1920.

Da Persico, G. B.: *Descrizione di Verona e della sua provincia*, Verona, 1920.

Collection de Son Excellence feu le Prince Alexis Orloff. Catalogue, Paris, 1920 (it contains a series of the most beautiful drawings by T. grouped according to subjects; among them the 'Annunciation' and the 'Flight into Egypt').

Fiocco, G.: *G. B. Tiepolo*, Florence, 1921 (2nd ed., 1926).

Hind, A. M.: *The etchings of G. B. Tiepolo*, in 'Print Collector's Quarterly,' 1921.

Kutschera-Woborsky, O.: *Neuentdeckung der Tiepolo Fresken im grossen Saal des Kastells zu Udine*, in 'Repertorium für Kunstwiss.' 1922.

Tarchiani, N.: *Mostra della Pittura Italiana del '600 e del '700*. Catalogue, Rome–Florence, 1922.

Voss, H.: *Ueber Tiepolos Jugendentwicklung*, in 'Kunst und Künstler,' 1922.

Caversazzi, C.: *Il ritratto di G. B. Tiepolo*, in 'Emporium,' 1923.

Fogolari, G.: *Dipinti giovanili di G. B. Tiepolo; nuovi acquisti e attribuzioni delle Gallerie dell'Accademia di Venezia*, in 'Bollettino d'Arte,' 1923.

Ongaro, M.: *Il Palazzo Ducale di Venezia*. Venice, 1923.

Sedlmaier u. Pfister: *Die Fürstbischöfliche Residenz zu Würzburg*, Munich, 1923.

Dolfin, B. G.: *I Dolfin patrizi veneziani nella storia di Venezia dal 452 al 1923.* Milan 1923.

Moschini, G. A.: *Dell' incisione in Venezia* (after the ms. in the Museo Corrèr), Venice, 1924.

Foratti, A.: *G. B. Tiepolo in Friuli,* in 'Le Vie d'Italia,' 1924, pp. 865–871.

Modigliani, E.: *Capolavori veneziani del '700 ritornati in Italia,* in 'Dedalo,' 1924.

Franceschini, G.: *La Villa Valmarana,* in 'Illustrazione Italiana,' August, 1924.

Ojetti-Tarchiani-Dami: *La Pittura Italiana del '600 e '700.* Milan, 1924.

Fogolari, G.: *Le Gallerie di Venezia,* Milan, n.d. (1924).

Mayer, L.: *Lorenzo Tiepolo,* in 'Bollettino d'Arte,' 1924–25.

Modigliani, E.: *Settecento Veneziano nelle raccolte private milanesi,* in 'Illustrazione Italiana,' Christmas Number, 1924–25.

Arese, P. M.: *Il Palazzo e la Raccolta Castiglioni a Vienna,* in 'Illustrazione Italiana' No. 13, March 29th, 1925.

Catalogo della Pinacoteca Querini-Stampalia, Venice, 1925.

Fiocco, G.: *Lorenzo Tiepolo,* in 'Bollettino d'Arte,' 1925.

Fiocco, G.: *Palazzo Pesaro,* in 'Rivista di Venezia,' November, 1925.

Nugent, M.: *Alla Mostra della Pittura Italiana del '600 e del '700.* 2 vols., S. Casciano, 1925.

Sánchez-Cantón, F. J.: *Lorenzo Tiepolo pastellista,* in 'Archivio Español de Arte y Arqueologia,' 1925.

Steif, M.: *Alte Meister im Maehrischen Privatbesitz,* in 'Belvedere,' I, 1925.

Lorenzetti, G.: *Venezia e il suo estuario,* Milan, 1926 (2nd ed. 1944).

Stix, A.–Froelich Bum, L.: *Die Zeichnungen der Venezianischen Schule. Beschreibender Katalog der Zeichnungen der Albertina,* vol. I, Vienna, 1926.

Brunetti, M.: *La Scuola Grande di S. Rocco,* in 'Rivista di Venezia,' August, 1927.

Coletti, L.: *La Pinacoteca Comunale di Treviso,* in 'Bollettino d'Arte,' 1927.

Eigenberger, R.: *Die Gemäldegalerie der Akademie der bildenden Künste.* Vienna, 1927.

Venturi, A.: *Studi dal vero.* Milan, 1927.

Fiocco, G.: *Aggiunte di F. M. Tassis alla Guida di A. M. Zanetti,* in 'Rivista di Venezia,' 1927, pp. 141–176.

Hadeln, D. v.: *Handzeichnungen von G. B. Tiepolo.* 2 vols., Munich and Florence, 1927.

Ojetti, U. (and collaborators): *Il Ritratto italiano dal Caravaggio al Tiepolo, alla Mostra di Palazzo Vecchio.* Bergamo, 1927 (the section on the Venetian Portrait of the 18th century is by A. Ravà).

Sánchez-Cantón, F. J.: *Los Tiepolos de Aranjuez,* in 'Archivio Español de Arte y Arqueologia,' 1927, p. 1 ff.

Vitali, L.: *Nuove Stampe di G. B. Tiepolo,* in 'Bollettino d'Arte,' 1927.

Posse, H.: *Der Triumph der Amphitrite von G. B. Tiepolo,* in 'Zeitschrift für Bildende Kunst,' 1927–28, p. 369 ff.

Molmenti, P.: *Sempre il Tiepolo,* in 'Dedalo,' I, 1927–28.

Beltrami, L.: *'Cose viste' ad uso di amatori d'arte ed affini.* Milan, 1928.

Damerini, G.: *I Pittori veneziani del '700.* Bologna, 1928.

Molmenti, P.: *Tiepolo e la Villa Valmarana.* 1928 (the 1st ed. in French is of 1880).

Catalogo della Mostra del Settecento Italiano. Venice, 1929.

Catalogue of the National Gallery, Trafalgar Square. London, 1929.

Fiocco, G.: *La Pittura italiana del '600 e '700.* Bologna, 1929.

Fiocco, G.: *La Pittura veneziana alla Mostra del '700,* in 'Rivista di Venezia,' 1929.

Hautecoeur, L.: *La Peinture au Musée du Louvre, II, Ecoles étrangères.* Paris, 1929.

Ausstellung aus Privatbesitz, Exhib. Catalogue, Düsseldorf, 1929.

Sánchez–Cantón, F. J.: *Bocetos y dibujos de Tiepolo,* in 'Archivio Español de Arte y Arqueologia,' 1929, pp. 137–143.

Moschini, V.: *Disegni del '700 alla Mostra di Venezia,* in 'Dedalo,' 1929–30.

Ricci, C.: *Eroi, Santi ed Artisti.* Milan, 1930.

De Vito–Battaglia, S.: *Il bozzetto del Tiepolo per il soffitto della Sala delle Guardie a Madrid.* Rome, 1931.

De Vito–Battaglia, S.: *Qualche opera inedita di G. B. Tiepolo,* in 'Rivista di Archeologia e Storia dell'Arte', 1931.

De Vito–Battaglia, S.: *Le opere di G. B. Tiepolo nella chiesa dell'Ospedaletto a Venezia,* in 'Rivista di Archeologia e Storia dell'Arte,' 1931.

Fiocco, G.: *The Castiglioni Tiepolos at Vienna,* in 'The Burlington Magazine,' April, 1931.

Fogolari, G.: *Il bozzetto del Tiepolo per il trasporto della Santa Casa di Loreto,* in 'Bollettino d'Arte,' July, 1931.

Gradenigo, P.: *Guida alla Pinacoteca dei Concordi di Rovigo.* Rovigo, 19.31

Catalogue of the Exhibition of Italian Art, Royal Academy 1930. London, 1931.

Moschini, V.: *La Pittura Italiana del Settecento.* Florence, 1931.

Lonati, V.: *G. B. Tiepolo a Verolanuova,* in 'Brescia,' IV, No. 12, December, 1931, pp. 48–49.

Pinetti, A.: *Inventario della Provincia di Bergamo.* Rome, 1931.

Posse, H.: *Die Briefe des Grafen F. Algarotti an den sächsischen Hof und seine Bilderkäufe für die Dresdner Gemäldegalerie, 1743–1747,* in 'Prussian Jahrbuch,' Beiheft, 1931.

De Vito–Battaglia, S.: *G. B. Tiepolo.* Bergamo, 1931 (Rome, 1932).

Venturi, L.: *Pitture italiane in America.* Milan, 1931 (English ed., 1933).

Fogolari, G.: *La modella del Tiepolo,* in 'Illustrazione Italiana,' Christmas Number, Milan, 1931.

De Vito–Battaglia, S.: *Una piccola opera giovanile di G. B. Tiepolo,* in 'Vita Artistica,' Rome, March–April, 1932.

G.V.–U.M. (Vale e Masotti): *La Chiesa della Purità, Notizie storiche—Per nozze.* Udine, 1932.

Mendez, C.: *Tiepolo,* in 'Pantheon,' July, 1932.

Arslan, W.: *G. B. Tiepolo e G. B. Morlaiter,* in 'Rivista di Venezia,' 1932.

Morassi, A.: *Il Museo Poldi-Pezzoli in Milano.* Rome, 1932.

Ojetti–Fogolari–Moschini and others: *Il Settecento Italiano.* Milan–Rome, 1932.

Siple, S.: *Recent acquisitions in America,* in 'The Burlington Magazine,' February, 1932.

Fiocco, G.: *Due nuovi Tiepolo,* in 'Dedalo,' June, 1932.

Argan, G. C.: *Un bozzetto inedito di G. B. Tiepolo,* in 'L'Arte,' 1933.

Lorenzetti, C.: *Un'opera di G. B. Tiepolo proveniente dalle Marche,* in 'Rassegna Marchigiana,' 3–4, 1933.

Brizio, A. M.: *Unpublished Drawings by G. B. Tiepolo,* in 'Old Master Drawings,' 1933.

Catalogo delle Gallerie dell'Accademia di Venezia. Bologna, 1933.

Fry, R.: *Cleopatra's Feast by G. B. Tiepolo,* in 'The Burlington Magazine,' September, 1933.

Modigliani, E.: *Dipinti noti o mal noti del Tiepolo,* in 'Dedalo,' 1933.

Venturi, L.: *Italian Paintings in America.* Milan, 1933. (Italian ed., 1931).

Somaré, E.: *Tiepolo* (Coll. 'Grandi Maestri del colore'), No. 22, Bergamo, 1934.

Lorenzetti, G., and Planiscig, L.: *La Collezione dei Conti Donà dalle Rose a Venezia* (Sale Catalogue). Venice, 1934.

Morassi, A.: *La Galleria dell'Accademia Carrara di Bergamo.* Rome, 1934.

Italiaansche Kunst in Nederlandsch Bezit (Catalogue). Amsterdam, 1934.

Morassi, A.: *The young Tiepolo,* in 'The Burlington Magazine,' February–March, 1934.

Calabi, E.: *La Pittura a Brescia nel '600 e '700. Catalogo della Mostra.* Brescia, 1935.

Catalogo della Mostra degli acquisti e doni pervenuti al Museo Civico Corrèr. Venice, 1935.

Catalogue-Exposition de l'Art Italien, Petit Palais. Paris, 1935.

Catalogue de la collection W.B. (Blumethal). Paris, Galerie Charpentier, 1935.

van Marle, R.: *La pittura all' esposizione d'arte antica italiana di Amsterdam,* in 'Bollettino d'Arte,' March, 1935.

Lafuente-Ferrari, E.: *Grabados, dibujos de Tiepolo.* Madrid, 1935.

Lorenzetti, G.: *Quadri di Teodoro Matteini e di G. D. Tiepolo,* in 'Rivista di Venezia,' July, 1935.

Lorenzetti, G.: *Tre note tiepolesche,* in 'Rivista di Venezia,' August, 1935, pp. 394–95.

Modigliani, E.: *Catalogo della R. Pinacoteca di Brera.* Milan, 1935.

Morassi, A.: *More about the young Tiepolo,* in 'The Burlington Magazine,' October, 1935.

Santangelo, A.: *Un capolavoro del Tiepolo ed altri inediti del Fontebasso,* in 'La Critica d'arte,' 1935.

Mayer, A. L.: *Tiepolo*, in 'Revista Española de Arte,' IV, September, 1935, p. 309.

Voss, H.: *Italienische Malerei des 17. u. 18. Jahrhunderts* (Katalog der Ausstellung in Wiesbaden). Wiesbaden, 1935.

Cipollato, A.: *Le nouveau Musée du XVIIIe siècle vénitien* (Pal. Rezzonico), in 'La Revue de l'Art ancien et moderne,' 1936, V, pp. 246–254.

Lorenzetti, G.: *Ca' Rezzonico* (Catalogue). Venice, 1936.

Goering, M.: *Italienische Malerei des 17. und 18. Jahrhunderts.* Berlin, 1936.

Arslan, W.: *Studi sulla pittura del primo Settecento veneziano*, in 'La Critica d'arte,' April, 1936.

Coletti, L.: *Zwei Entwürfe von Tiepolo*, in 'Pantheon,' 1936.

Avena, A.: *Il Museo di Castelvecchio a Verona.* Rome, 1937.

Della Pergola, P.: *Tre ritratti del Tiepolo*, in 'La Critica d'arte,' 1937.

Fiocco, G.: *G. B. Tiepolo in Ispagna*, in 'Nuova Antologia,' April, 1937.

Fiocco, G.: *Tiepolo*, in 'Enciclopedia Italiana.' Rome, 1937.

Froelich-Bume, L.: *An Exhibition of Italian Baroque paintings*, in 'The Burlington Magazine,' August, 1937.

Lorenzetti, G.: *Mostra delle Feste e Maschere veneziane.* (Catalogue), Venice, 1937.

Morassi, A.: *Disegni antichi della collezione Rasini.* Milan, 1937.

Morassi, A.: *An unknown early work by G. B. Tiepolo*, in 'The Burlington Magazine,' February, 1937.

Pallucchini, R.: *Un gruppo di disegni inediti del Tiepolo*, in 'La Critica d'Arte,' 1937.

Popham, A. E.: *The drawings at the Burlington Fine Arts Club*, in 'The Burlington Magazine,' February, 1937.

Catton-Rich, D.: *Paintings, Drawings and Prints by the Tiepolos*, Chicago, 1938 (Catalogue of the Loan Exhibition in the Art Institute at Chicago).

Fiocco, G.: *An early work by G. B. Tiepolo*, in 'Art in America,' October, 1938.

Froelich-Bume, L.: *Notes on some works by G. B. Tiepolo*, in 'The Burlington Magazine,' February, 1938.

Morassi, A.: *Yet more about the young Tiepolo*, in 'The Burlington Magazine, October, 1938.

Siple, S.: *Three Exhibitions of XVIIIth Century Art*, in 'The Burlington Magazine,' May, 1938.

Catalogue of the Exhibition 'Tiepolo and his Contemporaries,' Metropolitan Museum, New York, 1938.

Stechow, W.: *The two Tiepolos*, in 'Art in America,' 1938.

Cervellini, G. B.: *Per una revisione di G. M. Urbani de Gheltof*, in 'Civiltà moderna,' 1939.

Goering, M.: *Ein neuentdecktes Mädchenbildnis von G. B. Tiepolo*, in 'Pantheon', 1939.

Goering, M.: *G. B. Tiepolo*, in 'Thieme-Becker Künstlerlexikon,' Leipzig, 1939.

Moschetti, A.: *An unpublished early work by G. B. Tiepolo*, in 'The Burlington Magazine,' 1939.

Parker, K. T.: *Some observations on Guardi and Tiepolo*, in 'Old Master Drawings,' 1939.

Pittaluga, M.: *Note sulle acqueforti di G. B. Tiepolo*, in 'L'Arte,' 1939.

Read, B.: *Identified drawings by G. B. Tiepolo*, in 'The Burlington Magazine,' November, 1939.

Morassi, A.: *Brescia, Catalogo delle cose d'arte.* Rome, 1939.

Constable, W. G.: *A ceiling painting by G. B. Tiepolo*, in 'Bulletin of the Museum of Fine Arts,' Boston, Mass., June, 1940.

Fasolo, G.: *Guida di Vicenza*, Vicenza, 1940.

Middeldorf, U.: *An unusual drawing by G. B. Tiepolo*, in 'Bulletin of the Art Institute of Chicago,' April–May, 1940, pp. 54–57.

Fiocco, G.: *Pitture del Settecento italiano in Portogallo*, Rome, 1940.

Hegemann, H. W.: *G. B. Tiepolo.* Berlin, 1940.

Lorenzetti, G.: *Ca' Rezzonico* (Catalogue). Venice, 1940. 2nd ed. (the 1st is of 1936).

Wehle, H. B.: *The Metropolitan Museum* (Catalogue, Italian School). New York, 1940.

Goering, M.: *Veronese und das Settecento*, in 'Prussian Jahrbuch,' 1940.

Catalogue of Paintings and Sculpture, National Gallery of Art. Washington, 1941.

Morandotti, A.: *Mostra della Pittura Italiana del Settecento* (Catalogue). Rome, 1941.

Morassi, A.: *G. B. e D. Tiepolo alla Villa Valmarana*, in 'Le Arti,' April–May, 1941.

Morassi, A.: *D. Tiepolo*, in 'Emporium,' June, 1941.

Pallucchini, R.: *Gli incisori veneti del Settecento* (Catalogue of the Exhibition). Venice, 1941.

Porcella, A.: *I Tiepolo e i tiepoleschi*, in 'L'Arte,' December, 1941, pp. 169–181.

Santifaller, M.: *Die Radierungen G. B. Tiepolos. Anmerkungen zur Erforschung der Quellen ihrer Formwelt*, in 'Pantheon,' 1941.

Schierbatcheva, M.: *The Hermitage Tiepolos from Palazzo Dolfin*, in Russian, in 'Art Review' (Hckycctbo), Leningrad, 1941.

Fogolari, G.: *Lettere inedite del Tiepolo* (preface by N. Barbantini), in 'Nuova Antologia,' I, September, 1942.

Gradenigo, P.: *Commemoriale, Diario et Annotazioni curiose occorse in Venezia ecc.* (Ms. in the Museo Corrèr in Venice), edited by L. Livan. Venice, 1942.

Lorenzetti, G.: *La pittura veneziana del '700.* Novara, 1942.

Modigliani, E.: *La collezione Luigi Albertini.* Rome–Milan, 1942.

Morassi, A.: *Novità e precisazioni sul Tiepolo*, in 'Le Arti' (two articles) December, 1941–January, 1942; April–May, 1942.

Schaub-Koch, E.: *Tiepolo*, in 'Ateneo Veneto,' 1942.

Vigni, G.: *Disegni del Tiepolo.* Padua, 1942.

Sánchez-Cantón, F. J.: *Catalogo de los cuadros, Museo del Prado.* Madrid, 1942.

Fiocco, G.: *Tiepolo in Ispagna*, in 'Le Arti,' 1942–43.

Fernandez, J.: *Tiepolo, Mengs and Don Raphael Ximeno y Planes*, in 'Gazette des Beaux-Arts,' 1942, pp. 345–362.

Morassi, A.: *L'ora del Tiepolo*, in 'Emporium,' vol. XCVII, 1943.

Hetzer, T.: *Die Fresken Tiepolos in der Würzburger Residenz.* Frankfurt a M., 1943.

Morassi, A.: *G. B. Tiepolo.* Milan–Bergamo–Rome, 1943 (2nd ed., 1950).

Vigni, G.: *Note su G. B. e D. Tiepolo*, in 'Emporium,' July, 1943.

Goering, M.: *Wenig bekannte und neu gefundene Werke von G. B. Tiepolo*, in 'Pantheon' No. 6, October–December, 1944.

Bassi, E.: *Problemi dell' incisione veneta del Settecento*, in 'Emporium', July–December, 1944, p. 37 ff.

Morassi, A.: *Opere giovanili del Tiepolo*, in 'L'Arte,' January–June, 1944.

Pallucchini, R.: *Nota per G. B. Tiepolo*, in 'Emporium,' January, 1944.

Gallo, R.: *I Pisani ed i Palazzi di S. Stefano e di Stra.* Venice, 1945.

Morassi, A.: *Tiepolo e la Villa Valmarana.* Milan, 1945.

Pallucchini, R.: *Gli affreschi di G. B. e G. D. Tiepolo alla Villa Valmarana.* Bergamo, 1945.

Valentiner, W. R.: *A late work by G. B. Tiepolo: St. Joseph and the Christ Child*, in 'The Detroit Art Institute Bulletin,' 1945.

Borenius, T.: *Later Italian paintings from Titian to Tiepolo.* London, 1946.

Francis, H. S.: *Tiepolo's Adoration of the Magi drawings*, in 'The Cleveland Museum Bulletin,' January, 1946.

Glück, G.: *Gemäldegalerie des Kunsthistorischen Museums in Wien.* Vienna, 1946.

Longhi, R.: *Viatico per cinque secoli di pittura veneziana.* Florence, 1946.

Lorenzetti, G.: *Il quaderno del Tiepolo al Museo Corrèr di Venezia.* Venice, 1946.

Pallucchini, R.: *I Capolavori dei Musei Veneti* (Exhib. Catalogue). Venice, 1946.

Petrucci, A.: *Le Acqueforti del Tiepolo*, in 'La Fiera Letteraria,' December 26th, 1946.

Gerstenberg, K.: *Die Fresken Tiepolos in der Residenz Würzburg*, in 'Das Kunstwerk,' 1946, I and II.

Avena, A.: *Capolavori della pittura veronese* (Exhib. Catalogue), Verona, 1947.

Benesch, O.: *Venetian Drawings of the Eighteenth Century in America.* New York, 1947.

Barbantini-Lorenzetti-Mariacher: *Catalogo della Mostra delle Tre Scuole.* Venice, 1947.

Grabar, J.: *The Tiepolos in Archangel and Tiepolo's self-portrait* (in Russian), in 'Hckycctbo,' No. 2, 1947.

Morassi, A.: *Mostra della Pittura del Seicento e Settecento in Liguria* (Exhib. Catalogue), Genoa, 1947.

Pallucchini, R.: *Trésors de l'art vénitien.* (Exhib. Catalogue) Milan, Lausanne, 1947.

Pallucchini, R.: *Opere inedite o poco note alla Mostra 'Trésors de l'art vénitien' di Losanna,* in 'Emporium,' June, 1947.

Mariacher, G.: *La riaperta quadreria del Museo Corrèr,* in 'Emporium,' November, 1948.

Puerari, A.: *Mostra di antiche pitture dal XIV al XIX secolo.* (Exhib. Catalogue), Cremona, 1948.

Clemen, P.: *Tiepolo und die bayerisch-fränkische Rokokomalerei,* in 'Gesammelte Aufsätze,' Düsseldorf, 1948.

Marconi, S.: *Le Gallerie dell'Accademia di Venezia* (Catalogue), Venice, 1949.

Mariacher-Pignatti: *Civico Museo Corrèr, Catalogo della Quadreria.* Venice, 1949.

Morassi, A.: *Settecento inedito* (1st article) in 'Arte Veneta,' 1949.

Muraro, M.: *Mostra del restauro dei Monumenti e opere d'arte danneggiate dalla guerra* (Catalogue), Venice, 1949.

Richardson, E. P.: *Masterpieces of Painting and Sculpture from the Detroit Institute of Art* (Exhib. Catalogue), Detroit, 1949.

Bassi, E.: *L'Accademia di Belle Arti di Venezia nel suo bicentenario.* Venice, 1950.

Florisoone, M.: *Les dessins vénitiens du XVe au XVIIIe siècle.* Paris, 1950.

Mariacher, G.: *Nota sulla pala di Rampazzo di G. B. Tiepolo,* in 'Arte Veneta,' 1950, vol. p. 153.

Brunetti-Lorenzetti: *Venezia nella storia e nell'arte.* Venice, 1950.

Zampetti, P.: *La Mostra della Pittura Veneta nelle Marche.* (Catalogue of the Exhibition in Ancona), Bergamo, 1950.

Mariacher, G.: *Il Palazzo Ducale di Venezia.* Florence, 1950.

Morassi, A.: *Nuovi inediti del Tiepolo,* in 'Emporium,' November, 1950.

Pallucchini, R.: *La Mostra del bicentenario dell'Accademia Veneziana di Belle Arti,* in 'Arte Veneta,' 1950.

Pignatti, T.: *I ritratti settecenteschi della Querini-Stampalia,* in 'Bollettino d'Arte,' July–September, 1950.

Rosenberg, J.: *An oil sketch by G. B. Tiepolo for the 'Aeneas' ceiling in Madrid,* in 'Bulletin of the Fogg Art Museum,' Cambridge, Mass., March, 1950.

Morassi, A.: *Settecento inedito* (2nd article), in 'Arte Veneta,' 1950.

Berenson, B.: *G. B. Tiepolo,* in 'Illustrazione Italiana,' June, 1951.

Bassi, E.: *Un ricordo del viaggio in Germania di G. B. Tiepolo,* in 'Emporium,' 1951, pp. 75–76.

Catton-Rich, D.: *Time and Tiepolo,* in 'Art News,' October, 1951, pp. 17–19.

Ivanoff, N.: *Una postilla tiepolesca,* in 'Ateneo Veneto,' July–December, 1951.

Trentin, G.: *G. Battista, G. Domenico e Lorenzo Tiepolo incisori.* Venice, 1951.

Dazzi, M.: *Scheda per il Procuratore di G. B. Tiepolo,* in 'Arte Veneta', 1951.

Mazzariol-Pignatti: *Itinerario tiepolesco.* Venice, 1951.

Lorenzetti, G.: *Mostra del Tiepolo, Catalogo.* Venice, 1951.

Cf. 'Arte Veneta,' vol. 1951, pp. 232, 233, for the various Italian and foreign articles on the Tiepolo Exhibition, Venice, 1951.

Delogu, G.: *Tiepolo.* Bergamo, 1951.

Pignatti, T.: *Disegni del Tiepolo,* in 'La Fiera Letteraria,' June, 1951.

Pallucchini, R.: *La Pittura veneziana del Settecento* (Lezioni Universitarie), Bologna, 1951.

Morassi, A.: *Omaggio al Tiepolo,* in 'Arti,' March–April, 1951.

Pignatti, T.: *Novità su Lorenzo Tiepolo,* in 'Le Arti,' No. 4, 1951.

Vigni, G.: *Tiepolo.* Florence, 1951.

Maubert, A.: *Sur les traces de Tiepolo,* in 'Les Nouvelles littéraires,' July, 1951.

Bg., R.: *Il mistero di un secondo Tiepolo a Palazzo Dugnani,* in 'Famiglia meneghina,' January, 1951, pp. 8–9.

Pignatti, T.: *Tiepolo.* Milan, 1951.

Galbiati, G.; *Itinerario della Pinacoteca Ambrosiana* (Catalogue), Milan, 1951.

Emanuelli, E.: *Revisioni alla Mostra del Tiepolo,* in 'Panorama dell'Arte Italiana,' Turin, 1951.

Pignatti, T.: *G. B. Tiepolo e i suoi tempi,* in 'Nuova Antologia', 1951.

Barbantini, N.: *Tiepolo,* in 'Arti e Costume,' Milan, 1951.

Watson, F.: *Eighteenth Century Venice.* (Catalogue of the Exhib. at the Whitechapel Gallery). London, 1951.

Del Bianco, M.: *Documenti su due pale di G. B. Tiepolo progettate per S. Marco a Roma,* in 'Atti dell' Istituto Veneto di Scienze, Lettere ed Arti', 1951-52, pp. 283-290.

Richardson, E. P.: *Venice 1700–1800 (an Exhibition of Venice and the Eighteenth Century),* Detroit, Institute of Arts, 1952.

Watson, F.: *Reflections on the Tiepolo Exhibition,* in 'The Burlington Magazine,' 1952, pp. 40–44.

Cristini, G.: *I Tiepolo di Verolanuova,* in 'Brescia,' November–December, 1952, pp. 9–13.

Benesch, O.: *Marginalien zur Tiepolo Ausstellung in Venedig,* in 'Alte und Neue Kunst,' Vienna, 1952.

Baroni, C.–Dell'Acqua, A.: *Tesori d'arte in Lombardia,* Milan, 1952.

Dussler, L.: *Die Tiepolo Ausstellung in Venedig,* in 'Kunstchronik,' 1952, pp. 1–5.

Morassi, A.: *Settecento inedito* (3rd article), in 'Arte Veneta,' 1952.

Raimondi, A.: *Il Tiepolo a Bergamo nella Cappella Colleoni,* in 'L'Eco di Bergamo,' November 26th, 1952.

Gerstenberg, K.: *Tiepolos Weltbild in Würzburg und Madrid,* in 'Zeitschrift für Kunstgeschichte,' 1952.

Cailleux, P.: *Tiepolo et Guardi dans les collections françaises* (Exhib. Catalogue), Paris, 1952.

R. P. (Pallucchini): *Tiepolo e Guardi alla Galleria Cailleux,* in 'Arte Veneta,' 1952.

Riccoboni, A.: *Un tiepolesco in Valtellina: Cesare Ligari,* in 'Arte Veneta', 1953, pp. 175 ff.

Bassi-Rathgeb, R.: *Un Domenico Tiepolo e un Cesare Ligari ignorati a Lovere,* in 'Arte Veneta', 1953, p. 177 ff.

Ragghianti, C. L.: *Tiepolo a Trieste,* in 'Sele-Arte,' July–August, 1953.

Münz, L.: *Katalog der III. Sonderausstellung* (Vienna, Akademie). Vienna, 1953.

Sánchez-Cantón, F. J.: *J. B. Tiepolo en España,* Madrid, 1953.

Missiani, L.: *G. B. Tiepolo,* in 'Gazzetta del Veneto,' March 27th, 1953.

Mazzotti, G.: *Le Ville Venete,* Treviso, 1953.

Tiepolo, 150 disegni dei Musei di Trieste (Exhib. Catalogue), Florence, Palazzo Strozzi, 1953.

Münz, L.: *Führer durch die Gemaeldegalerie der Akademie der Bildenden Künste,* Vienna, 1954.

Muraro, M.: *Guida di Venezia.* Venice, 1954.

Ronci, G.: *Dal Caravaggio al Tiepolo* (Exhib. Catalogue), Sao Paulo, Brazil, 1954.

European Masters of the Eighteenth Century (Exhib. Catalogue by B. Ford, J. Byam-Shaw, F. Watson), Royal Academy, London, 1954-55.

Morassi, A.: *Some 'modelli' and other unpublished works by Tiepolo,* in 'The Burlington Magazine,' January, 1955.

Russoli, F.: *La Pinacoteca Poldi Pezzoli,* Milan, 1955.

Mazzini, F.: *Fra' Galgario e il Settecento* (Exhibition Catalogue), Bergamo, 1955.

Morassi, A.: *Tiepolo,* London, 1955 (other editions in Italian and German).

Vigni, G.: *Note sull' attività del Tiepolo a Madrid ed a Würzburg e sul Quaderno Corrèr,* in 'Atti del Congresso di Storia dell'Arte', Venice, 1955.

Mostra del Settecento Veneziano (Exhibition Catalogue), Villa Comunale, Milan, 1955.

Levey, M.: *Tiepolo's Altar-piece for S. Savaltore at Venice,* in 'The Burlington Magazine', 1955.

Watson, F.: *G. B. Tiepolo: a masterpiece and a book,* in 'Connoisseur,' November, 1955, pp. 212-216.

Fiocco, G.: *Cento antichi disegni veneziani,* Exhibition Catalogue, Fondazione Giorgio Cini, Venice, 1955.

von Freeden, M.–Lamb, C.: *Tiepolo. Die Fresken der Würzburger Residenz.* Munich, 1956.

Morassi, A.: *Fasti e nefasti del Settecento Veneziano*, in 'Emporium,' January, 1956.

Someda de Marco, C.: *Il Museo Civico e le Gallerie d'arte antica e moderna di Udine*, Udine, 1956.

Riccoboni, A.: *Opere giovanili poco note o inedite di G. B. Tiepolo*, in 'Arte Veneta', 1956, p. 165 ff.

d'Ancona, P.: *Gli affreschi del Tiepolo al Palazzo Clerici*. Milan, 1956.

Gioseffi, D.: *Pittura Veneziana del Settecento*. Bergamo, 1956.

Lorenzetti, G.: *Venezia e il suo estuario*. Rome, 1956.

Riccoboni, A.: *Un nuovo Tiepolo a Milano*, in 'Emporium', 1956.

Magagnato, L.: *Disegni del Museo Civico di Bassano*, Exhibition Catalogue, Venice, Fondazione Giorgio Cini, 1956.

Valcanover, F.: *Ritratto Veneto da Tiziano al Tiepolo*, Exhibition Catalogue, Warsaw, 1956.

Bialostocki, J.: *Mostra della Pittura Italiana nelle Collezioni Polacche*, Exhibition Catalogue, Warsaw, 1956.

Martin-Mery, G.: *De Tiepolo à Goya*, Exhibition Catalogue, Bordeaux, 1956.

Voss, H.: *Die Flucht nach Aegypten*, in 'Saggi e Memorie di storia della arte,' Venice, 1957.

Levey, M.: *Tiepolo's 'Empire of Flora,'* in 'The Burlington Magazine,' March, 1957, pp. 89–91.

Levey, M.: *The modello for Tiepolo's altar-piece at Nymphenburg*, in 'The Burlington Magazine,' August, 1957, pp. 256–261.

Pilo, G. M.: *Lazzarini e Tiepolo*, in 'Arte Veneta,' 1957, pp. 215–219.

Muraro, M.: *Disegni Veneti della Collezione Janos Scholz*, Exhibition Catalogue (Fondazione Cini), Venice, 1957.

Biasutti, G.: *I Libri 'De scossi, e spesi' del Card. Daniele Delfino ultimo Patriarca di Aquileia*. Udine, 1957.

Levey, M.: *Tiepolo's treatment of classical story at Villa Valmarana*, in 'Journal of the Warburg and Courtauld Institutes,' vol. XX, 1957, July–September, pp. 298–317.

Donzelli, C.: *Pittori Veneti del Settecento*. Florence, 1957.

Richardson, E. P.: *An unrecorded painting by Tiepolo*, in 'Bulletin of the Detroit Institute of Art,' 1957–58, No. 4, pp. 80–81.

Valentiner, W. R.: *Tiepolos 'Banquet of Cleopatra'*, in 'North Carolina Museum of Art Bulletin', 1957.

Benesch, O.: *Tiepolo und die malerische Aufgabe des Freskos im Settecento*, in 'Münchner Jahrbuch der bildenden Kunst', 1957.

Morassi, A.: *The discovery of a new painting by Tiepolo*, in 'The Connoisseur,' November, 1958, p. 178 ff.

Morassi, A.: *Giambattista Tiepolo's 'Girl with a lute' and the clarification of some points in the work of Domenico Tiepolo*, in 'The Art Quarterly,' summer, 1958, pp. 177–186.

Haskell, F.: *Algarotti and Tiepolo's 'Banquet of Cleopatra,'* in 'The Burlington Magazine,' June, 1958, pp. 212–213.

Precerutti-Garberi, M.: *Di alcuni dipinti perduti del Tiepolo*, in 'Commentari,' April–June, 1958, pp. 110–123.

Fillol, G.: *Los echos de el Palacio de el Pardo*, in 'Arte y Hogar,' December, 1958, pp. 34–38.

Marzoli-Feslikenian, M.: *Tiepolo*, Milan, 1958.

Vardanega, A.: *Il Rosario dei 'Gesuati' di Venezia nei monocromi di Tiepolo*, in 'Arte Cristiana,' No. 10–11, 1958, pp. 84–88.

Parker, K. T.: *Disegni Veneti di Oxford*, Exhibition Catalogue (Fondazione Cini), Venice, 1958.

Mrozinska, M.: *Disegni veneti in Polonia*, Exhibition Catalogue, Venice, (Fondazione Giorgio Cini), 1958.

Europäisches Rokoko, Exhibition Catalogue, Munich 1958.

Voss, H.: *Un taccuino di disegni del Tiepolo giovane*, in 'Saggi e memorie di storia dell'arte,' No. 2, pp. 316–322, Venice, 1959.

Morassi, A.: *Disegni veneti del Settecento nella Collezione Paul Wallraf*, Exhibition Catalogue (Fondazione Giorgio Cini), Venice, 1959.

Byam-Shaw, J.: *A sketch for a ceiling by Domenico Tiepolo*, in 'The Burlington Magazine', December, 1959, p. 447.

Huttinger, E.: *Venezianische Malerei*. Zurich, 1959 (French ed., Lausanne, 1959).

Levey, M.: *Painting in XVIII Century Venice*. London, 1959.

Italian Paintings and Drawings at 56 Princes Gate, London, 1959.

Morassi, A.: *Giambattista Tiepolo—Painter of 'macchiette,'* in 'The Burlington Magazine,' June, 1959, pp. 227–232.

Mariacher, G.: *Per la datazione di un'opera perduta di Giambattista Tiepolo*, in 'Arte Veneta,' 1959–60, XIII–XIV, pp. 237–238.

Rizzi, A.: *I Tiepolo 'critici d'arte,'* in 'Arte Veneta,' 1959–60, XIII–XIV, pp. 239–242.

Muraro, M.: *L'Olympe de Tiepolo*, in 'Gazette des Beaux-Arts,' January, 1960, pp. 19–34.

Levey, M.: *Two Paintings by Tiepolo from the Algarotti Collection*, in 'The Burlington Magazine,' June, 1960, pp. 250–257.

Battisti, E.: *Postille documentarie su artisti italiani a Madrid e sulla collezione Maratta*, in 'Arte antica e moderna,' No. 9, 1960, pp. 77–89.

Chamot, M.: *Some collections of western art in Russia*, in 'The Burlington Magazine,' February, 1959, pp. 47–53.

De Logu, G.: *La Pittura Veneziana dal XIV al XVIII secolo*, Bergamo, 1959.

Byam-Shaw, J.: *Two drawings by Domenico Tiepolo, and a note on the date of the Frescoes at the Villa Contarini-Pisani*, in 'The Burlington Magazine', December, 1960, p. 529 ff.

Pallucchini, R.: *La Pittura Veneziana del Settecento*, Venezia-Roma, 1960.

Pignatti, T.: *Il Museo Correr di Venezia* (Catalogue), Venice, 1960.

Knox, G.: *Catalogue of the Tiepolo drawings in the Victoria and Albert Museum*, London, 1960.

Levey, M.: *Tiepolo and his age*, in 'Art and ideas in Eighteenth-century Italy', published by Istituto Italiano di Cultura, IV, London, 1960.

Precerutti-Garberi, M.: *Asterischi sull'attività di Domenico Tiepolo a Würzburg*, in 'Commentari', July-December, 1960.

Lavrova, O. I.: *The sketch by Tiepolo 'Death of Dido' and the Valmarana Frescoes*, in 'Bulletin of the Institute of art-history of the Russian Academy of Sciences', No. 13–14, 1960, p. 165 ff.

Lavrova, O. I.: *Two Saints, sketch by G. B. Tiepolo*, in 'Bulletin of the Pushkin Museum', 1960, p. 49 ff.

Haskell, F.: *Francesco Guardi as vedutista and some of his Patrons*, in 'Journal of the Warburg and Courtauld Institutes', Nos. 3-4, 1960.

La Peinture Italienne au XVIIIe siècle (Exhibition Catalogue), Petit Palais, Paris 1960-61.

Rizzi, A.: *Il fiore della Galleria d'Arte antica di Udine*, in 'Avanti cul Brun', Udine, 1961, p. 283 ff.

ILLUSTRATIONS

THE OLD TESTAMENT

1 – 31

1. Fall of the Rebel Angels. *Udine, Palazzo Arcivescovile*

2. Adam Tempted by Eve. *Udine, Palazzo Arcivescovile*

3. Abraham and the Angels. *Madrid, Duke of Luna-Villahermosa Coll.*

4. Abraham and the Angels. *Madrid, Prado*

5. Abraham and the Angels. *Venice, Scuola di S. Rocco*

6. Sacrifice of Isaac. *Udine, Cathedral*

7. Rebecca at the Well. *Athens, Museum of Fine Arts*

8. Jacob Wrestling with the Angel.
Udine, Palazzo Arcivescovile

9. The Sacrifice of Melchisedek.
Buenos Aires, Museo Nacional de Bellas Artes

10. Rebecca at the Well. *New York, Private Coll.*

11. Hagar in the Desert. *Udine, Palazzo Arcivescovile*

12. Jacob's Dream. *Udine, Palazzo Arcivescovile*

13. Joseph Receiving Pharaoh's Ring. *London, Dulwich College Gallery*

14. The Finding of Moses. *Melbourne, National Gallery of Victoria*

15a. The Brazen Serpent. *Venice, Accademia*

16. The Brazen Serpent. *Munich, formerly Drey Coll.*

15b. The Brazen Serpent. *Venice, Accademia*

17. Joshua Commanding the Sun to Stand Still. *Milan, Museo Poldi-Pezzoli*

18. 'Capriccio' on the Finding of Moses. *Bergamo, Private Coll.*

19. Moses Saved from the Waters. *Milan, E. Moizzi Coll.*

29–30. Two Prophets. *Udine, Palazzo Arcivescovile*

31. Susanna and the Elders. *Hartford Conn., Wadsworth, Atheneum*

THE NEW TESTAMENT

32 – 64

32. The Annunciation. *Leningrad, Hermitage*

33. Rest on the Flight into Egypt. *Padua, S. Massimo*   34. Annunciation. *Madrid, Duke of Luna-Villahermosa Coll.*

35. The Circumcision. *Bassano, Museo Civico*

36. The Flight into Egypt. *Bellagio, Princess Torre e Tasso Coll.*

37. The Flight into Egypt. *Berlin, formerly Private Coll.*

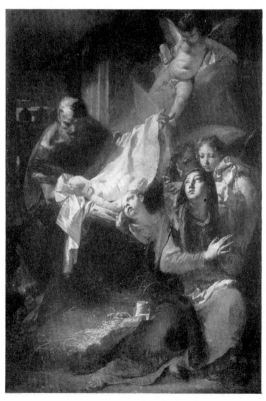

38. The Adoration of the Infant Jesus. *Venice, S. Mark's, Sacristy of the Canons*

39. The Flight into Egypt. *San Diego, Fine Arts Gallery*

49. The Last Supper. *Desenzano, Parish Church*

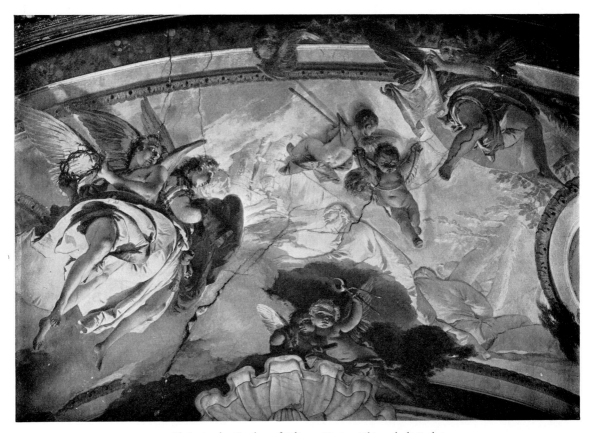

50. Christ in the Garden of Olives. *Venice, Chiesa degli Scalzi*

51. Christ in the Garden of Olives. *Stamford, Burghley House*

52. Ecce Homo. *Caen, Musée*

53. Ecce Homo. *Geneva, A. Pereire Coll.*

54. The Procession to Calvary. *Berlin, Gemäldegalerie*

55. The Crucifixion. *Venice, formerly Brass Coll.*

56. Christ Crucified, with God the Father.
Udine, Cathedral

57. The Crucifixion. *Vierhouten, van Beuningen Coll.*

58. The Crucifixion. *Burano, S. Martino*

59. The Deposition, *London, National Gallery*

60. The Deposition. *Zürich, Hausammann Coll.*

61. The Resurrection. *Udine, Cathedral*

62. The Resurrection. *Vicenza, S. Stefano*

63. The Deposition. *London, National Gallery*

64. The Ascension. *New York, Private Coll.*

79. The Immaculate Virgin. *Udine, Chiesa della Purità.* – 80. Madonna and Child with an Angel. *Bergamo, Private Coll.*

81. Madonna of the Rosary. *London, formerly J. B. Robinson Coll.* – 82. Madonna and Child. *Springfield, Museum of Fine Arts*

83. Madonna with Three Saints. *Bergamo, formerly Piccinelli Coll.* – 84. Madonna with Three Saints. *Zürich, Private Coll.*

85. Madonna with Five Saints. *Budapest, Museum of Fine Arts*

86. Madonna with Saints. *London, National Gallery*

87–88. The Miracle of the Holy House of Loreto. – 87. *Venice, Accademia.* – 88. *London, Earl of Rosebery Coll.*

89–90. S. Dominic Instituting the Rosary. – 89. *Milan, M. Crespi Coll.* – 90. *Berlin, Gemäldegalerie*

91. Madonna and Child with S. Antony and an Abbot. *Banbury, Upton House, Bearsted Coll.*

92. Madonna of the Rosary. *Milan, Museo Poldi-Pezzoli*

93. S. Dominic in Glory. *Venice, Chiesa dei Gesuati*

94. The Virgin Hearing the Prayers of S. Dominic. *Formerly Cambridge, Mass., Fogg Art Museum*

95. The Virgin Hearing the Prayers of S. Dominic. *Venice, Chiesa dei Gesuati*

96. Madonna with SS. Dominic and Hyacinth. *Chicago, Art Institute*

97. Holy Family with S. Gaetano. *Venice, Accademia*

98. Madonna del Carmelo with S. Catherine and the Archangel Michael. *Piove di Sacco, S. Martino*

99. Madonna with SS. George and Anthony Abbot. *Rome, Spalletti- Trivelli Coll.*

100. Madonna with SS. Catherine, Charles Borromeo and John Bishop. *Milan, Private Coll.*

101. Madonna with S. Giustina and the Little S. John. *New York, Lilienfeld Coll.*

102. Madonna with SS. Rose, Catherine and Agnes. *Venice, Chiesa dei Gesuati*

103. Madonna with S. Anthony of Padua. *Venice, Count Cini Coll.*

104. Madonna Appearing to S. John Nepomuk. *Venice, S. Polo*

105–106. The Assumption of the Virgin. – 105. *S. Daniele del Friuli, Cathedral.* – 106. *Ascott, National Trust, A. de Rothschild Coll.*

107. The Assumption of the Virgin. *Würzburg, Residenz*

108. Mystic Marriage of S. Catherine, S. John and The Infant Baptist. *Zürich, Hausammann Coll.*

109. The Patron Saints of the Crotta Family. *Frankfurt, Staedel Institute*

110. S. Augustine and Other Saints.
London, National Gallery

111. The Baptism of Constantine.
Folzano, Parish Church

112. Madonna with the Girdle.
Pirano, S. Maria della Consolazione

113. Apotheosis of S. Louis Gonzaga. *London, Count Seilern Coll.*

114. S. Dominic in Glory. *Venice, Accademia*

115. The Communion of S. Lucy.
Milano, Museo Civico

116. The Martyrdom of S. Sebastian.
Cleveland, Museum of Art

117. S. Fidelis of Sigmaringen Crushing Heresy.
Turin, Pinacoteca

118. The Communion of S. Lucy.
Venice, SS. Apostoli

119. The Martyrdom of S. Sebastian.
Diessen, Convent Church

120. S. Fidelis of Sigmaringen Crushing Heresy.
Parma, Pinacoteca

121. The Discovery of the True Cross. *Venice, Accademia*   122. The Discovery of the True Cross. *Venice, Accademia*

123-125. The Martyrdom of S. Agatha. – 123. *Paris, Broglio Coll.* – 124. *Padua, Santo.* – 125. *Paris, Broglio Coll.*

148. S. Joseph with the Christ Child, and other Saints. *Venice, Accademia.* – 149. Apotheosis of S. Bernard. *Milan, S. Ambrogio*
150. The Assumption with S. Theresa and a Bishop Saint. *Brescia, Count F. Lechi Coll.*

1. Penitent Magdalen. *Naples, Lauro Coll.* – 152. Miracle of S. Patrick of Ireland. *Padua, Museo Civico.* – 153. Martyrdom of S. Theodora. *Milan, Falck Coll.*

154

157

160

154–162. S. Roch. – 154. *Venice, formerly Gatti-Casazza Coll.* – 155. *Strasbourg, Musée.* – 156. *Milan, Count Cicogna Coll.*
157. *S. Marino (Calif.), Huntington Library and Art Gallery.* – 158. *Milan, Count Cicogna Coll.* – 159. *Cambridge, Fogg Art Museum*
160. *Philadelphia, Johnson Coll.* – 161. *Venice, formerly Private Collection.* – 162. *Sydney, Nat. Gallery of New South Wales*

163

166

169

163–171. S. Roch. – 163. *London, Count Seilern Coll.* – 164. *Milan, F. Marinotti Coll.* – 165. *Milan, D. Anghileri Coll.*

166. *Bennebroek, von Pannwitz Coll.* – 167. *Besançon, Musée.* – 168. *Berlin, Gemäldegalerie*

169. *London, formerly Bowyer Nichols Coll.* – 170. *Bennebroek, von Pannwitz Coll.* – 171. *Vicenza, Count da Schio Coll.*

172

175

178

172. S. Francis of Paola. *Munich, formerly Böhler.* – 173. S. Vincent Ferrer. *Milan, Venier Coll.* – 174. S. Cajetan. *Rio de Janeiro, Museu Nacional de Belas Artes.* –
175. S. Sebastian. *Rome, Private Coll.* – 176. S. Martin Bishop with a Chorister Boy. *Venice, Museo Corrèr.* – 177. S. Blaise with the Portraits of a
Young Woman and a Man. *Venice, Museo Corrèr.* – 178. S. Joseph with the Christ Child. *Bergamo, S. Salvatore.* – 179. S. Anthony of Padua with
the Christ Child. *Madrid, Rodriguez Bauza Coll.* – 180. S. Norbert Archbishop of Magdeburg. *Paris, Private Coll.*

181–183. S. Francis of Paola. – 181. *Milan, O. Miani Coll.* – 182. *Piove di Sacco (Padua), S. Nicolò.* – 183. *Venice, S. Benedetto*

184. Apotheosis of S. Gaetano of Thiene. *Rampazzo, Parish Church.* – 185. S. John the Baptist. *Warwick Castle, Earl of Warwick.* –
186. S. Francis of Sales. *Udine, Museo Civico*

187. S. Peter of Alcantara. *Madrid, Royal Palace*

188. S. Mark. *Rome, Private Coll.*

189. S. Luke. *Padua, S. Lucia*

190. S. Charles Borromeo. *Cincinnati, Art Museum*

191. S. Peter. *Jacksonville, De Ette Holden Cummer Museum Foundation*

192. S. John the Baptist. *Zürich, Private Coll.*

193. S. John the Evangelist. *Venice, S. Francesco della Vigna*

194. S. Matthew. *Venice, S. Francesco della Vigna*

195. S. Francis receiving the Stigmata. *Madrid, Prado*

196. S. Joseph with the Christ Child. *Detroit, Art Institute*

197. S. Pascal Baylon. *Madrid, Prado*

198. An Angel bearing the Eucharist. *Madrid, Prado*

199. A Cherub with a Crown of Lilies and two Heads of Cherubim. *Formerly Munich, Caspari Coll.*
(The lefthand part is now in the Prado, Madrid; the righthand part was formerly with French, New York.)

200–201. Angels and Putti. *Udine, Chiesa della Purità*

202. S. Catherine of Siena. *Vienna, Kunsthistorisches Museum*   203. S. Catherine and Angels. *Venice, Private Collection*

204. Faith, Hope and Charity. *Venice, Scuola dei Carmini*

205. Prudence, Grace and Innocence. *Venice, Scuola dei Carmini*

206. Strength and Justice. *Venice, Scuola dei Carmini*

207. Meekness and Humility. *Venice, Scuola dei Carmini*

208–209. Angels bearing the Indulgences of the Carmelites. – An Angel with Scapular and another with Lilies. *Venice, Scuola dei Carmini*

210. Justice. *Bergamo, Colleoni Chapel*

211. Wisdom. *Bergamo, Colleoni Chapel*

212. Faith. *Bergamo, Colleoni Chapel*

213. Charity. *Bergamo, Colleoni Chapel*

214. Faith, Hope and Charity. *Venice, Chiesa della Pietà*

215. Justice and Peace. *Venice, S. Lazzaro degli Armeni*

216. Three Virtues. *Venice, S. Francesco della Vigna*

CLASSICAL MYTHOLOGY AND
ITALIAN EPIC POETRY

227 – 277

227. The Rape of Helen. *Milan, Borletti Coll.*

228. The Madness of Ulysses. *Milan, Borletti Coll.*

239. Apollo and Daphne. *Milan, Palazzo Archinto*

240. Apollo and Midas. *Bergamo, Private Coll.*

241. Diana and Actaeon. *Bergamo, Private Coll.*

242. Phaethon and Apollo. *Barnard Castle, Bowes Museum*

243. The Rape of Europa, after Veronese. *London, formerly Cliffe Coll.*

244. Venus and Vulcan. *Zürich, Private Coll.*

245. Venus and Vulcan. *Philadelphia, John G. Johnson Coll.*

246. Diana and Actaeon. *New York, formerly Maurice de Rothschild Coll.*

247. Apollo and Marsyas. *Venice, Accademia*

248. Diana and Actaeon. *Venice, Accademia*

249. Apollo and Marsyas. *Copenhagen, Royal Museum of Fine Arts*

250. Diana and Callisto. *Venice, Accademia*

252. Perseus and Andromeda. *Milan, Palazzo Archinto*

251. Perseus rescuing Andromeda. *New York, Frick Coll.*

254. Triumph of Hercules. *Manchester (New Hampshire), Currier Gallery of Art*

253. Allegory with Venus and Apollo. *New York, Mr. and Mrs. Heinemann Coll.*

255. Neptune and the Zephyrs. *New York,
Metropolitan Museum of Art*

256. Chariot of Aurora. *Williamstown, Sterling
and Francine Clark Art Institute*

257. Zephyr and Flora. *Venice, Palazzo Labia*

258. Allegory with Mars and Venus. *Paris, formerly Flameng Coll.*

259. Allegory with Mars and Venus. *Venice, Palazzo ex Pisani-Moretta*

260. Bacchus and Ariadne. *New York, Timken Coll.* – 261. Bacchus and Ariadne on Clouds. *London, formerly Eckstein Coll.*

262. Triumph of Zephyr and Flora. *Venice, Ca' Rezzonico*

263. Juno and the Peacock on Clouds. *Milan, M. Crespi Coll.*

273–275. Rinaldo and Armida. *Chicago, Art Institute*

276. Rinaldo and Armida in the Garden. *Lausanne, formerly Private Coll.*

277. Scenes from Gerusalemme Liberata. *London, National Gallery*

HISTORY

278 – 318

279. Family of Darius before Alexander (?). *Rome, Private Coll.*

278. Archimedes in the Serapeion of Alexandria. *Rome, Private Coll.*

292. Alexander and Bucephalus. *Paris, Petit Palais*

293. Summons to Cincinnatus. *Munich, formerly Caspari Coll.*

294. Triumph of Marius. *New York, formerly Castiglioni Coll.*

295. Triumph of Scipio. *Leningrad, Hermitage*

290. Death of Sophonisba. *Paris, Patino Coll.*

291. Scene from Roman History. *Milan, formerly Private Coll.*

286. Betrothal. *Copenhagen, Royal Museum of Fine Arts*

287. Timoclea and the Thracian Commander. *Washington, National Gallery of Art, Samuel H. Kress Collection*

288. Gifts offered to Cleopatra. *Pavia, Necchi Coll.*

289. Tarquin and Lucretia. *Augsburg, Museum*

284. Alexander and Campaspe in the Studio of Apelles. *Paris, Louvre*

285. Mucius Scaevola before Porsenna. *Würzburg, University Museum*

282. Alexander and Diogenes. *Bologna, Ettore Modiano Coll.*

283. Family of Darius before Alexander. *Würzburg, University Museum*

281. Family of Darius before Alexander. *Milan, M. Crespi Coll.*

280. Family of Darius before Alexander. *Montecchio Maggiore, Villa Cordellina*

302. Jugurtha before the Roman Consul. *Baltimore, Walters Art Gallery*

303. Jugurtha before the Roman Consul. *London, formerly C. Smith Coll.*

304. The Continence of Scipio. *Milan, Palazzo Dugnani*

305. Scipio and the Slave. *Milan, Palazzo Dugnani*

306. The Capture of Carthage. *New York, formerly Castiglioni Coll.*

307. The Continence of Scipio. *Montecchio Maggiore, Villa Cordellina*

308. The Continence of Scipio. *Madrid, Count de Mora Coll.*

309. Caesar contemplating the severed head of Pompey. *Modena, formerly L. Giusti Coll.*

310. The Banquet of Cleopatra. *Paris, Musée Cognacq-Jay*

311. Banquet of Cleopatra. *Archangel Museum, formerly Jusupov Gallery*

312. Maecenas presenting the Arts to Augustus. *Leningrad, Hermitage*

313. The Meeting of Anthony and Cleopatra. *Archangel Museum, formerly Jusupov Gallery*

314. Triumph of Aurelian. *Turin, Pinacoteca*

315. Marriage of Barbarossa. *London, National Gallery*

316. Investiture of Bishop Harold. *New York, Metropolitan Museum*

317. Reception of the Emperor Henry III at the Villa Contarini alla Mira. *Paris, Musée Jacquemart-André*

318a. Nicola Soderini sent to the Roman Senate as Delegate by the Republic of Florence. *Nervesa, Villa Soderini*

318b. Entry into Florence of the Gonfaloniere Pier Soderini. *Nervesa, Villa Soderini.*

ALLEGORIES

319—409

319. Olympus. *Zürich, Hausammann Coll.*

321. Apotheosis of the Spanish Monarchy. *New York, Mr. and Mrs. Wrightsman Coll.*

320. Apotheosis of the Spanish Monarchy. *New York, Metropolitan Museum*

322. Time discovering Truth. *Venice, Palazzo Barbarigo*

323. Time discovering Truth. *Basle, Von Hirsch Coll.*

324. Time Abducting Beauty. *Paris, formerly Cotnareanu Coll.*

325. Time Unveiling Truth. *Vicenza, Villa Loschi al Biron*

326. Genius on Pegasus putting Time to flight. *Venice, Palazzo Labia*

327. Time discovering Truth. *Vicenza, Museo Civico*

328. Allegory of Poet Soderini (?). *Paris, formerly Fauchier-Magnan Coll.*

329. Time discovering Truth. *New York, Wildenstein*

342. Triumph of Amor. *Paris, formerly Trotti-Nicolle Coll.*

341. Triumph of Venus. *Madrid, Prado*

343. Fortitude and Wisdom. *Milan, Museo Poldi-Pezzoli*   344. Allegory of Fortitude and Wisdom. *Udine, Museo Civico*

345. Allegory of Fortitude and Wisdom. *Venice, Ca' Rezzonico*

370–371. Merit and Nobility. *Vicenza, Villa Loschi al Biron.* – 372. Two allegorical Figures with an Obelisk. *Sarasota, Ringling Museum*

373. Allegory of Summer. *Venice, Palazzo Papadopoli-Arrivabene*   374. Allegorical Figures. *Venice, Palazzo Barbarigo*

368. Allegory of Magnanimity. *Milan, Palazzo Dugnani*

369. Apotheosis of a Warrior. *Cologne, Baron Guillaume Coll.*

365. Allegory of Fortitude, Temperance, Justice and Truth. *Vicenza, Villa Loschi al Biron*

366. Mars. *Vicenza, Villa Loschi al Biron*

367. Genius. *Vicenza, Villa Loschi al Biron*

361. Fidelity with Love. *Vicenza, Villa Loschi al Biron*

362. Courage crowned by Glory. *Vicenza, Villa Loschi al Biron*

363. Charity dispensing Alms. *Vicenza, Villa Loschi al Biron*

364. Modesty putting Pride to Flight. *Vicenza, Villa Loschi al Biron*

357. Aurora and Flying Putti. *Sarasota, Ringling Museum*

358. Angel of Fame. *Providence, School of Design*

359. Industry triumphing over Idleness. *Vicenza, Villa Loschi al Biron*

360. Innocence driving away Vice. *Vicenza, Villa Loschi al Biron*

356. Apotheosis of a Warrior. *Cleveland, Museum of Art*

355. Diana, Apollo and a Goddess. *London, Dulwich College Gallery*

354. Triumph of Flora. *San Francisco, M. H. de Young Memorial Museum*

352. Allegory of the Rezzonico-Savorgnan Marriage. *Verona, Museo di Castelvecchio*

353. Chronos entrusting Cupid to Venus. *E. Ferreira Pinto Basto Coll.*

349. Allegorical Figure. *Venice, Count Cini Coll.*

350. Allegory of Merit. *Boston, Museum of Fine Arts*

351. Triumph of Virtue and Fortitude. *Florence, Contini-Bonacossi Coll.*

346–347. Allegory of Fortitude and Wisdom. – 346. *London, Dulwich College Gallery.* – 347. *Montecchio Maggiore, Villa Cordellina*

348. Allegory of Virtue and Fortitude. *Milan, Palazzo Gallarati-Scotti*

343. Fortitude and Wisdom. *Milan, Museo Poldi-Pezzoli*   344. Allegory of Fortitude and Wisdom. *Udine, Museo Civico*

345. Allegory of Fortitude and Wisdom. *Venice, Ca' Rezzonico*

342. Triumph of Amor. *Paris, formerly Trotti-Nicolle Coll.*

341. Triumph of Venus. *Madrid, Prado*

375–378. Aritmetica – Grammatica – Metafisica – Geometria. *New York, Metropolitan Museum*

379–380. Allegorical Female Figures. *Amsterdam, Rijksmuseum*

381. Putti holding medals with War Scenes. *Udine, Castello*

382–383. Allegories of Painting and Sculpture. *Venice, formerly Palazzo Barbarigo*

384. Putti holding medals with War Scenes. *Udine, Castello*

385–386. Allegories of Poetry and Music. *Venice, formerly Palazzo Barbarigo*

387–388. Praying Figures on a Balcony. *Venice, Accademia*

389–390. Spectators on the Balcony. *Paris, Musée Jacquemart-André*

391. Fame announcing to the Spectators the Arrival of Emperor Henry III. *Paris, Musée Jacquemart-André*

392–395. Allegorical Figures. – 392–3: *Milan, A. Bolchini-Bonomi Coll.* – 394–5: *New Haven, Yale University*

396–397. Allegorical Figures. *Stra, Villa Pisani*

398. Peace and Justice. *Paris, Musée Jacquemart-André*

399–400. Allegorical Figures. *Stra, Villa Pisani*

401. Four Flying Putti carrying Grapes. *Leningrad, Hermitage*

402. Decorative Panels. *London, formerly Agnew*

403. Putto with Grapes. *Paris, Duc de Talleyrand Coll.*

404. Putto with Ears of Corn. *Paris, Duc de Talleyrand Coll.*

405. Allegory of a Queen crushing Vice. *New York, Wildenstein*

406. Allegory of Truth and Abundance. *New York, Metropolitan Museum*

407. Allegory. *Vicenza, formerly Palazzo Trento-Valmarana*

408. Allegory of Age and Death. *Milan, Private Coll.*

409. Group of Figures. *Berlin, formerly Voss Coll.*

PORTRAITS AND
MISCELLANEOUS SUBJECTS

410 – 422

410. Head of an old Oriental. *Trieste, Rusconi Coll.*

411. Head of an old Man. *Paris, formerly Orloff Coll.*

412. Head of an old Oriental. *San Diego, Fine Arts Gallery*

413. Head of an old Man. *New York, formerly Wildenstein*

414. Girl playing a Mandoline. *Detroit, Art Institute*

415. Euterpe. *Barcelona, Museo de Arte*

416. Lady with a Parrot. *Oxford, Ashmolean Museum*

417. Boy holding a Book. *New Orleans, Museum of Art*

418. Boy with a Dog. *London, Hamalton Trust*

419. Astronomer. *London, Marquess of Dufferin Coll.*

420. Pulcinellos' Kitchen. *Paris, Cailleux Coll.*

421. Le Polichinelle coupable. *Paris, formerly Besnard Coll.*

422. Arms of the Barbarigo-Sagredo Family. *Venice, formerly Donà dalle Rose Coll.*

ADDENDA

423 – 429

423. The Crucifixion. *Udine, Cathedral*

424. Madonna Enthroned. *Paris, Private Collection*

425. Beata Laduina. *Milan, formerly B. Crespi Gallery*

426. Antia and Abrocome at the Feast of Diana. *Venice, Accademia.*
(Painted by Amigoni and repainted in large part by Giambattista Tiepolo.)

427. Girl with Basket of Fruit and Flowers.
Zürich, Private Collection

428. Head of an old Oriental.
Zürich, Private Collection

429. Study of a Nude Man from the Back. *Paris, Private Collection*

CHRONOLOGICAL TABLE

1696

March 5th or thereabouts: Tiepolo is born in Venice in the parish of S. Pietro di Castello, Corte di S. Domenico. *Gio. Batta Figliolo del sig.r Domenico q. Zuanne Tiepolo Mercante, Parcenevole di vascello, et della sig.a Orsetta giogali* ('Gio. Batta, son of Domenico, son of Zuanne Tiepolo Merchant, shareholder in a ship, and of Orsetta, married couple'. 'Giogali', wrongly thought to have been the family name of Tiepolo's mother, means 'married couple'). Da Canal, in his *Vita di Gregorio Lazzarini*, written in 1732 and published by G. A. Moschini, Venice 1809, says: *G. B. Tiepolo, figliolo di Domenico, mercante di negozi da nave, nato il dì quinto del marzo dell'anno 1697* ('G. B. Tiepolo, son of Domenico, trader in shipping, born on the fifth day of March in the year 1697'). Da Canal is wrong about the year, which was certainly 1696. It may be noted that the old style Venetian calendar (*more Veneto*) began the year on March 25th.

April 16th: Baptized in the church of S. Pietro di Castello, the patrician Giovanni Donà being his godfather. His baptismal certificate is on page 6, Book 18, of the parish baptismal registers.

1697

March 12th: Death of his father at an early age. His mother and her five children are left in comfortable circumstances.

1715 or 1716

The Sacrifice of Isaac. His first public work, in the church of S. Maria dei Derelitti, known as the Ospedaletto. Da Canal, *op. cit.*, says that Tiepolo painted it when nineteen years of age. The date 1716 is, however, inscribed (not by Tiepolo) on a book held by a prophet in the same series, and may be contemporary.

1716

The Crossing of the Red Sea. A lost work, painted at the age of twenty, in competition with other artists, which was exhibited and, according to Da Canal, *op. cit.*, 'applauded on the day of S. Roch'.

1717

Tiepolo's name appears for the first time in the records of the 'Fraglia', or Guild, of painters. From this it may be deduced that Tiepolo had already left the workshop of his master Lazzarini. Da Canal, *op. cit.*, says: *gli è stato discepolo, quantunque si dipartisse dalla di lui maniera diligente, giacchè tutto spirito e foco ne abbracciò una spedita e risoluta* ('He was a pupil of his (Lazzarini's), although he departed from his diligent manner and, all spirit and fire, adopted one rapid and free'). The Museo Civico in Venice owns a copy, made by G. A. Moschini, of the books of the 'Tanse' or 'Luminarie' (records of the Guild), in which were recorded the names of the members of the 'Fraglia'. The list of painters begins in 1539 and ends in 1780, being divided into four parts. In the third, which begins in 1687, G. B. Tiepolo's name may be found at the date 1717; in the fourth (1726–80) it figures repeatedly from 1726 to 1753. From 1761 to 1775 in the same list may be found the name of Domenico, and in 1761 that of Lorenzo (Nicoletti, *Lista di nomi d'artisti . . .* in 'Ateneo Veneto', Nov.-Dec. 1890).

1717 or 1719

Repudiation of Hagar (Milan, Rasini Coll.). First signed and dated work.

1719

November 21st: Marries Cecilia Guardi, sister of the painters Antonio and Francesco. Their nine children were: Anna Maria born 1722, Giovan Domenico born 1723, who died in childhood, Elena Maria born 1726, Giovanni Domenico born 1727, Giuseppe Maria born 1729, Angela Maria born 1731, Francesco Antonio born 1732, Orsetta Gaspara born 1734, Lorenzo Baldissera born 1736.
The marriage certificate is in the Cancelleria Patriarcale in Venice.

1720

Il grande Teatro delle Pitture e Prospettive di Venezia published by Lovisa. G. B. Tiepolo and Silvestro Maniago made drawings for this volume. (Moschini, 1815, Preface, p. XXIX.).

c. 1722

Da Canal, *op. cit.*, records that *Fu pittore del Doge Cornaro nella cui ricca abitazione presiedeva alla distribuzione delle cose pittoriche, oltra all'avervi fatto più sopraporte con ritratti e quadri di buon gusto* ('He was painter to Doge Cornaro (1709–22) in whose fine house (now the Palazzo Mocenigo a San Polo) he superintended the painted decoration, besides doing many overdoors with portraits and pictures in excellent taste'). No trace of these now remains.

c. 1725

Completed the decoration in fresco and on canvas of the Palazzo Sandi in Corte dell'Albero, documented by Da Canal, *op. cit.* The frescoes are still in the Palazzo Sandi; the canvases are now at Castelgomberto.

1725

July 30th: 'Pre' Gioseffo', writing from Udine to a friend, states that the Archbishop Dionisio Dolfin is making in his palace a staircase the like of which was not to be found in all Italy. He is probably referring to the frescoes which Tiepolo was painting, representing the *Fall of the Rebel Angels* (Morassi, in 'Le Arti', 1942, p. 97).

1726

June 4th: Martedì 4 giugno 1726 – Ill. signori . . . deputati della città sedenti nel loro auditorio: Osservata la supplica presentata dalli Signori Governatori della Ven. Confraternita del St.mo Sacramento nella chiesa del Duomo di questa città, hanno deciso concordemente . . . di poter abbellire con Pitture sacre di mano del celebre Pittor Tiepolo interiormente la Cappella eretta dalla Città al Santo Sacramento . . . ('Tuesday, 4th June, 1726. The illustrious deputies of the city, in council, having considered the petition presented by the Lords Governors of the Venerable Confraternity of the Holy Sacrament of the Cathedral Church in this city (Udine), have unanimously decided . . . to permit the embellishment with paintings of sacred subjects from the hand of the celebrated painter Tiepolo the interior of the Chapel erected by the City to the Holy Sacrament . . .'). The petition of the Governors is appended (Atti pubblici, t. 86, pp. 37, 38. The document is preserved in the City Archives at Udine, vol. ms. FX c.53, Fabbrica del Duomo nuova).

1731

April 14th: A document, published by Felice Calvi in 1885 in the genealogy of the Casati (this document could not be found by Morazzoni, *La sede della Scuola Superiore femminile A. Manzoni*, Strenna benefica . . . Milan 1918, tip. Pirola) records the text of a letter sent from Venice by Tiepolo to the Conte Giuseppe Casati of Milan, in which he expresses himself thus: *ma quanto a dar principio a detta opera, Lei sa benissimo che se prima non è terminato in Casa Archinto, ove mi corre il mio primo impegno, io non posso; ma bensì preferire la S. V. Ill. ad ogni altro come a voce m'impegnai e presentemente gli rinnovo il mio impegno, e con tutto questo spero di servirla avanti il termine della stagione . . .* ('You will know that I cannot begin this work (Palazzo Casati, later Dugnani) until the work in the Casa Archinto is finished, since my first duty lies there; but assuredly preferring your illustrious Lordship to all others, as I have verbally undertaken and here renew my pledge, and with all this I hope to serve you before the end of this season . . .'). Tiepolo is working on the frescoes in the Palazzo Archinto. The date 1731 appeared on the ceiling of the main saloon, now destroyed. The work is not only documented by the letter printed above, but also by Lattuada, *Descrizione di Milano*, vol. III, p. 150, of the 1737 edition: *I forastieri se ammessi ne' quarti di essa, potranno godere di tante pitture de' più eccellenti maestri, come di Tiziano, Buonaruota, Parmegianino, Procaccino, Giordano, come delle altre a fresco fatte nelle vôlte del nuovo quarto dal celebre Tiepolo Veneziano . . .* ('Visitors admitted into the rooms of this (Casa Archinto) can enjoy many pictures by the most excellent masters, such as Titian, Buonarroti, Parmigianino, Procaccino, Giordano, as also the frescoes done in the vaults of the new rooms by the celebrated Venetian Tiepolo . . .'). So also Bianconi, *Guida di Milano*, 1795, p. 214: *Nelle vôlte poi di varie camere può il dilettante di pittura vedere alcune opere del nostro Lanzano, sempre molto sbrigativo, molte del celebre Tiepolo . . .* ('In the vaults of the various rooms the amateur of painting may see some works by our Lanzano, always very expeditious, and many by the celebrated Tiepolo . . .').

September 4th: The Governors of the Luogo Pio at Bergamo invite Tiepolo to paint the cupola of the Cappella Colleoni with appropriate subjects. (Molmenti, 1909, p. 128.)

1732

Publication of *Verona illustrata* by Scipione Maffei, with reproductions of ten Roman portrait busts and two statues, engraved by Zocchi after drawings by Tiepolo. Maffei praises highly the work done by Tiepolo who certainly drew the statues from the originals in Verona, some years before 1732, probably when he painted for S. Sebastiano *Heliodorus pillaging the Temple*, now in the Museum.

February 26th: The councillors of the Luogo Pio after having confirmed the deliberation of September 4th, 1731, to decorate the Colleoni Chapel with new pictures, establish that: *sia data ampia libertà e facoltà alli Ill. mi Galeazzo Vertova Conte e Cavagliere e Giulio Carrara Dott. di far fare le dette pitture da quel soggetto che dalla loro prudenza sarà stimato migliore, e di stabilire il prezzo dell'opera. . . . Firmati: Pietro Andrea Colleoni Sott.—Giov. Batt. Novati* ('liberty and authority were given to Signori Galeazzo Vertova, Count and Knight, and Giulio Carrara, Doctor, to get these pictures made by a painter whom their prudence will esteem as the best and to settle the price of the work. . . . Signed: Pietro Andrea Colleoni, Deputy.—Giov. Batt. Novati.') (Document in the Archives of the Luogo Pio, Reg. no. 44, p. 136; A. Raimondi, in *L'eco di Bergamo*, November 26th, 1952.) It would be interesting to know which were the pictures in the Chapel before the restoration and the new decoration by Tiepolo. Pasta, *Pitture notabili di Bergamo*, was not well informed about them; Ridolfi mentions a military subject as a work by G. B. Castelli called 'Il Bergamasco'; Muzio records some figures of Saints in the vaults and the story of the so-called 'Four generalships of Colleoni' at the four corners.

August 21st: Another meeting took place and the councillors of the Luogo Pio mentioned the imminent arrival of the painter under contract to paint the vaults. Vertova and Carrara were also given permission to arrange for the decoration of the lunettes as well. (Document in the Archives of the Luogo Pio, Reg. no. 44, p. 141; A. Raimondi, in *L'eco di Bergamo*, November 26th, 1952.) From this document can be determined the period in which Tiepolo executed the fresco in the vaults. On August 21st the painter was not yet in Bergamo, but on September 30th he was working in the Chapel (see the following document).

September 30th: The name of the painter designated to decorate the Chapel is recorded firstly in the documents and only incidentally in a note of payment for some restorations made in the same Chapel *in occasione delle pitture a fresco* executed by 'Giov. Batt. Tiepolo'. (Document in the Archives of the Luogo Pio, Reg. no. 44, p. 143; A. Raimondi, *loc. cit.*).

1733

From the *Descrizione di tutte le pubbliche pitture di Venezia . . . ossia Rinnovazione delle Ricche Miniere di Marco Boschini . . . offerta a . . . A. M. Zanetti*, Venice 1733, p. 486: '*In questi giorni nella Chiesa di S. Giuliano sarà posto un quadro sopra la colonna dritta dell'Altar maggiore con la Vergine, il Bambino, e S. Giuseppe opera del celebre Giovambattista Tiepolo.*' ('In these days will be placed in the church of S. Giuliano a picture over the right column of the high Altar with the Virgin, the Child, and S. Joseph, a work by the celebrated Giovambattista Tiepolo.')

July: Contract relating to the new frescoes in the Cappella Colleoni with the agreement that *sig. Gio. Batt. Tiepolo pittore Ven.o abbia con la possibile celerità a portarsi in Bergamo a dipingere: I° Nelle tre nicchie della cappella suddetta le seguenti istorie, cioè in una il Battesimo di Gesù Cristo, nell'altra la Predicazione nel deserto e nella terza la Decollazione di S. Giovan Battista con quel maggior numero di figure possibili* ('Gio. Batt. Tiepolo painter of Venice, shall with all possible speed go to Bergamo and there paint: I. In the three niches of the above mentioned chapel the following histories, that is, in one the Baptism of Jesus Christ, in the other the Preaching in the desert and in the third the Decollation of S. John the Baptist, with the largest number of figures possible'). (Archives of the Accademia Carrara in Bergamo.) Tiepolo dated these frescoes 1733.

During the period when Tiepolo was painting the Colleoni Chapel he often visited the studio of Fra' Vittore Ghislandi, and was interested by his technique (sometimes painting with the finger tips). Tassi writes that Ghislandi painted the portrait of Tiepolo (about which we have no other information) as he had painted the portraits of other artists as 'M. Salomone' (certainly Adler), Pietro Gilardi, Francesco Polazzi, Angelo Palia, Bartolomeo Nazari, Antonio Zifrondi (Cifrondi), the sculptor Andrea Fantoni and others. (F. M. Tassi, *Vite de' pittori scultori . . . bergamaschi*, Bergamo 1743, vol. II, p. 66.)

In the City Archives of Udine is a note by the Patriarch Dionisio Dolfin that he had spent 356 Venetian Lire on an altarpiece—a *S. Francis of Sales*—in the church of S. Mary Magdalen of the Oratory (of S. Philip Neri) in Udine. This is certainly the picture in the Museo Civico commissioned from Tiepolo by the Patriarch himself.

1734

April 10th: Letters from Tiepolo to Lodovico Feronati of Bergamo, in which he speaks of the instruction given to his pupil Giovanni Raggi. The letter is preserved in the Accademia Carrara, Bergamo. (Caversazzi, *Emporium*, 1899; Sack, 1910, p. 63; Fogolari, *Nuova Antologia*, September 1st, 1942, p. 33.)

September 6th: From the *Atti Consigliari* in the Archives of the Luogo Pio in Bergamo it is known that the councillors of the Luogo Pio commissioned from Tiepolo another work, a frieze which had to be added to the decorations in fresco in the Chapel. This frieze was never executed, as we learn from a document dated September 6th, 1734: *Letta la lettera del Sig. Giov. Battista Tiepolo diretta al Sig. Don Giov. Fanti del g.o 26 Agosto passato qual dice di non poter venire più presto della ventura primavera ad operar nella Capela di q. to Pio Luogo nella facitura del frizo attorno alla stessa . . . è stato ordinato che per il sud. to Sig. Fanti gli sia risposto che non potendo il d.o Sig. Tiepolo venire nel corrente autunno a far l'accordo, e dar principio all'opera, ancor gl'Ill.mi Presidenti attuali di q. to Pio Luogo non vogliono ora deliberare a riguardo che in principio del futuro Gen.o scadono di carica e saranno eletti soggetti, a quali lasciano la cura di far fare l'opera sud.ta* ('after having read the letter from Signor Giov. Battista Tiepolo painter addressed to Signore Don Giov. Fanti on 26th August in which he says he is not able to come before next spring to paint in the Chapel of this Luogo Pio the decoration of the frieze around it . . . it was resolved that the above mentioned Signor

Fanti should answer that since Signor Tiepolo cannot come in the autumn to make an agreement, and to begin the work, the Presidents now in charge do not wish to deliberate at the present about the matter because at the beginning of next January they will no longer be in charge and other men will be elected to whom they commit the care of this undertaking....) (Document in the Archives of the Luogo Pio, Reg. no. 45, p. 55; A. Raimondi, *cit.*, 1952.) From this document we learn that Tiepolo finished the frescoes in the Colleoni Chapel at the end of 1733 or a little later. In the spring of 1734 he was working in the Villa Loschi al Biron and this work did not allow him to come back to Bergamo for the decoration of the frieze.

The letter from Tiepolo mentioned in the document, addressed to Sig. Fanti on August 26th, 1734, is lost.

November 6th: The books *De scossi, e spesi* (The Credit and Debit books) of Cardinal Daniele Delfino (1734–62) show a payment *Al sig. Zuanne Indorador per tre Quadretti della SS. Vergine del Tiepolo L. 33.* The three small canvases by Tiepolo, representing the Virgin, are not identifiable (or perhaps are lost). (Perhaps one of these was the painting now in Paris, Private Coll., see *Catalogue.*) (G. Biasutti, *I Libri 'De scossi, e spesi' del Card. Daniele Delfino ultimo Patriarca d'Aquileia,* Udine 1957.)

November 17th: Another letter from Venice to Feronati of Bergamo, in which Tiepolo writes that he had spent three months in Vicenza *per un forte impegno . . . che per destrigarmi ò dipinto si può dire giorno e notte senza respiro* ('on a difficult work . . . which to have done with I painted, one may say, day and night without respite'). This refers to the frescoes in the Villa Loschi al Biron, commissioned from Tiepolo by the Conte Nicolò Loschi in 1734, as is recorded on a stone plaque *in situ.* The letter is preserved in the Accademia Carrara, Bergamo. (Fogolari, 1942, pp. 33, 34.)

December 27th: Contract ordering the *Martyrdom of S. Agatha* for the Cappella Buzzaccarini in the Basilica of S. Anthony in Padua. The Governors of the Shrine of the Saint passed the following judgement on the picture: *Esposta la pala di S. Agata del pittore Chiepoletto al giudizio dei molti Reverendi Padri e notabili signori Presidenti, dei quali essendo stata giudicata plausibile e degna di questo gran tempio . . .* ('The altarpiece of S. Agatha by the painter Chiepoletto being exhibited to the judgement of the Very Reverend Fathers and distinguished Governors, it was by them adjudged laudable and worthy of this great temple . . .'). (Gonzati, *Basilica di S. Antonio,* Padova, 1854, vol I, Doc. CXXV.) The altarpiece was not exhibited until 31.1.1737. At this date Tiepolo received 80 *zecchini d'oro.*

1736

Count Tessin, Swedish Minister in Venice, is charged by his King to find a painter capable of decorating the Royal Palace in Stockholm, and he replies with an interesting letter (25.5.1736), since besides flattering praises of Tiepolo, it contains in a few words an opinion of the painters contemporary with him. (Canaletto, Cimaroli, Pittoni, Piazzetta, Brustolon, Polazzo, Nogari, Antonio Joli): *9⁰ Tiepolo, dit Tiepoletto est fait exprès pour nous. Il est sectataire de Paul Véronèse; – Ainsi comme vous le dites fort bien: Tout est dans ces Tableaux richement vêtu jusqu'aux gueux etc. Mais n'est-ce pas la grande mode? Au reste, il est plein d'esprit, accomodant comme un Taraval, un feu infini, un coloris éclatant, et d'une vitesse surprenante. Il fait un tableau en moins de temps, qu'il n'en faut à un autre pour broyer les couleurs. Comme il est actuellement occupé chez le Noble Cornaro pour 5 à 6 mois: ainsi je n'ai jamais pû obtenir une Reponse positive; cependant il paroit disposé à venir. Mais ce que vous me dites des Finances, me fait trembler. Etc. '*(9th. Tiepolo, called Tiepoletto, is just the man for us. He follows the style of Paolo Veronese, as you yourself have remarked. Everyone in these pictures is richly dressed, even the beggars, etc. But is this not the fashion? In fact, he is full of wit, as compliant as Taraval (Guillaume Th. Taraval, a French painter, who worked in Stockholm), has a boundless imagination, brilliant colour and an amazing speed. He does a picture in less time than another takes to grind his colours. As he is at present busy for 5 to 6 months for the patrician Cornaro, I have never been able to obtain a positive reply; nevertheless, he seems disposed to come. But what you tell me about finances, makes me tremble. Etc.'). No agreement was arrived at;

according to Tiepolo, because of unsatisfactory remuneration; according to Tessin, because of Tiepolo's extravagant demands. (Sirén, *Dessins et tableaux . . . dans les collections de Suède,* Stockholm 1902, p. 107; De Vesme, *Le peintre-graveur italien,* Milan 1906, p. 376.) The reference to Cornaro is probably related to the frescoes at Merlengo.

1737

January 29th: Tiepolo acknowledges receipt of the payment for the canvas on which he was to paint the altarpiece with *S. Augustine and other Saints,* once in the church of S. Salvatore in Venice and destroyed by fire in the eighteenth century. *Ricevo io sotto scrito dal Rev. mo Pr.e Abbatte Grandis Lire Sesanta due, per pagamento della tella che deve servire p. la palla val. L. 62. Gio Batta Tiepolo* (Mariacher, in 'Arte Veneta', 1959–60, XIII–XIV, p. 238.) (Documents in the Archivio di Stato, Venice.) See also July 15, 1738.

May: Contract for the ceiling of the church of S. Maria del Rosario ai Gesuati. The execution of the work was delayed and it was not finished until October, 1739. (Venetian State Archive; Archives of the monastery of the Gesuati.)

In Milan, working in the church of S. Ambrogio. Lattuada, *op. cit.,* vol. IV, 1738, is the evidence for this: *mentre nell'anno 1737 fu ristorata tutta la Cappella, con l'aggiungerle due laterali rappresentanti l'uno il Martirio di S. Vittore e l'altro il Naufragio di S. Satiro, fatti a tempra dal rinomato Tiepolo Dipintore Veneziano . . . Alla sinistra della medesima Cappella si trova la sacristia de' Monaci, ricca di preziosissimi arredi . . . e colla vôlta in cui fu rappresentato S. Bernardo in gloria dal rinomato Tiepolo vineziano.* ('while in the year 1737 the whole chapel was restored, with the addition of two laterals, one representing the Martyrdom of S. Victor, and the other the Shipwreck of S. Satiro, done in tempera by the renowned Tiepolo, painter of Venice . . . On the left of the chapel is the sacristy of the monks, rich in precious hangings . . . and with the vault in which is represented S. Bernard in Glory by the renowned Venetian Tiepolo'). It may be remarked that these paintings are in fresco, not tempera.

June 25th: Tiepolo receives the sum of L. 660 for the execution of the two altarpieces, one representing *SS. Hermagoras and Fortunatus* (Udine, Cathedral), the second with the *Guardian Angel* (originally in the church of S. Maria Maddalena dei Filippini, Udine; now in the Museo Civico, Udine). Both altarpieces were commissioned by the Cardinal Daniele Delfino. (Biasutti, 1957, *cit.*)

1738

June 6th: Tiepolo is paid L. 440 for the execution of the altarpiece of *Christ crucified and God the Father,* commissioned by the Cardinal Daniele Delfino for the altar of the SS. Trinity in the Cathedral of Udine (Biasutti, 1957, *cit.*)

July 15th: Tiepolo acknowledges receipt of the payment for the execution of the altarpiece of *S. Augustine and other Saints,* commissioned by the Cornaro Family and destined for the church of S. Salvatore in Venice: *Ricevutto lo sotto scrito dal P.e R.mo Habbe di S. Salvatore di Venezia Lire ottocento e sei per fatura di una palla di altar di raggione delle Ecc.me Casse Cornero val Lire . . . L. 800. Jo Gio Batta Tiepolo.* (Mariacher, in 'Arte Veneta', 1959–60, p. 238.)

1739

The manuscript chronicle written by the Augustinian Canon, Giuseppe dall'Abaco (1718–93), Munich State Library, Cod. germ. 1769–70, mentions the picture by Tiepolo dated 1739 – the *Martyrdom of S. Sebastian* – still in the church at Diessen. *Il terzo altare è consacrato al Santo Martire di Cristo Sebastiano, la cui immagine è un'opera singolarmente eminente del celebre pittore veneziano Tiepolo, che generalmente dai conoscitori viene lodata in tutti i particolari ed ammirata come uno dei migliori quadri della nostra chiesa.* ('The third altar is consecrated to Christ's Holy Martyr Sebastian, whose image is an especially eminent work of the celebrated Venetian painter Tiepolo, which is generally praised by connoisseurs and admired as one of the best pictures in our church').

In another manuscript in the Parish Archives of Diessen (*Chronologia quintuplex*, 1768), is the laconic statement *S. Sebastian, altar-Blatt, diepolo Venetus, 600 fl.*

October: The whole fresco decoration of the ceiling of the Gesuati church is finished. Tiepolo had submitted his projects in Spring, 1737. In February, 1738, he received a first payment of 8370,10 Venetian lire. In October, 1739, when the frescoes were finished, he received a further 4030 lire, making a total of 12.400,10 lire. (Venetian State Archive; Archive of the Gesuati Monastery.)

December 21st: Deliberations of the governors of the Scuola del Carmine over the choice of Tiepolo, *decantato il più celebre fra virtuosi* ('acclaimed the most celebrated among the *virtuosi*') to decorate the ceiling of the Audience Chamber. In this document it is clearly stated that Tiepolo was going to be in Milan at the beginning of 1740 (for the Palazzo Clerici). The documents are in the Venetian State Archives.
(Urbani de Gheltof, *Tiepolo e la sua famiglia*, Venice 1879, p. 100.)

1740

January 19th: Tiepolo agrees to the terms offered by the Governors of the Scuola del Carmine, and proposes two different versions of the themes and subjects for the work commissioned from him on December 21st, 1739 (Urbani de Gheltof, *op. cit.*, 1879). The large ceiling-fresco of the *Madonna del Carmelo with S. Simeon Stock* is dated 1740.

In this year Tiepolo paints the ceiling of the Palazzo Clerici in Milan. This is attested by an anonymous Milanese poet who dedicated verses to Tiepolo's 'singular merit' *in occasione che si trova a Milano a dipingere nella casa di S. E. il marchese Don Giorgio Clerici nell'anno 1740.* ('on the occasion of his being in Milan to paint in the house of his Excellency Marquis Don Giorgio Clerici, in the year 1740'). (Milan, publ. by Bolzini, 1740.)

The triptych in S. Alvise is first mentioned in the *Guida* by Albrizzi of 1740 (p. 171): the *Flagellation* and the *Crowning with Thorns*, which, together with the *Way to Calvary* (the large central canvas), form the triptych of the Passion.

In this year a book by Natale Dalle Laste and Marco Forcellini, *Opere di m. Sperone Speroni*, Venice, Domenico Occhi, was published, which contains (vol. I) the engraving of the portrait of Sperone Speroni painted by Titian in 1544. This engraving, by Giuseppe Patrini of Parma, is interesting because it was etched from a drawing by G. B. Tiepolo after the original which the painter probably saw when it was in the collection of the Canon Annibale Capodilista. The etching is inscribed: *J. B. Tiepolo delin. ex Titiano* and *Joseph Patrini sculp.*

1743

Spring: Count Algarotti leaves Dresden in March to go to Venice as envoy of King Augustus III to acquire old paintings and to commission modern canvases from the most famous Venetian painters (Piazzetta, Pittoni, Tiepolo, Amigoni, Zuccarelli). Tiepolo is charged to paint for the Royal Gallery of Dresden 'Caesar in a square of Alexandria contemplating the severed head of Pompey'. The painting was sent to Dresden in 1746 and is now lost. (Algarotti, *Opere*, VI, p. 35; Posse, 1931, Beiheft.) The *bozzetto* for it is to be identified with the painting once in the Giusti Coll., Modena, present whereabouts unknown (M. Precerutti-Garberi, in *Commentari*, April-June 1958, p. 114, Pl. XLVI, fig. 1).

June 2nd: Girolamo Zanetti (1713–81) writes in his memoirs (published by F. Stefani, Archivio Ven., t. XXIX, p. 97): *2 giugno. Pentecoste 1743. Nella Scuola della Beata Vergine de' Carmini vicino ai p.p. di quella Religione furono oggi per la prima volta mostrati pubblicamente i comparti del soffitto dipinti di nuovo da Gio. Batta Tiepolo eccellentissimo pittore de' nostri giorni sopra tutti gli altri.* ('2 June. Pentecost 1743. In the Scuola of the Blessed Virgin of the Carmine, adjacent to the Fathers of that Order, the compartment of the ceiling newly painted by Gio. Batta Tiepolo, most excellent painter of our times above all others, were today for the first time publicly shown). He adds, however, that the central

part has not yet been begun. (Venetian State Archives, publ. by Urbani, *op. cit.*)

June 17th: Letter of Algarotti from Venice to Count Brühl in which he testifies to the great esteem Tiepolo had for Paolo Veronese. It is known that Algarotti acquired for Augustus III the *Rape of Europa* by Veronese. He writes: *Tous les Peintres de Venise en sont amoreux, Tiepoletto entr'autres, qui a étudié toujour d'après Paul Veronese m'a dit lui meme, qu'il regarde cette Europe comme bien au dessus de celle, qui est dans le Palais du Doge, et qu'il vouloit meme en donner au dessus de 200 ducats d'or pour la mettre dans la Chambre où il peint affin de l'avoir devant les yeux comme une leçon et un etude continuelle.*

In another letter of July, 1743, to Brühl, Algarotti again refers to the *Rape of Europe: J'ai consulté particulièrement Tiepolo, qui a étudié toujours et imité si bien la manière de Paul Veronese. Il a été longtems en extase devant ce tableau. . . .*' (Principal Archive of Saxony, Dresden; Posse, 1931, pp. 41, 45.)

July 19th: Algarotti writes to Count Brühl from Venice begging for the title of 'Sur-Intendant des Bâtiments et Cabinets du Roi'. On this occasion, to obtain the intercession of Brühl, he commissioned from Tiepolo two pictures as gifts to the minister. There is a clear reference in the letter: *L'un representera les Beaux Arts ammenez par Mécène au Trône d'Auguste. . . . L'autre représentera l'empire de Flora qui change en endroits délicieux les lieux les plus sauvages.* The first is to be identified with *Maecenas presenting the Arts to Augustus*, now in the Hermitage, Leningrad, where are visible *dans le lointain au delà du Tibre . . . le Palais de votre Excellence et ses hortos pensiles* mentioned in letter. The second is the *Triumph of Flora* now in the de Young Memorial Museum in San Francisco, in which is identifiable *dans le lointain la belle Fontaine du Jardin de votre Excellence modellée par Mr. Mattielli.* (Principal Archive of Saxony, Dresden; Posse, 1931, p. 49; Levey, *Burlington Magazine*, March, 1957, p. 89.)

July 31st: Private agreement by which Tiepolo undertakes to paint the *Martyrdom of St. John, Bishop of Bergamo*, for 100 *zecchini*. The altarpiece was put up in the same year and is still in the Cathedral of Bergamo. (Biblioteca Capitolare, Ms. *Libro per l'opera pia di fare li sei quadri e compire li ornamenti del Coro della Cattedrale*, doc. July 31st–August 6th, 1743; Pinetti, *Inventario, della Provincia di Bergamo*, Rome, 1931, p. 67.)

September 4th: From the *Note des dépenses faites pour S. M. le Roi de Pologne*, by Count Algarotti and preserved in the Museo at Treviso: *donné à M. Tiepolo qui a été l'entremetteur du marché, un présent en argenterie et chocolat pour le valeur de L. 1148.* The picture bought by Algarotti through Tiepolo was the famous *Madonna* by Holbein, then in the Casa Delfino in Venice. A further gift was given to Tiepolo in silver plate, wax and chocolate for his help in the acquisition of the *Three Sisters* by Palma. (L. Ferrari, *L'Arte*, III, p. 152 ff., 19; Posse, 1931, p. 55.)

September 6th: Letter of Algarotti from Venice to Brühl in which he states that he acquired for Augustus III the above mentioned *Madonna* by Holbein and refers to the gift he made to Tiepolo: *par l'entremise du Peintre Tiepolo pour mille sequins soixante ducats d'or . . . et j'ai fait présent à Mr. Tiepolo d'un pièce d'argenterie avec du chocolat pour la valeur de cinquante sequins environ et d'un Canne avec une bequille d'ambre montié en or. Mr. Tiepolo a assuré mon par son sçavoir faire épargné pour le moins deux cents sequins au Roi.*

October 1st: Tiepolo, by a *scrittura privata 13 sett. p.p. ha stabilito l'accordo con i Rev. Padri Carmelitani* ('private agreement 13 Sept. last, has agreed with the Rev. Carmelite Fathers') to paint the ceiling of their church, with the assistance of G. Mengozzi-Colonna in the ornamental parts. (Document in the Venetian State Archives, Archives of the Carmelitani Scalzi, B.9, fasc XVI, publ. in Molmenti, 1909, p. 79; Fogolari, in 'Bollettino d'arte' July, 1931, pp. 18–32.)

October 4th: For the acquisition of two pictures by Borgognone for Augustus III, Tiepolo was chosen by Algarotti, *pour le maniment de ces deux affaires*, and was presented with *deux pièces d'argenterie avec quelque bagatelle pour la valeur de 46 ducats d'or.* The gift was noted also in the 'Note de Depences' of Algarotti.
(Letter of Algarotti to Brühl, Principal Archive of Saxony, Dresden; Posse, 1931, p. 59.)

October 26th: Letter from Tiepolo to Algarotti: *. . . Io non ho dato raggua-glio del mio arrivo in Montichio ne pure del mio soggiorno perchè così mi ha commandato . . . Tutta volta ho già terminato otto chiari scuri e quasi sono arrivato alla metà del soffitto tanto che mi lusingo anzi sicuro lo finirò per li 10 o 12 dell'entrante mese.* ('. . . I have given you no account of my arrival in Montichio, or of my stay here, because thus you desired me . . . Nevertheless, I have already finished eight *chiaroscuri* and have arrived almost at the middle of the ceiling, so much so that I flatter myself as certain to finish it by the 10th or 12th of the coming month'). This refers to the decoration, which still exists, of the Villa Cordellina at Montecchio Maggiore, near Vicenza. (Fogolari, 1942, pp. 34, 35; doc. in Bassano Museo Civico, Archivio Gamba.)

November 17th: Tiepolo is pressed by Algarotti to finish the *Triumph of Flora* and *Maecenas presenting the Arts to Augustus* for Count Brühl. (Letter of Algarotti to Brühl from Verona, Principal Archive of Saxony, Dresden; Posse, 1931, p. 62.)

1744

January 9th: Letter of Algarotti to Karl Heinrich Heinecken, in which he refers to the painter Matthias Österreich, a cousin of Heinecken: *Je l'ai recommandé à Mr. Tiepolo comme la personne du monde à qui je m'interesse le plus. Mr. Tiepolo est le meilleur Peintre de Venise l'homme le plus aimable qu'on puisse souhaitter et il a toute l'amitié imaginable pour moi. Il est engagé, Monseigneur, à avoir tout le soin imaginable pour les avance-ments dans la Peinture. . . .* (Dresden, Principal Archive of Saxony; Posse, 1931, p. 64.)

January 31st: From Venice Algarotti writes to Count Brühl about the *Banquet of Anthony and Cleopatra* by Tiepolo, now in Melbourne: *. . . J'ai cru convenable en apporter un autre* (painting), *qui put donner à Sa Majesté une juste idée de l'Ecole Venitienne dans le genre le plus noble et le plus majesteux. C'est un Tableau, que Mr. Tiepolo avoit commencé il ya quelquetemps* (sic) *pour d'autres et qu'il a bien voulu céder a mes instances et achever pour Sa Majesté. Il represente le Festin de Marc Antoine et de Cleopatre, et c'est tout ce que les Ecoles modernes peuvent donner de plus beau de plus noble et de plus riche. Je compte, Monseigneur lui en donner trois cent sequins; prix, que votre Excellence, quand même Elle n'ecouteroit point sa generosité ordinaire, jugera bien au dessous de l'excellence, de la grandeur, et du travail de l'Ouvrage. Il a plus que 8 pieds de haut sur 12 de large. Il va être achevé ces jours-ci avec ceux de votre Excellence, à qui on donne à present la dernière main.* (These last two pictures, executed by Tiepolo for Count Brühl, are the above mentioned *Triumph of Flora* and *Maecenas presenting the Arts to Augustus*, see above, July 19th, 1743.) (Principal Archive of Saxony, Dresden; Posse, 1931, pp. 64, 65.)

Also with regard to the Melbourne *Banquet*, Algarotti writing to Mariette, so praises the painting ('Relazione Storica', pp. 17 ff): *Io non parlo d'altri artifizj che sono in esso, della Esattezza della Prospettiva o del chiaroscuro, della bellezza delle pieghe, delle sceltezza delle forme, della vaghezza ed armonia de' colori e d'altri pregi che lo adornano esaltati a gara da una folla di Dilettanti, e Professori, che concorsero a vederlo appena ch'e' fu finito nelle stanze del Pittore* ('I don't speak of other artifices which are in it, of the exactness of the perspective or "chiaroscuro", of the beauty of the folds, of the perfect quality of the forms, of the charm and harmony of the colours and of other such values which adorn it and which were praised unanimously by a multitude of Dilettanti and Professors, who went all to see it as soon as it was finished in the room of the Painter'). (Algarotti, *Opere*, VIII, p. 33; Posse, 1931.)

Another enthusiastic mention of the *Banquet* in a letter of Algarotti to Mariette from Potsdam, 1751 (Algarotti, *Opere*, VI, p. 35).

March 5th: From the 'Note de Depences' of Algarotti: *payé à Mr. Tiepolo pour le Tableau de Marc Antoine et de Cleopatre pour S. M. 300 Sequins qui font L. 6.600* (Treviso, Museo Civico).

On the same day Tiepolo receives the partial payment of 50 *sequins* for the execution of *Caesar in a square of Alexandria contemplating the severed head of Pompey* ('Note de Depences', Treviso, Museo Civico).

July 17th: From a letter of Algarotti to Count Brühl, we know that Tiepolo was rewarded by Augustus III for his help in acquiring paintings for the Royal Gallery of Dresden: *J'ai donné, Monseigneur, la*

Tabatière de porcelaine de Mr. Zanetti et remis celle d'or à Mr. Tiepolo de la part de Sa Majesté (Dresden, Principal Archive of Saxony; Posse, 1931, p. 66).

1744-45

According to a list of payments and expenses from 1744 to 1745 for restorations made in the Palazzo Barbarigo in Venice, Tiepolo is said to have received 680 ducats for works executed in the Palace: '*A Tiepoletto come da Poliza n.24. . . . duc. 680.*' The payment refers to the *Allegory of Fortitude and Wisdom*, now in Ca' Rezzonico, Venice. (Archive Donà dalla Rose, Carte Barbarigo, Museo Corrèr; Lorenzetti, 1936, p. 28.)

1745

February 23rd: Ricevo io sottoscritto . . . ducati quattrocento correnti, quali sono ultimo residuo, e tolti dalli ducati tre mila per la pittura fatta da me nel soffitto della chiesa . . . ('I receive . . . 400 ducats, as the final payment and subtracted from three thousand ducats for the decoration I made in the ceiling of the church . . .'). It is the receipt in full for the payment Tiepolo had for the fresco in the Scalzi, Venice (Doc. in the Venetian State Archives.)

April 17th: The collaboration of Tiepolo with Mengozzi-Colonna in the Palazzo Barbarigo, Venice, is attested by a note of expenses made by Domenico Brunello for Pietro Barbarigo: '*A' li 17 aprile 1745: spese fatte per la cornise nella Camera dipinta da Mingozzi e Thiepoleto*' ('17th April, 1745: expenses made for the frame in the Room painted by Mengozzi and Tiepolo.') (Archive Donà dalle Rose, Carte Barbarigo, Museo Corrèr; M. Muraro, in 'Gazette des Beaux Arts,' I, 1960, p. 33, n. 5.)

1746

February 26th: Tiepolo receives 80 sequins as balance of the former account of March 5th, 1744, for the execution of *Caesar contemplating the severed head of Pompey* for Augustus III. (Algarotti, 'Note de Depences', Treviso, Museo Civico).

1747

Tiepolo dates the *Meeting of Anthony and Cleopatra*, formerly in the Jusupov Gallery, Archangel (Russia).

March 3rd: Sack, 1910, p. 87, publishes a letter, written by Tiepolo from Venice, which shows the cordial relations existing between the painter and the Cordellina family after the decoration of their Villa. Sack believes that the letter was written to Algarotti, but Fogolari, 1942, p. 35, suggests other possible recipients, for instance, A. M. Zanetti.

1749

Tiepolo is commissioned by the Conte di Montegnacco of Udine to paint the *Consilium in Arena*, recording the admission of the Count himself and of Count Florio into the Order of the Knights of Malta. (Joppi, in 'Pagine friulane', No. 9, Udine, 27.10.1889.) The painting is in the Museo Civico, Udine. The document is preserved in the Biblio-teca Comunale at Udine (Busta Malta). The painting was executed after 26.10.1749, the date of the letter from Count Montegnacco. It is interesting to note that, as is clear from the style, the execution was entrusted by Tiepolo to his son Domenico.

1750

May 29th: A letter from the Hofkammer of Würzburg to the banker Lorenz Jacob Mehling, resident in Venice, records that Prince Bishop Carl Philipp von Greiffenklau had learned with satisfaction that '*the celebrated fresco-painter signor Tiepolo had resolved to come to Würzburg to perpetuate worthily in Germany his own name and his own art and that the Bishop was eagerly waiting for him*'. Tiepolo was promised 3.000 florins for the journey and as part payment for the frescoes, one third payable at Tiepolo's departure and the balance at Tiepolo's arrival, before the beginning of the work. In the letter of May 29, the Hofkammer enclosed the plans of the Saloon which Tiepolo was to decorate, together with the description of the subjects chosen at Würzburg. But it was pointed out that the Bishop left Tiepolo free to execute his own ideas if he had better projects to submit. (Staatsarchiv Würzburg, Hofkammerprotokolle 1750–53; Freeden und Lamb, 1956, p. 25. The documents referring to Tiepolo's stay in Würzburg are reported also by Sedlmaier u. Pfister, 1923.)

August: At the middle of August, 1750, the son of the banker Mehling writes to Würzburg that Tiepolo had promised to set out soon on his journey (*ibidem*).

October 10th: Mehling and Tiepolo sign a preliminary contract, by which the painter undertakes to decorate *'carefully and diligently, according to the description of the subjects and the plans'* sent to him, the saloon of the Residenz, in a given time, except for the ornaments. For this work he was to receive 10.000 Renan florins in cash, plus all the necessary implements (Utensilien) and colours, beaten gold (geschlagenes Gold), free board and lodging (bares Geld) for himself and his companions (*ibidem*).

November 18th: Mehling sends the above-mentioned contract to Würzburg, together with a letter. It is evident that Tiepolo was about to start for Würzburg (*ibidem*).

December 12th: Tiepolo arrives in Würzburg with his two sons, Giandomenico, aged 23, Lorenzo, aged 14, and a valet. Five rooms have been reserved for him in the Residenz, facing the garden, in the northeast corner in front of the Rennweg. (Staatsarchiv Würzburg, Histor. Verein, Tagebücher des Hoffouriers Ms. q. 176; Freeden u. Lamb, 1956, p. 27).

1751

April 17th: The Prince Bishop visits Tiepolo in his studio to see the preparatory drawings, which were already begun. (Freeden u. Lamb, 1956, p. 28).

April 27th: Tiepolo begins to work in the great Saloon *malen und durchpauschen* (painting and using the "spolvero"). (Freeden u. Lamb, 1956, p. 28.)

May 8th: The central scene of the great Saloon, which Tiepolo began first, was progressing well. It was decided in the meantime to get the gilding executed, to take advantage of the scaffolding. The person responsible for the gilding was the painter of the Würzburg court, Franz Ignaz Roth. From the documents it is clear that, after the ceiling, Tiepolo executed the south-wall fresco with the *Marriage of Barbarossa* and then the other wall with the *Investiture of Bishop Harold*, which he dated 1752. (Staatsarchiv Würzburg; Freeden u. Lamb, 1956, p. 28.)

1752

February–March: The Prince Bishop visits Tiepolo in his studio, working at the two altarpieces for the Archiepiscopal Palace Chapel. One of these, the *Fall of the Rebel Angels*, is just signed and dated 1752. Tiepolo received for them 3.000 florins. (Staatsarchiv Würzburg; Freeden u. Lamb, 1956, p. 29.)

April 20th: The Prince Bishop visits Tiepolo again to see the projects of the Staircase, which the painter has already prepared. The commission to fresco the great Staircase was therefore given to Tiepolo before he finished the decoration of the great Saloon. (*Ibidem.*)

July 4th: The great Saloon is finished. It was called from then on, because of the fresco themes, 'Kaisersaal'.

July 29th: Tiepolo signs the contract for the fresco on the ceiling of the great Staircase, for which he was to receive 15.000 Renan florins. It may be assumed that the fresco was begun immediately to take advantage of the favourable season. (Staatsarchiv Würzburg; Freeden u. Lamb, 1956, p. 29.)

1753

Tiepolo signs and dates the ceiling-fresco with *Olympus and the Quarters of the Globe* on the Staircase of the Würzburg Residenz.
Tiepolo signs and dates the altarpiece executed for the Benedictines of Schwarzach, representing the *Adoration of the Magi* (now in the Alte Pinakothek in Munich).

November 8th: Tiepolo and his sons leave Würzburg to return home. (Staatsarchiv Würzburg; Freeden u. Lamb, 1956, p. 30.) The friendly relationship of the Tiepolos with the Würzburg court lasted for a long time, as is shown by the correspondence between the painters and the court. Three years after Tiepolo's departure from Würzburg, Giambattista received as a gift a portrait of the Prince Bishop, as token of esteem and *'costante affetto'* (Staatsarchiv Würzburg; M. Precerutti-Garberi, in 'Commentari,' 3–4, 1960, p. 282).

1754

Tiepolo dates one of the 22 monochrome frescoes executed for the Villa Panigai at Nervesa (later in Berlin and partially destroyed).

May 8th: The altarpiece of *S. John Nepomuk*, painted by Tiepolo, is exhibited in the church of S. Polo in Venice. The picture is also recorded by Zanetti, 1771, p. 467, and is still in the church. (*Commemoriali Gradenigo*, in Museo Corrèr Library, partly published by Livan, Venice, 1942, p. 11.)

May 21st: Letter from the Marquis de Vandières, *Surintendant des Bâtiments du Roi*, written from Versailles to the painter Natoire, then Director of the French Academy in Rome. Vandières gives instructions to Natoire to send some *pensionnaires* of the French Academy, on their way back to France, to copy the frescoes by Tiepolo in the Villa Contarini alla Mira, which Vandières considers interesting for the history of manner and costume. In the letter the frescoes are mentioned without the name of Tiepolo. (Montaiglon-Huiffrey, *Correspondance des Directeurs de l'Academie de France à Rome avec les Surintendants des Bâtiments*, XI, 1754–63, Paris, 1891, pp. 29–30.) As Vandières left Rome in March, 1751, he must have seen the frescoes on his way back to France. We know that Tiepolo left Venice in November, 1750, and therefore at this date the frescoes seem to have been already finished. (Byam-Shaw, in *The Burlington Magazine*, December, 1960, pp. 529–530.)

June 13th: Tiepolo begins the ceiling of the church of the Pietà in Venice, which was 'made visible' on August 2nd, 1755, together with two other compartments. (*Commemoriali Gradenigo*, pp. 12, 17.) Tiepolo was paid 500 *zecchini*.

1755

Early: Tiepolo's name appears among those of several painters and sculptors who were invited by the Riformatori dello Studio (the University Authorities) of Padua to compile the rules of the new Academy of Painting and Sculpture founded on September 20th, 1750, by the Venetian Republic. The Academy, which was in the Fondaco della Farina at S. Marco (the Fondeghetto) had for its first President *domino Giovanni Battista Tiepolo pittor*, appointed on February 15th, 1756, together with two councillors, the painter G. B. Pittoni and the sculptor G. M. Morlaiter. On August 21st, 1758, Pittoni succeeded Tiepolo as President (Dall'Acqua-Giusti, *L'Accademia e la Galleria di Venezia*, in 'Atti della R. Accademia di Belle Arti,' 1873). Tiepolo was also an honorary academician of the Accademia at Parma (Ricci, Rapporti di G. B. Tiepolo con Parma, Parma, 1896). See also the documents in Gradenigo, *Commemoriali*, p. 22; and E. Bassi, *L'Accademia di Belle Arti di Venezia*, Venice, 1950, pp. 7 ff.

1756

March 12th: Gradenigo, *Commemoriali*, p. 21, mentions a ceiling painted by Tiepolo in the Chiesa delle Capuccine presso San Gerolamo at Cannaregio. The work is not recorded in other sources, nor is there any trace of it.

May 10th: Letter from Algarotti to Giampiero Zanotti of Bologna, describing the frescoes by Tiepolo in the Villa Contarini at La Mira. (Algarotti, *Opere*, vol. VIII, p. 45.)

1757

March 8th: In a manuscript by Bartolomeo Foni, preserved in the archives of the church at Folzano: *Nel presente anno 1757 alli 8 di marzo fu dato incominciamento dallo stuccatore . . . e si spera pure nel prossimo dicembre di poter nicchiare nella sovasa dell'altar maggiore la pala effigiante S. Silvestro Papa che batizza l'imperatore Constantino, della quale si è accordato il contratto per il pezzo [sic] di zecchini cento col Signor Gio. Batta Tiepolo . . .* ('In this year 1757, on the 8th March, was begun by the plasterer . . . and it is hoped that by next December it will be possible to place in the frame of the high altar the altarpiece representing Pope Silvester baptising the Emperor Constantine, for which the contract has been agreed for the price of 100 zecchini with Signor Gio. Batta Tiepolo . . .'). The altarpiece, which is still *in situ*, was unveiled on September 30th, 1759. (Molmenti, 1909, p. 153.)

Summer–Autumn: Tiepolo is painting frescoes at the Villa Valmarana in Vicenza, working with his son Domenico. In a *carnival scene* in the 'Foresteria' there is recorded the name of Domenico with the date 1757, formerly wrongly read as 1737. (On the whole question see Morassi, in *Le Arti*, 1943.)

December 2nd: A document of the Senate records that Tiepolo lent 6,000 ducats to the Board of Works of the church of the Pietà. (Venetian State Archives, publ. in Molmenti, 1909, p. 41, n. 20.)

1758

June 29th: From the deliberation of the City Council of Este (Libro Consigli, XVI, 1742–59, c. 341–42): *Dai Magnifici Deputati . . . vien posta parte che sia data autorità . . . di procurare la scelta di un valente pittore . . . per formare la detta Pala, la quale rappresenti la Gloriosa Santa Tecla in qualità di protettrice di Este . . .* ('By the Lords Deputies . . . it has been decided that authority shall be given . . . for the choice of a worthy painter . . . to make the said altarpiece, which is to represent the Glorious S. Thecla in the guise of the protectress of Este . . .'). A letter, dated 1760, from Isidoro Alessi to the Bishop Sante Veronese (publ. by Franceschelli, *Este*, Stratico, 1882) states that: *La Vigilia del SS. Natale dell'anno scorso 1759 fu posto nella Tribuna il nuovo Quadro che rappresenta S. Tecla intercedente . . .* ('On the Vigil of the Holy Nativity of last year, 1759, the new picture which represents S. Thecla interceding was placed in the Tribune . . .'). (Molmenti, 1909, p. 119, n. 35.)

1759

Tiepolo signs and dates the altarpiece of the *Child Mary presented to God the Father* (now in Dresden.)

Tiepolo signs and dates the altarpiece of *S. Thecla delivering the city from the plague*, executed for the Cathedral of Este.

March 14th: Letter from Tiepolo to the Abbé Innocenzo Frugoni, Secretary of the Academy of Fine Arts in Parma (founded in 1758 by Philip I of Bourbon) in which the painter returns thanks for his appointment as 'Accademico di merito' (Honorary Academician). From this letter we learn that Tiepolo had just returned from Brescia.

In this connection it is interesting that the original intention of the Academy was merely to confer the title of *amatore* (connoisseur) upon Tiepolo but Anton Maria Zanetti, the historian of Venetian painting, wrote to Frugoni on September 9th, 1758, and pointed out the ineptitude of such a title for a painter famous throughout Europe. After this observation the Academy decided to appoint Tiepolo 'Accademico di merito'. These letters are preserved in the Archive of the Academy of Fine Arts in Parma. (C. Ricci, *Rapporti di G. B. Tiepolo con Parma*, Parma 1896.)

August 7th: Bernardo Scotti, a Venetian trader, delivers to Tiepolo colours for the ceiling decoration of the church of the Purità in Udine The list of the colours provides an interesting insight into the composition of his palette: *Terra gialla Romana chiara, Detta scura, Terra Rossa Mineral, Detta verdi di Verona fina, Detta Mezana, Detta in panni, fina, Detta nera mineral, Detta Ombra Brusada, Detta schietta, Ocria Romana, Smaltin soprafin, Nero di Feccia, Detta di Vida, Brunin sopra finissimo, Cinaprio nattivo Min.* Tiepolo signs the receipt of the delivery made *per conto di Sua Eminenza Dolfin* ('on account of His Eminence Dolfin'). (Archivio, Capitolare di Udine, sezione II, busta 52; Vale e Masotti, 1932, p. 25.) In the same month Tiepolo must have begun the decoration on the ceiling, while Domenico executed the eight *chiaroscuri* for the walls.

August 25th: During Tiepolo's stay in Udine for the frescoes in the church of the Purità, Cardinal Daniele Delfino (who so often engaged the painters) asks Giambattista and Domenico for *expertises* about 7 old paintings sent to Udine from Cividale, which were related to the worship of the Dominican Santa Benevenuta di Bojano, whose beatification was then in progress. The *expertises* were made separately by the two Tiepolos on August 25th, 1759. (Rizzi, in 'Arte Veneta', 1959–60, pp. 239–242.) (Documents preserved in the Archive of the Curia Arcivescovile of Udine.)

September 16th: The Patriarch Dolfin paid 5.500 lire to *Padre, e Figlio Tiepolo Pittori eccellenti, e de più accreditati di Venezia per le Pitture. . . . Soffitto, Laterali, e Palla* (Father, and son Tiepolo, excellent painters and among the most renowned of Venice, for the Paintings. . . . Ceiling, Laterals and Altarpiece). Besides the two Tiepolo received 482.8 lire *per farli venire e ricondur a Venezia, Oro, e Colori, oltre la spesa di 50 giorni trà Viaggi, Feste e Lavori* (for their coming and starting to Venice, gold, and colours plus the expenses of 50 days employed in journey, Feasts and works). At this date, therefore, the ceiling decoration with laterals and the altarpiece with the *Immaculate Virgin*, still on the high altar, were finished. (Archivio Capitolare di Udine; Vale e Masotti, 1932; Biasutti, 1957, p. 24.)

1760

There is evidence that Tiepolo in this year presented a picture to Louis XV, for which he was well rewarded. (Autograph letter from Amedeo Swayer, a noted collector of *objets d'art*, in *Epistolario Moschini*, in the Museo Civico, Venice; Molmenti, 1909, p. 25, n. 12. The letter is untraceable in this *Epistolario*, according to a communication kindly made to me by Dr. Pignatti of the Museo Corrèr.)

February 6th: Letter of Daniele Dolfin from Udine to G. B. Tiepolo. On September 5th, 1759, Daniele Dolfin, previously appointed cardinal and titular bishop of the church of S. Marco in Rome, intends to commission from Tiepolo two canvases to be placed in the church. (The canons of S. Marco had already initiated unsuccessful agreements with the painter Stefano Pozzi.) On September 15th, 1759, Girolamo Ruggia, the Roman secretary to Dolfin, makes known the decision of the cardinal. The subjects to be represented were the 'Bishop lowering the body of St. Mark into the urn' and the 'Glory of the Persian Martyrs Abdon and Sennen'. In the letter of February 6th, Daniele Dolfin writes that *sono attesi in Roma con impazienza li Quadri . . . E riguardo il prezzo, ho detto che saranno 400 scudi romani . . . so che meriterebbe di più . . .* ('The two canvases are awaited in Rome anxiously. . . . And regarding the price, I have said it will be 400 Roman scudi . . . I realize you merit more . . .') (Archivio Arcivescovile di Udine, Atti-Ordinari Udinesi, Cartolario II, Daniele Dolfin; Kutschera-Woborsky, in 'Kunstchronik', 1918–19, pp. 934–40; M. Del Bianco, in 'Atti dell'Istituto Veneto', 1951–52, Tomo CX, pp. 286–87.)

February 9th: Letter of Daniele Dolfin from Udine to Tiepolo, about the two canvases to be placed in S. Marco in Rome. In this letter the cardinal asks the painter to let him see some sketch for the pictures. (Bibl., see above.)

February 26th: Tiepolo writes from Venice to Daniele Dolfin that he hopes the canvases for S. Marco in Rome will be finished next summer: *Non mi determino però qual mese, posciachè li Quadri ad Oglio devono essere studiati e repplicati, tanto più questi . . . che capitar devono in Roma, dove le crittiche sono famigliari* ('I won't decide the month since the canvases have to be studied and repeated, and particularly those which have to go to Rome, where the criticisms are familiar'). (Bibl. see above.) Nevertheless Cardinal Dolfin, writing to his agent in Rome, G. Ruggia, on 22.1.1762, sends 300 *scudi* for the payment *per la faciture di due gran Quadri, che mancavano di dipingersi nella Chiesa di S. Marco del mio Titolo* ('for the execution of two large canvases which were not yet painted for the church of St. Mark'). Tiepolo had written to Dolfin that the paintings were shortly to be finished, but afterwards other pressing engagements and the departure to Spain prevent him from finishing the pictures. In fact, on 16.3.1761, Tiepolo informs Algarotti (see below) that he had, among other works, to paint two further canvases for a church in Rome, certainly to be identified with the ones commissioned by Dolfin.

May 10th: Letter from Venice to Algarotti: *Io pure secondo il mio impegno nell'ora che scrivo dovrei ritrovarmi a Milano, ma la gotta insolentissima . . . mi levò il modo onde poter sodisfare al mio impegno e difficilmente di poterlo più adempiere, posciachè subito che lo sono in stato dovrò fare il modello par la sala di Ca' Pisani, opera non tanto indifferente che mi terrà occupato per il corso di tre o quattro anni* ('I ought, according to my commitments, to be again at this moment in Milan, but the intemperance of gout . . . denied me the means of fulfilling my obligation, and with difficulty will I be able to meet it, since immediately that I am able I must make the *modello* for the saloon of Ca' Pisani, a not inconsiderable work which will keep me occupied for about three or four years'). (Fogolari, 1942, pp. 35–36.)

July 11th: Tiepolo answers the Academy of Parma about a projected competition for the execution of a painting. In this letter he states that *Nel tempo in cui mi pervenne il compitissimo foglio di S.V. Ill. ma 17 del giugno, fuori mi trovava dalla Patria . . .* ('At the time when your letter of the 17th June reached me, I was out of Venice . . .'). Tiepolo was certainly in Strà for the frescoes in the Villa Pisani. (Archive of the Academy of Parma; Ricci, 1896.)

September 1st: The King of England commissions from Tiepolo a great picture representing *Frederick of Prussia on horseback commanding a victorious army.* (Gradenigo, *Commemoriali,* p. 62.) Nothing else is known of this picture, which perhaps was never executed.

September 19th: Contract by which Tiepolo undertakes to decorate the central oval of the ceiling in the new audience chamber of the Scuola Grande di S. Giovanni Evangelista. This contract was never fulfilled on account of the work in hand at Strà and his departure for Spain. (Urbani, *Guida storico-artistica della Scuola di S. Giovanni Evangelista in Venezia,* Venice, 1895.)

October 23rd: Gradenigo, *Commemoriali,* p. 64, notes: *Il più acclamato onde storicamente pitturare soffitti per Sale, Stanza e Chiese a fresco, e a Oglio è Gio. Batta Tiepoletto* ('The most acclaimed in painting historically ceilings of Saloons, Rooms and Churches in fresco, and in Oil is Gio. Batta Tiepoletto').

1761

Zaccaria Betti, *Componimenti poetici,* Verona 1761, extols the paintings done by Tiepolo for the Palazzo Canossa in Verona.

A letter of Tiepolo, dated September 28th, 1761, to the Spanish ambassador in Venice (see below), proves that the painter was then working in Verona, certainly on the fresco in the Palazzo Canossa. Another letter (see below) of the Spanish ambassador in Venice to Marques de Squillace (December 5th, 1761) testifies that the fresco was finished in the middle of October, 1761.

March 16th: Letter from Venice to Algarotti: . . . *solo le accenno per di lei lume che senza fallo alcun alla fine del presente mese dovrò portarmi qualche giornata sopra Milano per una mia premura, ove non sarò per trattenermi se non dieci o dodici giorni soli . . . Il quadro della Cena . . . è da molto tempo avanzato et anco al suo fine . . . Io poi mi ritrovo al presente con molti impegni, il più grande è grandissimo sopratutti si è il dover dipingere il gran salone di Ca' Pisani a Strà, e sopratutto ancora due quadri per essere annicchiati in una chiesa di Roma, travalgiando tuttavia un gran soffitto in tella per la Corte de Moscovia . . .* ('I tell you for your information only that at the end of this month I must without fail go some way beyond Milan for a matter of great concern to me, which will not detain me less than 10 or 12 days . . . The picture of the Supper . . . has for some time been very forward and also at finishing point. . . . Thus I find myself at the moment with much work, the most important is the biggest of all, which is the painting of the great saloon in Ca' Pisani at Strà, and over and above that another two pictures to be placed in a church in Rome, while labouring the while on a large ceiling on canvas for the Court of Moscow . . .'). (Fogolari, 1942, pp. 36–37.) The painting of the *Last Supper* can possibly be identified with *Christ*

and the Magdalen in the House of the Pharisee ex-Barlow and now in Dublin. In the letter of April 4th 1761 mentioned below there is again a probable reference to this picture as finished.

April 4th: Another letter from Tiepolo to the Abbé Innocenzo Frugoni about the competition promoted by the Academy of Fine Arts in Parma. It seems probable that Lorenzo Tiepolo took part in this competition, since on April 18th, 1761, he addressed a letter to the Academy (see below). (Archive of the Academy of Fine Arts in Parma; Ricci, 1896.)

April 4th: A very interesting letter from Tiepolo to Count Algarotti, in which there is a reference to a portrait of the Count that the artist seems to have painted just then: . . . *et ora molti più l'impegno si prende per un tal ritratto per cui fa molto bene incoragirmi col mezzo della predetta sua compitissima lettera ben degna del di lei bell'animo. Quanto bramerei poter la godere al fianco mio come lo è la Vittoria che se ne sta a quello del Gran Ritratto cui tuttavia travaglio in tal maniera potrei starmene sicuro d'un felice esito; ma se non v'è la persona, me la prefiggerò presente per maggiormente riuscire nell'impegno.* ('. . . and now I have more and more to do my best for such a portrait so that you are right in encouraging me with that kind letter well worthy of your noble mind. How much I long to be able to have the pleasure of having you at my side like the Victory at the side of the Great Portrait for which I nevertheless am working in such a way that I can be sure of a good result; but if the sitter is not here, I shall imagine him as present for better success in my task.) There is no other record of this portrait. (Precerutti-Garberi, in *Commentari,* April–June, 1958, pp. 120–123.)

In the same letter Tiepolo writes that *me trovo occupato in Ca' Pisani, et in di' forse portar mi devo a Verona a dipingere una salla . . .* ('I am now occupied in Ca' Pisani and in a few days I have perhaps to go to Verona to paint a room . . .'). (Doc. in a Private Coll. of autographs and art documents, Turin; Baudi di Vesme, *Paralipomeni tiepoleschi,* Turin 1912, pp. 309 ff.).

April 18th: A letter of Lorenzo Tiepolo stating that his father is working on the fresco at Villa Pisani. (Ricci, 1896.)

June 10th: Two letters from Tiepolo to Innocenzo Frugoni, both concerning the competition for a picture (see above). In the second of them Giustino Menescardi is indicated as the winner of the competition with the charge to execute the painting for the Academy in Parma. (Archive of the Academy of Fine Arts, Parma; Ricci, 1896.)

August 10th: On this day the ceiling of the Scuola di S. Giovanni Evangelista (following Gradenigo, p. 76), *uscito dal pennello del vivente e celebre Gio. Batta Tiepolo* ('painted by the brush of the living and famous Gio. Batta Tiepolo') was unveiled. The work, commissioned from Tiepolo (see September 19th, 1760), was not executed by him but by Angeli.

September 26th: From a letter of the Duke of Montealegre, Spanish ambassador in Venice, to the Marques de Esquilache, minister of the King, we know that Charles III of Spain charged the 'Intendente General' in Venice, Count Gazzola, to come to terms with Tiepolo for his departure to the Spanish court. Tiepolo is said then to be working in Verona and was informed of the King's wish in a letter dated from Venice September 25th, 1761. (*Obra de Palacio, Legajo 452;* E. Battisti, in 'Arte antica e moderna', no. 9, 1960, p. 78.)

September 28th: Tiepolo writes from Verona to the Spanish ambassador in Venice, Duke of Montealegre, to accept the high honour of being invited to Spain. Tiepolo adds that Count Gazzola had already given him the plans of the oeuvre he had to undertake *ed in aggiunta le misure per quattro sopraporte da collocarsi nella sala del Trono à me destinata da dipingere, per poterne formar anticipatamente li miei studij, e modelli . . .* ('together with the sizes of four overdoors to be located in the Throne Room which has to be painted by me, in order to enable me to execute in advance my studies and sketches of the oeuvre . . .'). Besides Tiepolo requests a delay to fulfil the obligations already undertaken. Tiepolo's answer was sent together with a letter of Duke of Montealegre (dated October 3rd, 1761) to the Marques of Esquilache. (*Obra de Palacio, Legajo 452;* Battisti, *cit.,* 1960, p. 79.)

Tiepolo's letter seems to be a further proof that he executed at Madrid first the fresco of the Throne Room.

November 19th: Giambattista Tiepolo Pittore Veneziano rinomatissimo viene ricercato dal Monarca delle Spagne alla Rep.ca onde maggiormente infervorarlo passare sollecitamente a Madrid per sempre più rendere degno di S. Maestà quel reale soggiorno, mediante sì famoso pennello ('the very famous Venetian painter Giambattista Tiepolo was asked for by the King of Spain from the Republic to get him to go directly to Madrid, where his famous brush is to render the Royal Palace still more worthy of His Majesty'). Gradenigo, *Commemoriali*, p. 83.

December 5th: Letter from Venice of the Duke of Montealegre to the Marques de Esquilache reporting a conversation between the ambassador and Tiepolo. The painter, returned to Venice, apologizes for the delay in his departure to Spain and points to the difficulties of the engagements previously undertaken which kept him busy until last October. Montealegre reports that the 'supremo Inquisitore' Foscarini had pressed Procurator Pisani to release Tiepolo (who was working in the Villa Pisani at Strà, and evidently he was forced to finish the frescoes speedily. For his part Tiepolo does not seem glad to leave Venice, because of his age and the inclemency of the winter; he adduces many reasons for obtaining a further delay: his family, the marriage of one of his daughters. The Duke of Montealegre writes that Tiepolo still insists on postponing his departure until the next May. The letter mentions also the plans for Tiepolo's voyage to Spain: from Venice to Genoa and from there by ship to Antibes, where the journey was to continue by stage-coach to Barcelona and Madrid. Interesting is a passage which testifies to Tiepolo's justness and generosity. The Duke of Montealegre writes: *Yo alabé su generoso modo de pensar, y su justa confianza, persuadido que non se anganava, insisti no obstante en proveerlo de dinero, aun como de Amigo à Amigo, si gustaba, pero no se dexò vencer, y yo debo hacerle esta justicia en elogio de su proceder* ('I praised his generous way of thinking and his just confidence, convinced that he was wrong, and I insisted nevertheless on providing him with money, just as between friends, if he liked it, but he would not be persuaded and I must do him this justice, in praise of his demeanour.') (*Legajo 452. Pintores*; Battisti, *cit.*, 1960, p. 80–81.)

It is evident from the documents that Tiepolo was really forced to accept the new engagement at the Spanish court.

December 22nd: The painter announced his departure to Spain in two letters addressed (according to Molmenti), to the patrician Tomaso Farsetti (1720–93), a great patron of artists. Modern suggests that the letters were addressed to Algarotti. The first is dated December 22nd, 1761: *... mi disponevo d'avanzarle la Nottizia della chiamata mia alla Corte di Spagna al di Cui sommo onore avevo adderito con il tempo condicionato, per poter dar fine a molte opere di già avanzate e particolarmente alla Grandiosa Salla di Ca' Pisani, ed in seguito all'altre così anche dalla Corte stessa accordatomi, per cui quiettissimo e tranquillo se ne stava l'animo mio. Ma inaspettatamente chiamato da chi può comandare, me fu inzonto di subito prendere le mie mosse ... a fatica ho potutto aver tempo sino Febraro venturo ... Per quanto è a me notto, in Ispagna non haverò a fare che una salla cosichè mi lusingo in capo a due anni ritornarmene alla Patria ...* ('I was going to tell you the news of my summons to the Court of Spain, which highest honour I had accepted for a date to be agreed upon, so as to be able to finish many works already begun, particularly the Grand Saloon of Ca' Pisani, and then the other things, as had been granted me by the Court, so that my mind was undisturbed and tranquil about them. But unexpectedly summoned by him who is able to command I was bidden immediately to take my leave ... and with difficulty have I been able to get until next February ... From what I know, in Spain I shall have only one room to do, so that I flatter myself that in at most two years I shall return home'). (Letter preserved in the *Epistolario Moschini*, in the Museo Civico, Venice; Molmenti, 1909, pp. 25–26.)

1762

Tiepolo's intended departure to Spain is reported also by Alessandro Longhi, *Compendio delle vite dei pittori veneziani storici più rinomati. ...* Venice, 1762: *Si vocifera che nella presente primavera* (G. B. Tiepolo) *partirà per Madrid, ricevuto da quel monarca con onore particolare, conducendo seco Gio. Domenico suo figliuolo, diligentissimo imitatore di un tanto padre. Vive frattanto in patria signorilmente.* (It is rumoured that in the

present Spring he (G. B. Tiepolo) will leave for Madrid, received by that monarch with particular honour, bringing with him Gio. Domenico, his son, very diligent imitator of so great a father. He lives in the meantime in Venice like a rich gentleman.)'

January 9th: An autograph letter from Tiepolo to Algarotti states that Tiepolo had been in Treviso. We do not know why he went there: the only decoration by him known to have any connection with the city is that formerly in the Palazzo Onigo at Sant' Andrea (now in part in the Ringling Museum, Sarasota).

This letter also contains a reference to a picture commissioned from Tiepolo by Algarotti, an old copy of the Veronese *Last Supper* originally in Venice in the Chiesa dei Servi (now in the Louvre). The copy was bought by the Count for a few florins and was now to be touched up so that it would pass as Veronese's original *modello* for the large picture in the Louvre. The architecture had already been repainted by Visentini but Tiepolo's departure for Spain prevented him from doing anything. Other letters refering to this picture: 4.3.1760 from Algarotti to Tiepolo, 4.4.1761 from Tiepolo to Algarotti, three of 2.1.1762, 5.1.1762, 16.1.1762 from Algarotti to his brother Bonomo. All these documents are preserved: in the Royal Library, Turin, Cartella, *Algarotti-Guerra dei Sette Anni* (the three letters to Bonomo); in a Collection of Autographs bequeathed to the city of Turin by Count Nomis di Cossilla (the one from Tiepolo to Algarotti). See: Baudi di Vesme, *Paralipomeni Tiepoleschi, cit.*, p. 309 ff.

January 30th: The pressing request that he should leave for Spain is patent from a letter from the Duke of Montealegre Don Leopoldo de Gregorio, Spanish Ambassador in Venice, addressed to the Marques de Esquilache, Minister to the King: *... y me ha prometido abreviar sus disposiciones, y anticipar quanto mas le sera posible su viaje, quedando de acuerdo precisamente en que lo emprendera dentro del proximo mes de Marzo ...* ('and he has already promised me that he will cut short his commitments, and to make his journey as soon as he possibly can, having given his word that he will undertake it during the coming month of March ...'). (Archives of the Royal Household – Personal de Empleados; Molmenti, 1909, p. 41, n. 15.)

March 13th: The second letter addressed to Farsetti is dated March 13th: *Al presente sono alla fine del Modello della Gran Opera, che tanto è vasta, basta solo riflettere, che'è di cento piedi; tuttavia voglio sperare che l'idea compita sarà molto ben accomodata et adattata a quella Gran Monarchia, fatica grande ma per tal Opera ci vuol coraggio ...* ('At this moment I am finishing the *modello* for the great work, which is so huge, that it is sufficient to reflect that it is 100 feet; all the same I should like to think that the finished design will be suitable and appropriate to that great Monarchy, a heavy task but for such a work courage is needed ...'). (*Epistolario Moschini*, in Museo Civico, Venice; Molmenti, 1909, pp. 26–27.) This *modello* is now in Washington.

April 3rd: The Duke of Montealegre informs the Marques de Esquilache of Tiepolo's departure: *Debo dar à V. Ex.a el aviso de que el Pintor D.n Iuan Tiepolo, con dos hijos suyos, y en compañia de D.n Ioseph Casina, noble Paduano, negociante de espejos, y bien conocido en Madrid, emprendio ya su viaje el 31 del pasado y antes de expirar el mes de Marzo, segun me tenia ofrecido, dirigendose por la via de tierra en derechura a Barcelona y a esa Corte ...* ('I must inform your Excellency that the painter Don Iuan Tiepolo, with two of his sons, and accompanied by Don Ioseph Casina, Paduan nobleman, merchant in mirrors and well known in Madrid, started on his journey on the 31st of last month and before the end of March, as he had given me his word to do, travelling by land direct to Barcelona and to the Court ...'). (Archives of the Royal Household, Madrid, – Personal de Empleados; Molmenti, 1909, p. 41, n. 15.) This date is confirmed by Gradenigo (p. 85).

June 4th: After a tiring journey overland, Tiepolo arrives in Madrid and is welcomed by the Venetian Ambassador, Sebastiano Foscarini, whose guest he remained for a short time. The architect Sabatini informed the Marques de Esquilache of this. (Molmenti, 1909, p. 29; Sánchez-Cantón, *Tiepolo en Madrid* (lecture), Madrid, 1925, p. 8.)

June 10th: Applaudito fu il nuovo vessillo della Congregazione de' Preti di S. Maria Mater Domini, perchè di Arazzo d'oro e disegnato da Giambattista Tiepolo, ed intessuto da Antonio Dini Turinese ... ('The new banner of the Congregation of the Priests of S. Maria Mater Domini, of golden tapestry, designed by Giambattista Tiepolo and woven by Antonio Dini of Turin, was well received . . .'). Gradenigo, *Commemoriali*, p. 87. The banner is still in S. Maria Materdomini, Venice; the picture from which the banner was copied is now in Springfield Museum.

June 12th: The Marques de Esquilache exchanges letters with Francesco Sabatini, Court architect, charging him *di assistere il Professore veneziano con ciò che gli fosse necessario tanto per la casa quanto per tutt'altro* ('to assist the Venetian Professor with that which is necessary for his house and for all else as well'). Tiepolo had refunded to him the expenses of his journey, and was assigned the same salary as the painters Mengs and Corrado Giaquinto, that is, 2,000 doubloons annually, plus 500 ducats for a carriage. The letters of the Marques de Esquilache and Sabatini are in the documents transcribed by Baron Davillier, publ. in 'Bullettino di Arti e Curiosità Veneziane', A.III, pp. 171, 174, Venice, Ongania, 1880; Molmenti, 1909, pp. 29 and 42, ns. 21 and 22, also publishes them.

June 30th: Receipt for 2,800 reals given to Tiepolo by Sr. Alonzo Muriel, for the fitting-up of the lower apartment in the house of Don Antonio de Muriel Salzedo y Baldivieso, in the plaza of S. Martin, opposite the monastery of S. Martin. The church and plaza were demolished under King Joseph Bonaparte in 1809. (Archives of the Royal Household, *cit.*; Molmenti, 1909, p. 42, n. 23; Sánchez-Cantón, *G. B. Tiepolo en Espana*, Madrid, 1953, pp. 9–10.)

August 2nd: Letter from Sabatini to the Marques de Esquilache, concerning the furnishing of Tiepolo's house: *Paso à manos de V. E. el Recibo del medio año anticipado que he pagado por el alquiler de la casa en donde vive el Pintor D.n Iuan Bautista Tiepolo . . .* ('I send to your Excellency the receipt for the half year in advance which I have paid for the renting of the house in which the painter Don Iuan Bautista Tiepolo lives . . .'). The furnisher's bill is appended. (Archives of the Royal Household, *cit.*; Molmenti, 1909, p. 42, n.)

1763

Letter from Tiepolo to King Charles III, asking to be exempted from the so-called tax of the *Media anata*, as the King had conceded *a otros profesores que han tenido el mismo honor de servir à S.M.* (*Legajo 452. Pintores*; Battisti, *cit.*, 1960, p. 81.)

1764

Tiepolo signs the fresco of the *Apotheosis of Spain* in the great saloon of the Royal Palace of Madrid.

1767

January 4th: In a letter to Charles III, Tiepolo expresses his satisfaction for the consideration he had received at the Spanish Court and writes that he would be glad to remain longer in Spain offering to paint on canvas, as he had done in other Courts with success. The King annotated the letter ('*decreta a margine*') that Tiepolo should be given commission for works to be indicated to him by Padre Joaquin de Electa. (Sanchez-Cantón, 1953, p. 10.)

January 16th: Tiepolo asks the King for a consideration so as to furnish his house better and to prepare a suitable workshop. The King agrees

and in the same month Tiepolo had from the King's treasurer 12,000 reals. (Molmenti, p. 30, n. 42; Sack, p. 142.)

September 5th: Letter from Francesco Sabatini, chief architect of the Palace, from Madrid to Don Miguel de Muzquiz asking for *el Pintor de Camera D.n Juan Baptista Tiepolo, que en el dia està encargado de hacer siete quadros grandes al olio para la nueba Iglesia, y Combento que se costruye en el Real Sitio de Aranjuez* a new studio suitable for painting the seven canvases and *de la misma conformidad que la tiene en su casa el Pintor de Camera D.n Antonio Raphael Mengs* (It seems that the rivalry between Tiepolo and Mengs really existed). On October 1st, 1767, Don Miguel de Muzquiz grants the permission *paraque en la Casa donde vive* (Tiepolo) *se le disponga una Pieza a proposito para pintar al oleo* as was asked by Sabatini. (Battisti, *cit.* 1960.)

1768

January 31st: Lorenzetti (Exhib. Cat., Venice, 1951, p. XXI) says that Tiepolo was appointed Professor of Anatomy at the Academia de San Fernando in Madrid on January 31st, and that he resigned on March 6th of the same year, but this is refuted by Sánchez-Cantón (1953, pp. 11–12), who says that there is no trace of all this in the Academia records.

1769

August 29th: Tiepolo writes to the King's secretary, Miguel de Muzquiz, that the seven pictures for Aranjuez were finished and that he had requested instructions for their placing from the King's confessor, but that neither he nor his sons had been able to obtain the honour of speaking to the Father, who would not deign to answer their letters, which occasioned Tiepolo to think that he 'had not completed the task to his (Padre de Electa's) complete satisfaction, which would be a great mortification to me' (*no haber dado cumplimiento à mi encargo a su cabal satisfacción, que seria para mi la mayor mortificacion*). (Documents in Davillier, *cit.*, p. 42, no. 21; Molmenti, 1909, p. 192; Sánchez-Cantón, 1953, p. 11.)

We know from a letter of September 15th to the Marques de Muzquiz from Tiepolo that he was pleased to receive a commission to fresco the vault of the apse of S. Ildefonso in Aranjuez. Tiepolo presented two designs for the fresco to the King in September, but death prevented the execution of the work. (Molmenti, 1909, p. 193; Sánchez-Cantón, 1953, p. 11.)

1770

January 8th: Cecilia Guardi, Tiepolo's wife, acknowledges the rich gifts sent by her husband from Spain. (Venetian State Archives, sez. not.; Molmenti, 1909, p. 41, n. 20.)

March 27th: Tiepolo dies suddenly. His death certificate is in the registers of the church of S. Martin in Madrid and notes that *No pudo rezibir los S.tos Sacra.tos, murio en viente y siete del M.zo de mil setez.os y setenta* ('He could not receive the Holy Sacraments; he died on the 27th March of 1770'). His tomb in S. Martin has been demolished. (Molmenti, 1909, p. 42, n. 26; Sánchez-Cantón, 1953, p. 12.)

April 21st: Letters from Madrid inform Venice of Tiepolo's death, *il famoso pittore veneziano, anzi il più rinomato, . . . ben noto in Europa, in età di 72 anni, et il più laudato in Patria* ('The famous Venetian painter, indeed the most renowned . . . well known in Europe, aged 72, and the most highly praised in his country'). Gradenigo, *Commemoriali*, pp. 191–192.